GOOD
LOVING
GREAT
SEX

FINDING BALANCE WHEN YOUR SEX DRIVES DIFFER

GW00568187

GOOD LOVING GREAT SEX

FINDING BALANCE WHEN YOUR SEX DRIVES DIFFER

DR ROSIE KING

ARROW

To my darling husband Ross, who made all
my dreams come true.

Random House Australia Pty Ltd
20 Alfred Street, Milson's Point, NSW 2061
http://www.randomhouse.com.au

Sydney New York Toronto
London Auckland Johannesburg
and agencies throughout the world

First published in 1997
This Arrow edition published in 1998
Copyright © Rosie King 1997

All rights reserved. No part of this publication may be reproduced,
stored in a retrieval system, or transmitted in any form or by any means,
electronic, mechanical, photocopying, recording or otherwise, without
the prior written permission of the Publisher.

National Library of Australia
Cataloguing-in-Publication data:

King, Rosie
Good loving great sex.

ISBN 0 09 183907 6 (pbk).

1. Sex instruction. 2. Sex counselling. 3. Sex. I. Title.

306.7

Cover design Gayna Murphy
Text design Mark Davis
Illustrations by Bettina Guthridge
Typeset by Lynne Hamilton
Printed by Griffin Press

10 9 8

Contents

Introduction   *1*

Part 1   Guide to Desire   *5*

Chapter 1   The Desire Dilemma —
         Catastrophe or Challenge?   *7*

Chapter 2   The River of Desire   *20*

Chapter 3   The Psychology of Desire — Our Thoughts,
         Feelings and Relationships   *34*

Chapter 4   Pass Me the Ruler —
         Measuring Your Sex Drive   *43*

Chapter 5   Is My Sex Drive Normal?   *53*

Part 2   The Makings of a
        Mismatched Couple   *67*

Chapter 6   Flames of Passion —
         The Highs and Lows of Sex Drive   *69*

Chapter 7 His Desire, Her Desire —
           Bridging the Gap Between the Sexes   82
Chapter 8 Her Enhancers —
           Sugar and Spice and All Things Nice   101
Chapter 9 His Enhancers —
           Slugs and Snails and Puppy Dogs' Tails   115
Chapter 10 Pursuer/Distancer —
           A Vicious Cycle in Action   140

Part 3   Healing Your Relationship   153

Chapter 11 Good Loving — Caring and Communication   155
Chapter 12 Up Close and Personal — Intimacy and Trust 165
Chapter 13 Maintaining Love —
           Commitment, Respect and Equality   177
Chapter 14 Problem Solving — Conflict and Negotiation 191
Chapter 15 Creating Passion — Friends and Lovers   205

Part 4   Achieving Sexual Compatibility   223

Chapter 16 Getting Your Sex Life Back on Track   225
Chapter 17 Making it Easier to Say 'Yes' to Sex   251
Chapter 18 Putting the Sexual Hierarchy to Work   281
Chapter 19 Reducing Inhibitors of Sexual Desire   309
Chapter 20 Special Circumstances —
           Pregnancy and Breastfeeding, Menopause
           and Ageing   336

           Conclusion   357

           Resources   359
           Bibliography   365
           Index   367

Acknowledgements

My evolution as a sex therapist and educator has been warmly supported by many individuals. My wise and gentle mother, Margaret Goldfinch, gave me a wonderful gift when she taught me as a child that sex was a natural, enjoyable part of life. She also showed me that it is possible to combine family and a fulfilling career, and do both well. She has always been a role model for me.

After graduation from university, Dr Martyn Baker took me under his wing and into his practice, where I learnt that good medical care always deals with patients' sexual anxieties as well as their physical and emotional symptoms. He has always been a firm friend and a very generous colleague.

I thank Professor Deborah Saltman for recognising the educator in me and arranging my first undergraduate teaching job. She showed me that good education is as much about humour as it is about getting the message across.

The late Dr Derek Richardson, known fondly as the 'Godfather' of sex therapy in Australia, always believed in me and insisted I take risks even when I didn't want to. Taking risks was nothing new to Derek, who continues to be sadly missed.

My colleagues, clinical and otherwise, at the Australian Centre for Sexual Health provide a perfect multidisciplinary clinical and research environment for my work. I am lucky to work at a Centre that is recognised both nationally and internationally for its excellence. A special thanks to Di Retchless for all her help.

I appreciate very much the personal and professional support afforded to me by my regular supervision group. Thanks to you all — Serina Cauchi, Trisha Langford and Dr Margaret Redelman.

This book could not have been written without the long-distance help and support of my oldest friend, Eve Belson, and her partner, Gary Fudge. Their extraordinary unconditional generosity to me leaves me speechless. Thank you both.

Thanks to my wonderful sons, Ross and Stephen, who tolerated the writing of this book, which came and lived like a cuckoo in our family nest. Thanks to my beautiful step-daughters, Simone, Katherine and Elizabeth, for their computer expertise in times of crisis and for welcoming me into their lives.

Finally, my most heartfelt thanks go to my husband, Ross, who gives so much, so often, to so many, but most of all, to me.

Introduction

So you and your partner have differing levels of sex drive. Do you want sex more frequently than your partner does? Or is it the other way round? Perhaps one of you rarely feels like making love, while the other is hungry for sex all the time. Or you may be interested in sex — but not with your partner!

Problems with libido are common. Some people complain they have too much interest in sex, while others say they have too little or none at all. In my experience the most common complaint is that one partner has a higher sex drive than the other. These highs and lows often result in personal, sexual and relationship unhappiness, and contribute to the rising divorce rate.

Most of us grow up believing that when we find our true love, life will be a bed of roses. We will be perfectly matched in every way — emotionally, intellectually, spiritually and, of course, sexually. Welcome to the real world! Total relationship harmony exists only in the minds of romantic novelists, not in the hustle and bustle of everyday life. Most couples find that their sexual appetites differ at least some of the time. The differences may surface only under particularly difficult circumstances, or be apparent throughout the relationship. For some the difference in libidos is small; for others, the gap between their levels of interest in sex is big enough to drive a truck through.

Differing libidos are common. As a sex and relationship therapist with almost 20 years' experience, I am convinced that a set of perfectly matched sex drives is as rare as hen's teeth. Some couples are fortunate enough to discover positive ways to overcome their desire mismatch and, as a result, the negative effects on their relationships are minimal. Unfortunately, this is not always the case.

Many couples experience bitter disputes and ongoing unhappiness because of unresolved issues in their sex lives. Partners can end up mired in a sticky swamp of sexual conflict which may spell the end of their relationship. This is a tragedy, because differences in sex drive can be successfully overcome when partners are willing to alter their attitudes and change their behaviour.

The majority of couples facing a mismatch in sex drives need little more than practical information, mutual goodwill and commonsense strategies in order to deal with the issues. The program outlined in this book is designed to re-establish goodwill between partners with differing libidos. It offers practical strategies that allow partners to work together to get their needs met while feeling good about themselves, their relationship and their sexuality. These techniques are based on an understanding of what is normal, on having realistic expectations and exploring sexual options. Employing proven techniques from my clinical practice, couples can learn to cope with differences in desire. When partners are willing to work together on the problem, the bedroom can be transformed from a battleground back into a playground once more.

Author's note

The terms 'sex drive', 'sexual desire', 'libido', 'sexual interest' and 'sexual urge' are used interchangeably throughout this book. Some writers distinguish between biological sex drive and psychological sexual interest, but these terms are not relevant in this context.

Throughout this book when I refer to 'relationships', 'partners' and 'couples', these terms encompass all sorts of connections between human beings: married couples, live-in relationships, long- and short-term romances between men and women. The terms also refer to gay and lesbian couples. It is a myth that when two men or two women get together in a homosexual relationship they will automatically enjoy perfect sexual synchronicity. Many homosexual couples suffer from differences in their sex drives. Gay and lesbian couples will also benefit from the information and techniques outlined in this book.

Part 1

Guide to
Desire

The Desire Dilemma — Catastrophe or Challenge?

When Janine and Larry first met, they seemed a perfect match. Not only were they in love, but they really liked each other. Over time their relationship deepened and they decided to settle down together.

Initially they were equally enthusiastic about sex, but as the years passed a troubling pattern emerged. Janine was happy with sex twice a week, while Larry expected to make love every night. The more Larry wanted sex, the less interested Janine became.

After a while this 'sex problem' started to poison other parts of their relationship. They began fighting over little things and spending less time together. They stopped kissing and cuddling and started going to bed at different times. The romance faded and they began to avoid each other. Eventually they found themselves living separate lives.

Janine and Larry have differing levels of interest in sex. This common problem is known as DESIRE DISCREPANCY or DD.

Theirs is such a typical story that you might accuse me of peeking into your life, even through your bedroom window. No, I'm not psychic. Problems with desire discrepancy manifest in a way that most couples find eerily familiar. This predictable sequence of events occurs when couples lack the skills to overcome the problems posed by their differing sex drives.

SEXUAL MISMATCH

It can be deeply disappointing for couples who are generally well matched to discover that they are a poor match once the bedroom door is closed. DD may be evident from the start: he wants sex more than she does, or vice versa. Or like Larry and Janine, partners may be well suited in the early stages of their relationship, only to find that serious desire differences start to emerge over time.

Many couples find that their problems with sex drive leak out of the bedroom and poison other areas of their relationship. Has your relationship been affected by DD? Do you cuddle and kiss less often than you used to? Has the fun and romance faded from your relationship? Do you feel less comfortable just being around your partner? Do you ever feel like you're living with a stranger?

Over time, even a small difference in sexual interest can cause tension and unhappiness. Do you find that your arguments always seem to boil down to bitter words about sex — words that hurt and can't be taken back, and that eat away at the love and trust in your relationship?

If you answered 'Yes' to any of these questions, be reassured that you are not the only couple facing these difficulties. I receive thousands of letters each year asking for advice about sexual problems in 'A Rosie Love Life', my column in *Woman's Day* magazine. By far the most common anxieties are loss of sexual interest and differing sex drives. The following letters are typical.

> Dear Dr Rosie,
> My husband and I have been married for eight years and have three small children. Although I love him very much, I no longer have any sexual feelings towards him. I enjoy a kiss and a cuddle, but he always wants to go further. We haven't made love for nearly six months and I feel so guilty. He's cranky with me and the kids, and we fight about sex all the time. Please help me save my marriage.

Dear Dr Rosie,
My wife is always nagging me for sex. When I don't come through
with the goods, she accuses me of being gay or having affairs with
other women. I've never cheated on her. It's just that she always criti-
cises me in and out of bed and I'd rather masturbate than make love.

If differing sex drives is your problem, you're definitely not alone.
Many couples experience this problem at some stage in their relationships. Let's take a look at a typical couple, those Nursery
Rhyme favourites — Jack and Jill, now all grown up and more
than best friends.

Jack and Jill were destined to fall in love. After all, they had
enjoyed a mutual childhood interest in buckets, water and wells!
Jack, fully recovered from his head injury, had been away in the
city studying irrigation methods, while Jill had been to university
to learn business management skills. Reunited in their late twenties, they found they still shared many interests. The chemistry
between them was sizzling and it wasn't long before they set the
wedding date.

After a fairytale wedding they left for their honeymoon and
embarked on the intimate physical side of their married life. Jack
was a caring and sensitive lover, while Jill's interest in lovemaking
surprised Jack. For such a shy girl, she was 'hot to trot' morning,
noon and night. Both Jack and Jill knew they had found their perfect match.

Over the next two years they worked hard to build up their
irrigation business. Because of work demands, they had less time
to spend together. Money was tight and there wasn't much to
spare for a night out at the cinema or a quiet dinner for two. They
were often tired and stressed out at the end of a long day and
argued more frequently.

Jill found that her interest in sex was steadily diminishing.
Jack's sulky, irritable reaction when she said 'No' to sex didn't
help matters.

As the months wore on, Jill started going to bed earlier and
earlier. She made sure she always wore her daggiest pyjamas in an
attempt to deter Jack's sexual advances. Even though she was
longing for some hugs and kisses, she tried to steer clear of him,

just in case he pushed her for sex. He couldn't even give her a cuddle without getting 'wandering hands'. When she did have sex with him, it was because she felt guilty, not because she felt horny. She began to view sex as a burden, just another demand in her long and weary day. She felt pressured and resentful towards Jack. They stopped kissing hello and goodbye and soon they were rarely touching at all. Jill felt that Jack only wanted sex, not her.

Meanwhile, Jack was feeling rejected and confused. In the beginning Jill couldn't keep her hands off him, but now he was having trouble scoring even a peck on the cheek. She went to bed early while he watched the late night movie, and he knew she pretended to be asleep when he got into bed. If he initiated sex, she'd either turn away or say she had a headache. When she did give in, he knew she wasn't enjoying their lovemaking and just wanted to get it over with.

Jack wasn't just missing sex, he was also missing the closeness, affection and sense of connection he and Jill once had. Yet she kept pushing him away. He couldn't help making sarcastic comments in front of others, like 'Sex? What's that — I can't remember!', even though he knew it only made things worse. Jack finally decided to do something about the situation. He bought Jill a magazine in which couples described their erotic experiences. Jill threw it in the garbage. Jack later retrieved the magazine and used it when he secretly masturbated to let off excess sexual steam on his own.

Every time they had an argument, Jack and Jill seemed to end up fighting about sex. Jill accused Jack of being interested in nothing but sex, while he claimed she had a 'sexual problem'. The more she rejected him, the more angry he became and the more he pursued her for sex. The more he chased her, the more she backed away.

This is a fairytale without a happy ending. In Nursery Rhyme Land there were no sex therapists or relationship counsellors — no-one to turn to for help.

Jack and Jill weren't the only ones experiencing difficulties. Jack Sprat's hearty wife confided to Jill one day that her husband was not only lean physically, but he was also lean in the sex drive department. She expected sex like clockwork each Saturday night, and he insisted on staying up till all hours doing crosswords. Jack Sprat's roly-poly wife had even considered going on a diet to gain her man's attention!

Whether your experience of desire discrepancy fits the Jack and Jill model (where the male has a higher interest than the female), or that of Mr and Mrs Sprat who have the opposite problem, no doubt you found elements in their stories that are similar to your own. Unfortunately, unless both these couples get help, the outlook is very dim indeed.

TYPICAL MISTAKES WE ALL MAKE

Jack and Jill are in a dilemma. They know they have a problem, but everything they do to solve it seems to make the situation worse. They are making all the typical mistakes that prevent partners from working together as a team to solve the DD dilemma:

- They have no knowledge about the true nature of sexual desire.
- Their expectations about what sex should be like in a long-term relationship are unrealistic.
- They blame each other for the problem; each considers the other to be 'abnormal'.
- They are caught in a vicious cycle where Jack chases Jill for sex at every opportunity, while Jill tries to avoid his overtures as much as she can. They are slowly but surely drifting apart.
- They don't have the communication and negotiation skills to resolve their difficulties and so they feel totally stuck.
- Jack and Jill believe they have a serious sexual problem. They both agree that in a healthy relationship these sorts of sexual differences shouldn't occur.

Be your own sex therapist

Can you recognise elements of your own situation in Jack and Jill's story? Perhaps you and your partner are making similar mistakes when you try to handle your difficulties.

How much do you know about the inner workings of sexual desire?
Have you been blaming each other for the problem?
Do you think your partner is abnormal?
Do you find it difficult to talk about sex together?
Do you feel stuck and unable to solve your dilemma?

Let's examine Jack and Jill's mistakes more closely.

Lack of knowledge about sexual desire

Jack and Jill can't really be blamed for their lack of knowledge about sexual desire. After all, no mention is made of desire or desire problems in sex education programs. Parents rarely mention desire to their children, except to warn of the dangers of 'succumbing to lust'.

> **Jack:** Sex education? Dad took me to a Father and Son night and we saw a movie about how chickens reproduce. That was about it, I'd say.
> **Jill:** Mum gave me a talk about periods and told me not to lead boys on or I'd get into trouble.

We need to know how sex drive works if we are to overcome problems with DD. Trying to fix something when you don't know how it works is asking for trouble. Take my car, for example. I know a lot about sex but very little about car engines. Recently my car broke down on the freeway. The mechanic who answered my call for help was able to tell at a glance what was wrong and how to fix it. When differing levels of sexual interest start to cause problems in a relationship, most people are like me with my car. They know very little about the mechanics of their sexual desire, so they have no idea how to fix problems when they arise.

Understanding the nature of sex drive is fundamental to solving desire problems. Only by becoming familiar with what is 'under the bonnet' of our sex drive can we hope to have a smooth journey on the highway of love!

Unrealistic expectations about sex in a long-term relationship

Both Jack and Jill expected their lust level to sizzle forever, just as it did in the early months of their relationship. They also expected their sex life to flourish despite their difficult day-to-day circumstances and their very typical relationship difficulties. Neither realised that desire normally

> Marriage is popular because it combines the maximum of temptation with the maximum of opportunity.
>
> G.B. SHAW
> IRISH PLAYWRIGHT

fluctuates from minute to minute, depending on each partner's emotional and physical wellbeing and the state of their relationship. When their unrealistic expectations of passionate, frequent sex were not met, they both felt cheated and angry.

> **Jack:** When we got married, I thought: Great — sex every day for the rest of my life!
> **Jill:** I just assumed that because we loved each other we'd automatically want sex at the same time. If I didn't want it, then he wouldn't want it. Boy, was I wrong.

Like Jack, most of us assume that the passionate interest in sex experienced by lovers early in their relationship must be normal, a benchmark by which to measure our sexual relationship in later years. We are totally unprepared for the inevitable changes in sex drive as our relationship matures. We expect life and love to remain the same although we turn from a couple into a family, move house, change jobs, and face unemployment, financial difficulties and bereavement.

Jill has fallen prey to another popular myth about sex drive — that a couple's interest in sex will magically match up if they truly care about each other.

Blaming and judging your partner

> **Jack:** If Jill would just loosen up about things, we wouldn't have a problem. She should lighten up, relax and enjoy sex more, then all our problems would be solved.
>
> **Jill:** All he thinks about is sex, sex, sex. If he could keep his mind above his belt for a few minutes, we wouldn't have the difficulties we're having now.

Faced with DD, partners will often throw the hot potato of blame backwards and forwards until their hands are burnt and one or the other decides to give up the game (and often the relationship). DD is a couple problem. Both partners must take responsibility for their contribution to the situation and both need to make changes. Solving DD requires teamwork. The good news is that being part of the problem means you can be part of the solution, too.

Jack and Jill also engage in the popular pastime of making the other person wrong. Usually it goes something like this: He's a sex maniac and she's frigid. Or: He's a sexual failure and she's insatiable. In the majority of cases, neither partner is sexually abnormal. Couples simply don't have the know-how to approach this problem with the sensitivity and compassion it requires.

Believing that you're entitled to sex

Jack and Jill have differing levels of sexual interest, but both are normal. However, as the lower desire partner, Jill is much more likely to feel abnormal and to be blamed for the DD problem because of society's fickle attitudes to sex.

Currently, society dictates that a high libido is 'normal' and anything less is abnormal or inadequate. These days everybody, regardless of age, sex or relationship status, should be thinking of sex every waking moment, otherwise there is something seriously wrong with them. If the higher drive partner wants sex, then it is their partner's job to provide it.

This attitude of sexual entitlement can lead to behaviour that is totally unacceptable under any circumstances in a relationship.

Deprived of their 'rightful' sexual frequency, higher drive partners may become insistent, relentlessly initiating sex and demanding satisfaction. It is not unusual to find higher drive partners criticising the sexuality of their partners and blaming them for the sexual difficulties in the relationship. One client I counselled gave his wife the nickname 'Fridge' to remind her of her inadequacies. Sadly, emotional, sexual and physical abuse is also reported under these circumstances.

If your partner has a higher interest in sex than you do, you are likely to be seen as the one with the 'problem'. If only *you* would change and want more sex, then hey presto — no problem!

> I am happy now that Charles calls on my bedchamber less frequently than of old. As it is, I now endure but two calls a week and when I hear his steps outside my door I lie down on my bed, close my eyes, open my legs, and think of England.
>
> LADY HILLINGDON

Sexual attitudes swing like a pendulum, from permissive to repressive and back again, each swing taking around a hundred years. In the Victorian era, at the close of the 19th century, a low interest in sex among women was considered godly, chaste and perfectly normal, while a high sex drive was seen as a moral failing. Women were expected to close their eyes 'and think of England', and men were seen as victims of shameful lust they could barely control.

How times have changed! In the 1990s a high sex drive is the ultimate sexual accessory for both men and women. Women are currently expected to get wet at the drop of a hat, let alone a man's pants! Men, too, are expected to be consumed with sexual thoughts and urges. These days it's tough to admit to feeling lukewarm about sex.

Tina and Charlie had been married for eight years and lived with their two young sons in the country. Tina no longer felt any interest in sex with Charlie. This was causing problems in their marriage and they sought the advice of a marriage counsellor in the closest large township. The counsellor, a man in his fifties, did not have any training in the area of sexual desire difficulties.

When Charlie explained that he wasn't getting enough sex, the counsellor immediately turned his focus to Tina. 'Why are you withholding sex from Charlie?' he asked. He pointed out that men have bodily needs and that it's a wife's duty to fulfil them. He blamed Tina for the problem and wondered aloud why Charlie had stayed with her for so long. The couple left with Tina in tears. That night, Charlie told Tina that unless she gave him more sex he would either leave her or have an affair.

There is no such thing as an entitlement to sex. Sex is a matter of negotiation and compromise between two partners, not a relationship right. In recent years the emphasis in DD work has fortunately begun to shift from deciding which person in the relationship has the 'problem', to a concept of shared responsibility for the sexual relationship.

A vicious cycle

When DD occurs, relationships can rapidly get out of kilter. The more the higher drive partner presses for sex, the more the lower drive partner withdraws and avoids sex. The higher drive partner may become demanding and impatient, angry and critical. The lower drive partner shuts down. Both partners start to relate to each other in ways that are toxic to the relationship. Resentment, anger, frustration, guilt and despair are common side effects of this vicious cycle. This pursuer/distancer cycle is described in full in Chapter 10.

Poor communication and negotiation skills

DD is made worse by a couple's lack of communication and poor problem-solving skills. Few people feel comfortable talking about sex. In fact, we are more likely to communicate our interest in sex or lack of it with our faces and our bodies than with words. Our non-verbal communication about sex works fine until a problem crops up. Problem-solving skills like negotiation and compromise require in-depth discussion about sex, a topic which most people find very difficult to broach, let alone explore thoroughly.

Believing differences in sex drive shouldn't occur in a healthy relationship

Couples who have differing levels of interest in sex are often told they have a sexual problem, a sexual dysfunction or a sexual disorder. This labelling is based on the erroneous belief that 'normal' couples should have a perfectly matched set of sex drives from day one of their relationship.

Contrary to current popular opinion (even some professional opinion), couples who experience differing levels of interest in sex (desire discrepancy, or DD) are not abnormal, nor are they suffering from a sexual 'dysfunction' or 'disorder'. They are experiencing a sexual inevitability.

DESIRE DISCREPANCY — A SEXUAL INEVITABILITY

Why an inevitability? Sex drive naturally fluctuates according to what is going on in our lives and our relationships — up one day and down the next. It is unrealistic to think that one partner's sex drive will wax and wane at the same rate as the other's.

The vast majority of couples will encounter mismatched sex drives at some stage in their relationships. The mismatch may be mild or severe, short or long-term. Irrespective of the degree of the mismatch, the experience of DD is normal in long-term romantic relationships. Normalising desire discrepancy is the crucial first step in resolving the differences.

RESOLVING DESIRE DISCREPANCY

Effective treatment of desire problems requires a *total relationship approach*, not just a sexual one. To resolve a desire mismatch, a couple must first accept that DD is normal. Any damage to the relationship must be healed and the toxic cycles of pursuing and distancing interrupted. Finally, the couple needs to learn how to negotiate sexual styles and activities, as well as sexual frequency.

A MORE POSITIVE VIEW

Desire differences need not spell marital discord or disaster. The proof of the pudding is that not all couples who have a disparity in sex drives necessarily see themselves as having a difficulty. Many couples learn to compromise and cope with the differences, working with the problem rather than against it. They figure out practical ways to deal with the differences, adjusting their relationship over the years. They attack the problem and not each other.

Instead of viewing this inevitable difference in sexual needs negatively, and labelling the situation a sexual catastrophe, why not see DD as a challenge? Working hand-in-hand with your partner to overcome your desire mismatch has many advantages. Apart from accruing the obvious sexual benefits, you will also gain personal and relationship growth, a deeper understanding of each other's needs, and a strengthening of your mutual sexual and love bonds. In addition, skills learnt from successfully dealing with sexual difficulties can be usefully employed outside the bedroom to deal with other issues causing conflict.

Given the right tools and the motivation to work together, every couple with desire discrepancy who wishes to improve their sexual compatibility will be able to do so. Some couples may need the added support of professional counselling from a sex or relationship therapist, but most people should be able to work together to improve their relationships and their sex lives once they have been taught how to deal with DD.

Key Points ⋅ϑ⋅

Desire discrepancy is not only common, it is normal and inevitable at some time in all long-term relationships. What is not inevitable is the unhappiness and conflict that most couples experience when sex drives differ.

Our ideas about what is sexually normal go in and out of fashion. Currently, a high level of sexual interest is in fashion. Anything less is wrongly regarded as inadequate or abnormal.

When a couple has the skills and willingness to work together to achieve sexual compatibility, DD need not cause problems in the relationship.

DD is a challenge, not a catastrophe. It is an opportunity for personal, sexual and relationship growth.

The River of Desire

T o overcome the challenges posed by differences in desire, you need to understand the origins of sexual desire and the factors that increase or decrease your interest in sex. Armed with this practical information, you can then start to work on overcoming desire discrepancy.

THE ORIGINS OF SEX DRIVE

If you ask people where their sex drive comes from, you will get a smorgasbord of answers. Some think it's *hormonal* — a product of the chemical cocktails circulating in our blood. Others think it's *all in the mind* — purely psychological, based on our feelings and thoughts. The romantics among us say that sexual desire emanates *from the love and trust found in a close relationship*. More practical people might say it is a natural *reflection of good health and wellbeing*.

So who is right? They all are! Our sex drive originates in the brain, and is influenced by our hormones, our physical wellbeing, our thoughts and feelings, and the quality of our relationship. The origins of our sex drive are both biological and psychological. They can be readily understood by using a simple model.

THE RIVER OF DESIRE

Human sexual desire has many characteristics in common with a large river system. Just as a river is made up from many different sources of water, sex drive comes from a variety of biological and psychological sources. A river may run in full flood or dry up completely. Sex drive also ebbs and flows, modulated by your health, emotional wellbeing and the state of your relationship.

A river begins its life in the mountains as streams, which join together to form a body of water that flows across the plains to the sea. The waters cannot be separated once they are joined. Nor can you know by looking at the river which volume of water originally came from which source.

Sex drive is created in the same way from a number of different sources. These sources can be classified into either biological sources or psychological sources, as shown in the table below.

SOURCES OF SEXUAL DESIRE

Biological Sources
Neurological sources
The neurological sources of desire include the brain and the nervous system of the body.

Hormones
The main desire hormone is the male hormone, testosterone, present in both men and women.

Physical wellbeing
Your physical health, or lack of it, can profoundly affect levels of sexual desire.

Psychological Sources
Personal wellbeing
What you *feel* and how you *think* can alter levels of sexual desire. Your *lifestyle* and *environment* will also affect your sexual interest.

Relationship wellbeing
Levels of desire will be enhanced by a happy, fulfilling relationship and inhibited by an unsatisfactory, conflicted coupling.

These five streams join to form the River of Desire.

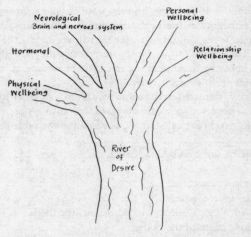

When the banks of your desire river are full, you think about sex more often, feel horny, and are more inclined to act and react sexually. If one or more sources of your river dry up or are dammed in some way, your river will dwindle to a trickle, with sex falling lower and lower on your list of priorities.

In the worst case scenario, the river may dry up altogether: no sexual thoughts, no sexual feelings, no sexual responses or overtures. In short — a sexual drought!

This model makes it clear why your sex drive fluctuates. When things are good emotionally and physically, and your relationship is in good shape, desire can be present in abundance. When your relationship is full of conflict, or your health is poor or there are too many stresses, desire can fade away completely.

Each source of desire has a part to play in determining on any given day whether you will be frothing at the mouth for sex, or more interested in your butterfly collection than an erotic romp with your partner.

THE BIOLOGY OF DESIRE

Let's take a closer look at the biological factors that influence desire. (In Chapter 3 we'll examine the psychological sources of sex drive.)

Biological drive has its origins in your:
- neurological system — the brain and nervous system
- hormonal system
- physical wellbeing.

The biggest sex organ of all — the brain

To understand the contribution of the neurological system, you need to take the focus away from below the belt where the problem seems to lie, and concentrate on your major sex organ,

> My brain? It's my second favourite organ.
> WOODY ALLEN

which lies between your ears, not between your legs — *the brain*.

Your sex drive has its origins in the most primitive part of your brain, the limbic system and the hypothalamus.

Sex drive is generated by desire centres in the brain, similar to the

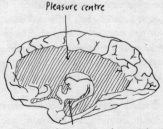

Pleasure centre

Sex, aggression and fear

way electric currents are produced by a generator. In some people the current produced is naturally high, and in others it is naturally low. Your 'sexual electricity' varies from day to day, even moment to moment. On a good day your sex drive may be high, but on the day you get fired, drive into a pylon in the parking station and fight with your partner, your libido will most likely be at an all-time low.

Your appetite for sex is regulated, just like your need for food and drink, by centres in the brain that enhance or inhibit your appetites. The difference between the sex drive and your drives of hunger and thirst is that no-one has yet died from a lack of sex!

Specific structures in the hypothalamus seem to control distinct aspects of sexual behaviour. The *active sexual behaviour centre* governs initiation of sex, and this area is larger in male brains than in female. Its action is based on the male hormone, testosterone. It is probably responsible for the fact that, as a broad generalisation, men are more likely to initiate sex than women.

The *receptive sexual behaviour centre* in the hypothalamus is associated with the female hormone, oestrogen, and promotes passive sexual behaviour. This centre works to make females more receptive to sexual advances.

Sexual desire and sexual arousal

Sexual desire means feeling horny or having an interest in sexual activity. *Sexual arousal* means being turned on and physically ready to participate in sex. For a woman this means lubrication, and for a man, erection.

There is a direct link between your levels of sex drive and your capacity to become sexually aroused. A person with high levels of desire will find it easier to become turned on. The opposite is also true. A low level of sexual interest will make sexual arousal harder to achieve. The desire centre in your brain is thought to affect your capacity for sexual arousal by stimulating or depressing the physical reflexes in the lowest (sacral) part of the spinal cord. No doubt this effect is supported by your own experience.

> **Judy:** My husband Paul doesn't realise that on low desire days I need a lot more time and energy to get turned on. He is always keen to have sex and gets turned on in a flash. The minute I think he's hurrying me, I turn off and then nothing works. I wish he'd understand that every day is different for me.

Fortunately, desire and arousal occur independently of each other. You don't need to feel horny to get turned on. If you are willing to be sexually involved, you can become aroused and enjoy sexual activity whether you experience desire or not.

Hormonal origins

Desire also has a hormonal basis. Hormones are powerful chemicals created by various organs of the body that travel in the bloodstream and activate other organs. Well-known examples of hormones include insulin from the pancreas and thyroxine from the thyroid gland. Sex hormones include the female hormones oestrogen and progesterone, and the male hormone testosterone. *Desire in both men and women is believed to be mainly fuelled by the male hormone, testosterone.*

Testosterone — the 'he' hormone
Testosterone in men comes mostly from the testes and is responsible for masculine characteristics such as facial and body hair, as well as for their deeper voices and more muscular physiques. Men's testosterone levels vary on a daily basis. Secretion is at its highest, often doubling, just after sunrise. Testosterone levels also rise when men fight, watch a violent film or TV show, exercise, win at sport (even at chess) and when they think about sex.

There is no direct correlation between a man's level of sexual interest and the level of testosterone in his blood, as *long as his testosterone level stays within normal limits*. In other words, a man who has a 'low normal' level of testosterone is just as likely to be the town stud as the man whose testosterone level is 'high normal'.

Testosterone production from the testes peaks during the twenties and thirties. This is followed by a slow decline in testosterone levels which affects libido in some men but not others. Some men at 50 have such low levels of testosterone that they lose all interest in sex, while others at 80 are still as keen as ever. It is known that men who drink and smoke to excess have reduced levels of testosterone in their blood. It's not just the level of testosterone that counts. As men age, their tissues become less responsive to this hormone. When a man experiences loss of sexual interest, especially if the problem comes on suddenly, a simple blood test can exclude a hormonal cause. This should be performed three times at eight-week intervals before testosterone replacement is initiated.

There are medical conditions that cause lowered levels of testosterone and result in lowering or loss of sexual desire. Men with advanced cancer of the prostate are sometimes advised to take hormones that suppress testosterone or to undergo orchidectomy (surgical removal of the testes) to prevent rapid tumour growth. This results in loss of sexual desire in these people.

> Dear Dr Rosie,
> My husband wants sex morning, noon and night. Is there any medication I can give him to reduce his sex drive?

In the old days a little bromide in soldiers' tea was believed to decrease their interest in sex. I doubt whether they noted any difference. Medication that reduces sex drive in men is now restricted to the treatment of sex offenders. Side effects include fatigue, weight gain and breast growth.

Sex hormones and female libido

Both male and female hormones have a part to play in female sex drive. Women produce testosterone and other androgens (chemicals which produce masculine characteristics) but at very low levels. Androgens are secreted, along with the female hormones oestrogen and progesterone, by the ovaries and also by the adrenal glands near the kidneys. Although women produce only tiny amounts of testosterone and other androgens, their bodies are extremely sensitive to them. For example, it only takes a small quantity of testosterone medication to give a woman the side effects of facial hair, acne or a deepening of the voice.

As men's testosterone level is 10 to 20 times higher than women's, it comes as no surprise that men generally have a stronger interest in sex than women. This does not mean that a man with a lower interest than his partner is abnormal.

Oestrogen and progesterone — the 'she' hormones

The influence of the female hormones, oestrogen and progesterone, on sex drive is not yet clear. Some women note fluctuations in sex drive according to their menstrual cycle: some peak at mid-cycle, others premenstrually, and some during or just after their period. Studies have shown a peak of testosterone levels around the time of ovulation, which may account for increased levels of sexual interest at that time.

Fluctuating levels of oestrogen throughout the menstrual cycle may in part account for changes in female desire. Oestrogen makes a woman more sensitive to sensual stimulation through the five senses. Thanks to oestrogen, a woman will be more or less receptive to sensual touch, to erotic smells and sights, and to the taste and sound of her partner at different times of the month.

This important oestrogen effect means that sensual aspects of a relationship are more significant to women than men — the amount and type of touching from her partner, the way he speaks to her, and his grooming and hygiene can increase or reduce her interest in making love with him.

It is widely known that women have a superior sense of smell compared with men. This oestrogen effect explains why women are so sensitive to body odours, both their own and others. A man might be blissfully unaware that he has knockout body odour and be totally surprised when his woman recoils in disgust from his 'manly odour'. I suppose we have oestrogen to blame for the fact that his gym shoes are more offensive to her than they are to him!

Women commonly feel uncomfortable and embarrassed about their own genital aromas, some even resorting to perfumed sprays to mask their scent. Yet most men love the musky sexual smell of women. Knowing that the sexes differ in this way may help some women to be more accepting of their natural body scents.

Progesterone, which is secreted mainly in the second half of a woman's monthly cycle, has an inhibiting effect on a woman's sexual and sensual responses. When progesterone levels are high, both sexes are less responsive to sexual attraction via body aromas and pheromones (sexual attractants that are undetectable to the human sense of smell). Women who use hormonal contraception

containing progesterone (the Pill, the Mini Pill or injectable progesterone) may notice a drop in sexual interest due to these effects.

There is still much to learn about the effects of female sex hormones on desire. Further research may help to shed light on the
role these hormones play in inhibiting or promoting sex drive.

Testosterone therapy — 'Give 'em all a shot!'

Given what we know about the enhancing effect of testosterone
on sex drive, it would seem reasonable to suggest that anyone
with a lowered level of sex drive might benefit from testosterone
therapy. There is one fly in this therapeutic ointment: Testosterone
replacement therapy only works when a person is low on natural
testosterone.

Unfortunately, many men with sexual difficulties who consult
their doctors are automatically prescribed a course of testosterone
injections. This treatment will only work if the man's own level of
testosterone is below the normal limits. By giving men with
normal testosterone levels additional testosterone, existing cancer
of the prostate, a common male malignancy, may be aggravated.
Testosterone replacement therapy should only be given to men
after blood tests have proved a deficiency in hormone levels and
the prostate gland has been thoroughly checked.

Most people are familiar with hormonal replacement therapy
(HRT) for women who have passed through the menopause.
Women who receive HRT with oestrogen and progesterone often
find that their sex drive is improved, but this is probably due to a
reduction in menopausal symptoms and an improved sense of general wellbeing, rather than a direct effect on sexual desire.

Research is currently being carried out to investigate the effects
of giving women tiny amounts of testosterone after menopause in
addition to traditional HRT with female hormones. Results suggest that testosterone does have a beneficial effect in women who
have lost sex drive after the menopause. Women on testosterone
replacement therapy also report a greater feeling of wellbeing and
zest for life.

What about giving young women testosterone therapy? Some
doctors prescribe testosterone injections for women who have
given birth 9 to 12 months earlier and still feel no return of desire.

Yet lowered desire for up to two years and longer is so common after a baby is born that it should be considered a normal experience. There are more effective ways to deal with loss of sexual interest and desire discrepancy than giving women injections of testosterone. In Chapter 20 we will discuss new mums and sexual desire in more detail.

The amount of testosterone needed to give sexual enhancement can also give some women unwanted side effects. It's not much fun being more sexually inclined if you get acne, start growing a beard and your voice drops to a deep baritone! Not only can side effects be troubling, but the effect of testosterone replacement on female desire is still very much under debate. This therapy may result in increased sensitivity of the female genitals rather than a greater interest in sex. Testosterone in women can cause enlargement of the clitoris and heighten its sensitivity to sexual stimulation. This enlargement may be permanent and can persist after therapy has ceased.

Hormones have an important role to play in generating sex drive, but it seems that giving quick-fix hormone treatments to either sex is only appropriate in special cases. *There is no place for indiscriminate administration of testosterone in either men or women for problems with sexual desire.*

Sexual chemistry

There are many body chemicals in addition to male and female sex hormones that influence sex drive and sexual response.

Dopamine is a neurotransmitter (brain chemical) responsible for your experience of sexual pleasure. Dopamine increases sex drive and sexual arousal, and promotes orgasm and sexual satisfaction. Another neurotransmitter, **Serotonin** facilitates warm social intimacy short of sexual activity. Serotonin promotes contentment, but it can inhibit both desire and orgasm.

Oxytocin, known as the 'cuddle chemical', facilitates the sensation of touch, together with feelings of attraction and bonding. Oxytocin is released into a woman's bloodstream when she begins suckling her baby, triggering the 'let down' reflex and releasing milk from the breasts. It has an obvious function in helping a mother bond with her baby. Oxytocin levels in the bloodstream in both men and women increase after a person is touched by another in a positive way. When a pattern of positive touching has been established, levels of oxytocin increase in the bloodstream when pleasurable touching is anticipated. It's not surprising we all look forward to a cuddle!

> Dear Dr Rosie,
> The only time my husband touches me is when he wants sex. We never hold hands, or kiss hello or goodbye, and he rarely gives me a hug. I'm sure I would be more keen to have sex with him if he met some of my needs for hugs and kisses.

One way to increase sex drive in a lower drive partner is to introduce regular affectionate kissing, hugging, holding and touching into your relationship — pleasurable touching that does *not* necessarily lead to sex. Consistent affection without sexual demands enhances sex drive by increasing levels of oxytocin in the bloodstream.

Prolactin is an important brain chemical that negatively affects sex drive. Prolactin reduces desire on its own, but it also lowers testosterone levels with obvious consequences. Prolactin levels are high during breast-

> The union of hands and hearts.
> JEREMY TAYLOR
> ENGLISH DIVINE

feeding to maintain milk production in the nursing mother. Prolactin levels surge during nausea, vomiting and fainting — no wonder so many pregnant and lactating women have a lowered interest in sex.

Adrenaline, your stress hormone, excites sexual responses in small amounts, but in excessive amounts it is a powerful passion killer.

DHEA and **DHEAS** (Dehydroepiandosterone and Dehydroepiandosterone sulphate) are testosterone-like chemicals secreted by the adrenal glands and by the limbic area of the brain. DHEA and DHEAS appear to have a positive effect on libido, stimulating sex drive in both men and women and promoting sexual arousal. Levels of these hormones increase after exercise and meditation.

This explains why exercise and deep relaxation techniques like meditation are not only good for you, they are good for your sexual desire as well.

DHEA and DHEAS levels reach a peak in the third decade of life and decrease slowly thereafter, so that levels are quite low by the age of 60, possibly making some contribution to decreasing interest in sex with age. These libido-enhancing hormones probably account for the fact that some women do not lose their sex drive after menopause, even though their ovaries stop producing testosterone. In years to come, we will no doubt be hearing more about these important steroid hormones.

As you can see, hormones have a lot to answer for when it comes to the highs and lows of sex drive. So far we have looked at two important biological factors in desire — the desire centres in the brain and the effects of hormones on desire. Next we need to take a look at how your physical wellbeing influences your interest in sex.

Physical Wellbeing

It is commonsense that an individual's physical wellbeing will have a profound influence on their interest in sex. Any form of physical malaise will decrease levels of sex drive. It may be pain — headache, backache, arthritis, toothache, period pain or fatigue, physical tension and other stress-induced physical symptoms. A short-term illness like a cold or flu, or a long-term problem like kidney failure or cancer will dampen sex drive. The medicines you use to treat illness may also affect your libido negatively. If you have questions about the impact of your health on your sexual function, consult your physician.

Be your own sex therapist

Could any of these conditions be inhibiting your or your partner's sex drive?

- fatigue
- physical tension
- acute and chronic pain
- chronic heart disease
- chronic lung disease
- any acute or chronic infection
- auto-immune diseases
- recurrent urinary tract infections
- recurrent vaginal thrush and other vaginal irritations
- kidney disease
- thyroid disease
- liver disease
- cancer
- high alcohol intake
- opiate addiction
- diseases of the nervous system
- anorexia nervosa
- muscle diseases
- painful intercourse
- malnutrition
- blood disorders
- metabolic diseases
- hormone disturbances
- chromosomal abnormalities.

Many drugs also reduce your libido, including:

- treatment with steroids (cortisone)
- some antidepressants and tranquillisers
- some blood pressure medications
- some diuretics
- some anti-ulcer medications
- some appetite suppressants in men
- progesterone administration
- cancer treatments — radiotherapy, chemotherapy and hormone therapy.

By looking after your health in general — eating a healthy diet, avoiding cigarettes, drugs and excessive alcohol, only taking essential medication, getting regular exercise and avoiding high levels of stress — you can maximise your level of sex drive.

The origins of sex drive are both biological and psychological. The **biological** factors include the brain and the nervous system, hormones and physical wellbeing.

High sexual desire makes it easier to get sexually aroused and low sexual interest makes it more difficult to get turned on through the action of the brain on the sexual reflexes in the lower part of the spinal cord.

The desire centres in the brain are activated or depressed by a number of hormones. The main desire hormone in both men and women is the male hormone, testosterone. Men produce 10 to 20 times more testosterone than women do, but women are highly sensitive to it.

The role played by the female hormones, oestrogen and progesterone, in sexual desire remains unclear. Oestrogen stimulates the senses, and progesterone inhibits them in both men and women.

Some women may benefit from the addition of testosterone therapy to their hormonal replacement therapy after the menopause. Indiscriminate administration of testosterone in either men or women is unhelpful and may be dangerous.

Any impairment in physical wellbeing may reduce sexual interest. What's good for you is also good for your sex drive.

The Psychology of Desire — Our Thoughts, Feelings and Relationships

Psychological drive for sex results from a combination of *personal* and *relationship* factors. Personal factors impacting on desire include:

- your thoughts and feelings
- your lifestyle and environment.

PERSONAL FACTORS — THINKING AND FEELING

What you think and how you feel can swell your River of Desire or dam it up completely.

The impact of feelings

Emotions play a vital role in the induction or suppression of your sex drive. If you are relaxed and happy, your sex drive is likely to rise; if you are stressed and angry, it will probably plummet.

Marian, 26, had lost interest in sex with her husband Grant over the previous 12 months. Recently she had been promoted to a management position and she believed that work stress was the reason she didn't want sex.

Marian was right — work was a factor. But so was the fact that her younger sister was suffering from an eating disorder and had been in and out of hospital for the last year. Her parents had split up and her alcoholic mother had come to live with her. Marian had a lot more than work stress to contend with.

Marian was diagnosed as suffering from severe depression in addition to her work stress, her anxiety over her sister, her anger at her father and her resentment of her mother. If Marian had experienced a high level of sex drive while carrying this emotional load, I would have wanted to know why!

In primitive times, to preserve the human race, desire was originally under the control of emotions. This survival mechanism prevented us from becoming sexually involved in circumstances that may be adverse or even dangerous to us. For example, without emotional modulation of desire, our ancestors might have procreated when they were too ill or too stressed to care for their offspring. Or, overcome by desire, they might have made sexual approaches to hostile partners who could have harmed or even killed them. Anger, anxiety and depression are still potent signals to shut down sexual activity. The influence of emotions on desire is no longer required to save the human race, but it remains an integral part of our sexual make-up and cannot be ignored or avoided.

Sex drive is reduced by all the uncomfortable feelings, including stress, guilt, shame, depression, resentment, anger, despair, hopelessness and worry. Reducing or resolving your uncomfortable feelings is a key step in increasing your desire for sex. Kylie's uncomfortable feelings related directly to sex.

> Kylie: I grew up in a family where sex was never discussed. My dad used to turn off the TV if there was a kissing scene in a movie. When my older sister got pregnant at 16, she was kicked out. I love my husband David, but whenever things get sexual I feel ashamed and scared. Even though David and I have been married for eight years, it still feels like my dad is watching everything we do. I'm working with a counsellor to overcome my shame and guilt about sex. I'm slowly becoming more relaxed, and recently I've started to enjoy making love with David.

Improving your sex life is not the only reason for mending your emotional wellbeing, but it certainly is a good one.

The impact of thoughts

Over years of counselling couples with desire difficulties, I have noticed an interesting phenomenon. This is the ability of individuals to think themselves 'into' and 'out of' sex. A person can literally think themselves 'into sex' by focusing on pleasant thoughts about sex and their partner, pleasing aspects of the relationship, satisfying sexual experiences in the past, and the positives to be gained from sharing sexual activity with their partner.

They can just as easily do the opposite by not thinking about sex at all or by concentrating on negative aspects of sex and their relationship. This 'stinking thinking' about sex and their partner reduces feelings of desire. Until this habit is pointed out, most people are unaware that they have any conscious control over their libidos.

A perfect example of thinking ourselves 'into' sex occurs during courtship. In the early weeks, months and years of romantic relationships, sex drive tends to peak because of this very mechanism. We only focus on positives about our partners and screen out the negatives — it's no wonder we have the hots for them!

Focusing on the positives and tuning out the negatives

A partner with lowered libido can increase desire by thinking more positively about their partner, their relationship and about sex. Of course, for this strategy to work the higher drive partner must consistently provide positive experiences for the lower drive partner to concentrate on.

When a couple has been having desire discrepancy problems for some time, they get into the habit of looking out for the negatives. Initially it can be very difficult for them to start thinking about each other in a positive way.

Early in her marriage to Morris, Ruth was sexually interested and keen to make love whenever they were able. Morris was a capable lover and Ruth felt sexually satisfied and happy with their relationship in general.

Things were fine until the birth of their first child, Samuel. Morris expected Ruth to stay at home and be a housewife and mother, just as his mother had done. Ruth's family was very different. After Ruth's father ran off, Ruth's mother and sisters worked together as a team sharing all the responsibilities.

Ruth wanted to keep working and expected Morris to share the household and parenting tasks with her. They were unable to resolve their conflicts, and over time Ruth became emotionally and sexually distant and eventually lost interest in sex completely. Morris felt rejected, cheated and abandoned, and often had temper tantrums.

When this couple first sought help, Ruth could barely find a good word to say about Morris. She complained about the way he looked, the clothes he wore, the way he smelt, his snoring, his eating habits, his tantrums, his demands on her. Over time, they worked through their domestic differences, but Ruth's sex drive remained at an all-time low.

Ruth still needed to 'focus on the positives and tune out the negatives'. Ruth's first task was to make a list of the reasons why she and Morris fell in love. She was then to mark off all those positive factors that were still a part of their relationship. Ruth was surprised to find how many things she still liked about Morris.

Further discussion revealed that Ruth's mother had a habit of bad-mouthing Ruth's father and men in general. Ruth had grown up with the sound of negativity against men ringing in her ears. Once she was aware of this learnt tendency to focus on bad points about men, she found it easier to see the positives of Morris and their relationship.

Morris, on the other hand, had a lot of work to do himself. Following my advice, he began to listen to Ruth's pleas for better hygiene and personal habits. His task was to find ways to help, nurture and support Ruth so that she felt loved, special and appreciated for what she did.

I encouraged both of them to acknowledge each other for their progress and to compliment each other whenever appropriate. Morris loved receiving praise and was keen to 'do more to get more'. Given the tools for change, this couple warmed to the task and were delighted as Ruth's sex drive gradually began to reappear.

Ruth still finds she has a tendency to slip back into her old habits of seeing only the bad and ignoring the good in Morris and, when she does, her sex drive starts to disappear again. Fortunately, both Ruth and Morris now know what to do to get their relationship and their sex life back on track.

This case study is a good example of how someone can think themselves out of sex and, given the right conditions, can think themselves right back into it again. However, it must be emphasised that it's not possible to focus on the positive in a relationship or in a partner when there are few or no positives to be appreciated. This is why *both parties* need to work hard to meet each other's needs outside the bedroom to ensure a hassle-free time inside the bedroom.

Our emotional and intellectual control over our libido is exciting, because it means that we can influence our sexual desire by the way we think and feel and the way we behave towards each other in a relationship.

Be your own sex therapist

For the lower drive partner
- Do you notice your partner's good points, or do you only see the negatives?
- Can you remember what attracted you to your partner in the first place?
- Do you think about how pleasurable sex might be for you, or do you only concentrate on unpleasant aspects of sexual activity?
- What effect do you think an improvement in your relationship might have on your sex drive?

For the higher drive partner
- Have you fallen into bad habits of neglecting your partner and your relationship so that all they can see is negatives?
- Can you see how your behaviour may have a part to play in your partner's lowered level of desire?
- What can you do to improve the situation?

PERSONAL FACTORS — YOUR LIFESTYLE AND ENVIRONMENT

Lifestyle and environmental factors also affect your level of interest in sex, acting via your thoughts and feelings.

Lifestyle

Sex does not occur in a vacuum. It is influenced by everything else that is going on in your life. Lifestyle factors that can positively influence desire are adequate recreation and relaxation, time spent pursuing hobbies and other interests, job satisfaction and reasonable working hours. On the other hand, couples who work long hours at jobs they hate, who are highly stressed and never take time out for themselves or their relationships are creating a lifestyle that is not conducive to experiencing sexual desire.

> **Kaye:** Norman travels for work and spends a lot of time overseas. He expects me to feel like sex the moment he gets off the plane. He's away for three weeks and I'm left with the kids, my job and the house to run. I'm worn out by the time he gets back and he's like a stranger to me. Even when he's home, he works such long hours that I lose touch with him. My sex drive is really suffering.

Environmental factors

'Environmental factors' refer to the situations in which you and your partner conduct your intimate sensual and sexual activities. Examples include the room you choose, the day of the week, the time of day. Factors that impact positively on desire include adequate privacy, a comfortable and pleasing environment, and adequate time for intimate, sensual and sexual activities. Music, lighting and atmosphere are all important factors, especially to women, whose sensual facilities, as we learnt, are heightened by oestrogen. Factors that inhibit sexual desire range from no lock on the bedroom door when kids are about, to a noisy, untidy, unattractive or dirty bedroom.

Many couples expect sexual activity to carry on independent of their environment. They believe that once you become passionately involved it won't matter where you are, what colour the sheets are or what time of day it is. This is true — when you are really turned on, very little matters — the trick is to get to those high levels of arousal. This is often possible only when the environment is conducive to sensual and sexual activity.

> **Joanna:** I know it seems odd, but I just can't make love when the bedroom is untidy. The worst thing of all is having one of the cupboard doors open. I can't relax. If we could spend just a few minutes before going to bed tidying up the bedroom, I'm sure I'd feel more like making love.

It is common for one partner to be more sensitive to the environment than the other. The less sensitive partner may scoff at their spouse's need for a sexier ambience. However, it is much wiser to alter your environment to make sex more inviting than it is to force an unappealing environment onto a sensitive partner.

Relationships and Desire

The final tributary flowing into the River of Desire is the Relationship Stream. Relationship factors have a profound effect on willingness to be sexual, through the feeling and thinking channels described above. Sexual desire is often an early casualty in a relationship that is not working well.

Let's compare two neighbouring households:

At No. 5 John Street live Paul and Kathy who bicker constantly, wounding each other with sarcasm. He delights in humiliating her in front of others, and she is famous in the neighbourhood for her bad temper and sharp tongue. They avoid each other as much as possible.

A couple like this would be hard pressed to feel passionate sexual interest for each other. What about their neighbours?

At No. 7 we find Rick and Marie, a couple who enjoy mutual respect and affection. They make an effort to make each other feel special and to nurture their relationship on a daily basis. They are happy and feel secure and relaxed with each other. Not surprisingly, these lovebirds are more sexually inclined towards each other than their warring neighbours.

Your sexual desire is deeply affected by the wellbeing of your relationship. Relationship factors that feed into desire in a positive way are:

- good communication
- plenty of affection unrelated to sex
- mutual decision making
- shared control of the relationship
- unconditional love and acceptance
- trust — fidelity and jealousy issues resolved
- romance
- commitment
- intimacy
- constructive conflict resolution
- companionship
- respect
- attraction to partner
- satisfying sensual and sexual skills
- companionship and fun
- feeling appreciated.

The lifeblood of your sexual desire flows from within your relationship. Relationships are like hothouse plants that need constant nurturing and attention in order to survive and grow. Mutual sexual desire is a beautiful fruit that grows only on healthy plants. If you don't feed, water and protect your plant, keeping it healthy and thriving, you can't expect a robust crop of fruit.

If you want to heal your sex life, you must first heal your relationship. The steps to a better relationship are described in Section 3 of this book, 'Healing Your Relationship'.

THE EVER CHANGING RIVER OF DESIRE

Using the River of Desire model, it becomes abundantly clear how and why our sex drive fluctuates from day to day, week to week, month to month. It also helps to explain why so many couples experience differences in levels of sex drive. The more we understand about how desire works, the better we are equipped to resolve problems with libido.

Key Points ◄◊►

How we feel and what we think can either promote or suppress sexual desire.

It is possible to think yourself into and out of sex. To enhance sex drive, focus on the positives and tune out the negatives about yourself, your partner, your relationship and your sex life.

Lifestyle and environmental factors impact on sexual desire through the way we think and feel.

Sexual desire is deeply affected by what is happening between two people in their relationship. To enjoy a happy, healthy sex life you need to build a happy, healthy relationship. Great sex comes from good loving.

4

Pass Me the Ruler — Measuring Your Sex Drive

I f newspapers and women's magazines are any guide, people are obsessed with measuring and comparing their sex drives. Headlines scream, 'Are you getting enough?' and 'Does your sex life make the grade?' Before we take on the daunting task of measuring sex drive, let's define it.

WHAT IS SEX DRIVE?

Defining sex drive is difficult. How can you define lust, passion or feeling horny? Sexual researchers have come up with this definition: *Sexual drive is the motivation and inclination to be sexual.* According to this definition, sexual desire motivates us — it prompts us to seek out sex and to act in a sexual way. Sexual desire also inclines us towards sex — it renders us willing to be sexual and more likely to respond to sexual overtures and opportunities.

MEASURING DESIRE

If desire is difficult to define, then measuring it is even more challenging. How do you measure horniness? You can't use a ruler, a tape measure or a measuring jug to quantify desire. It's like trying to measure an orgasm. (One wag recently told me there are only two types of orgasm — fantastic and great!) To measure sexual desire, perhaps we could count the frequency of intercourse — once a week, twice a week, once a month, once a year. But it's possible to have regular intercourse with your partner and feel no desire at all. Many of you will have experienced this yourselves.

Frequency of intercourse can never accurately reflect an individual's level of sex drive, because intercourse needs two people to tango. The higher drive partner is often having less sex than desired, while the lower drive partner endures more sex than they require. Lovemaking with your long-term partner may be an infrequent, passionless affair, but you could happily set the night on fire with someone else — *anyone* else! What does that say about your level of libido?

Can frequency of masturbation tell us anything? Not really. Some people masturbate with great enthusiasm but are like cold fish with their partners. To complicate matters even further, people with a high sex drive might choose to be celibate, and those who act in a chronically promiscuous fashion may experience very little sex drive at all. Measuring sex drive turns out to be a real can of worms!

Assessing your sex drive

Which sex drive are we talking about? Are we talking about the sex drive you experienced as a teenager? The lust you enjoyed when you first fell in love? The libido you felt when you or your partner was pregnant? The passion that flared when the two of you went for two weeks' holiday without the kids? Or the desire you felt (or didn't feel) just after you lost your job?

Desire can change from moment to moment. Your sex drive today could well be higher or lower than it was last week, last month or last year. Let's make an assessment of your current level of sex drive.

Be your own sex therapist

To find out more about your current level of sexual interest, answer these questions. Circle the appropriate answer.

Do you have pleasurable thoughts about sex during the day?
Usually/ Frequently/ Sometimes/ Rarely/ Never

Do you find it easy to get into the mood for sex?
Usually/ Frequently/ Sometimes/ Rarely/ Never

Do you ever initiate lovemaking?
Usually/ Frequently/ Sometimes/ Rarely/ Never

Do you find it easy to get aroused and to stay that way?
Usually/ Frequently/ Sometimes/ Rarely/ Never

Do you have sexual fantasies?
Usually/ Frequently/ Sometimes/ Rarely/ Never

Do you respond positively to your partner's sexual overtures?
Usually/ Frequently/ Sometimes/ Rarely/ Never

Do you masturbate?
Usually/ Frequently/ Sometimes/ Rarely/ Never

Do you miss sex if you haven't made love for a while?
Usually/ Frequently/ Sometimes/ Rarely/ Never

If you answered 'Usually' or 'Frequently' to most of the questions, you currently have a robust interest in sex. If 'Rarely' or 'Never' was your most frequent answer, then your interest in sex is on the lower side at present. 'Sometimes' places you slap bang in the middle.

Ask your partner to complete the quiz and then compare answers. Is your sexual interest currently higher than your partner's, or lower?

A Better Way

In my clinical practice I have always felt uncomfortable about describing partners as having either a 'higher sex drive' or a 'lower sex drive'. This comparative description taps into all those unhelpful judgments about what is 'normal' and which partner has the 'problem'. I needed a way of describing differing levels of sex drive that did not rely on comparison.

The answer came to me as I examined my own personal experience of sex drive. Thanks to years of serial monogamy and two marriages, I had worn the hat of both the higher and lower drive partner on different occasions. I had experienced both sides of desire discrepancy, wanting more sex than one partner and less sex than another. I knew the exciting highs of desire during romantic courtship and the miserable depths of losing interest in sex completely. It occurred to me one day that *how much* desire you experience is not as important as how you *express* that desire in your relationship. Sexual desire could be described more effectively in terms of behaviours than comparisons like higher and lower. For example:

- When my sex drive is at its highest I am *initiatory*, making sexual overtures and taking an active sexual role.
- When my sexual interest is a little lower I feel *receptive* to sexual overtures if my husband chooses to make them. I am sexually interested and keenly motivated to participate.
- A little more down the desire scale, I am *available* for sexual activity. My sexual motivation is not particularly high, but I'm quite happy to make love if my husband feels in the mood.
- When my sex drive drops even more, I am *neutral* about sex. I can take it or leave it. Although mostly I am willing to participate in sex, I am prompted to participate by reasons other than urgent physical desire — my enjoyment of my husband's body, my needs for closeness and intimacy, my pleasure at being desired.
- At my lowest, I am *disinterested* in sex. I don't particularly feel a need for sex and if I decide to engage in sexual activity with my husband I might choose not to get turned on. If my husband isn't very interested in making love, I'm content to give it a miss.

I called these differing expressions of sexual interest *desire behaviour zones* — initiatory, receptive, available, neutral and disinterested. Like most people, my desire behaviour changes from zone to zone, depending on what is going on in my life and my relationship.

DESIRE BEHAVIOUR ZONES

The beauty of desire behaviour zones is that they reflect the range of sexual interest from low to high without making judgments or comparisons. This new terminology freed me and my patients from comparative descriptions of sex drive — higher, lower, more, less — and from all the prejudices surrounding quantification of sex drive. Desire behaviour zones simply reflect how people act and react to each other sexually.

Desire behaviour zones and arousal

Level of desire (wanting sex) has a direct effect on capacity to get aroused (turned on), as described in Chapter 2. People in the disinterested zone find it requires more effort to get aroused, while those in the initiatory zone find getting turned on as easy as falling off a log. Regardless of desire level, if an individual is willing to get turned on and their partner knows how to help, sexual arousal is possible. However, once the right attitudes are in place, sexual activity can still be enjoyable and fulfilling without sexual arousal. This is discussed later in Chapter 16.

The main differences between these five behaviour zones are:

- *Awareness of interest in sex* — ranging from feeling horny about sex to feeling 'yawny'.
- *How interest in sex is expressed* — ranging from actively seeking out sex to having a 'why bother' attitude.
- *The time it takes to get aroused once sensual and sexual contact begins* — initiatory = faster to arouse; disinterested = slower to arouse.

Initiatory zone

People in the initiatory zone think about sex frequently and make verbal and non-verbal moves towards sex. They will actively seek out sexual opportunities and be responsive to sexual cues from others. Initiatory people are usually aware of feeling 'horny'. Some people are highly initiatory, while others are mildly initiatory.

Men are more likely to take on an initiatory role for two reasons. First, high testosterone levels boost their interest in sex even in adverse circumstances and, second, society *expects* men to be the sexual aggressors. Initiatory people find it very easy to move from desire (wanting sex) to arousal (being turned on). At this high level of sexual interest, desire and arousal can almost merge into one.

> **Rowan:** I just look at my girlfriend Misha and I get turned on. I can't tell the difference between wanting sex in my head and my body responding. When I feel horny, the next thing there's that old warmth in the groin. I'd describe myself as highly initiatory. When I want sex, I really want sex. And that's most of the time. I start most sexual stuff off between us, usually by kissing and cuddling Misha.

Receptive zone

In the receptive zone people are aware of an interest in sex but it is not usually compelling enough to make them initiate sex. However, they are receptive and happy to participate when their partner initiates it. They rarely make the first move and may not seek out sex unless they have to. They can be highly or mildly receptive to sexual advances. Moving into sexual arousal is usually easy for receptive people.

> **Terri:** I may not make the first move, but the moment I know that sex is on the agenda I'm ready and raring to go. I suppose if Wally didn't tap me on the shoulder first I'd get around to it, but it doesn't happen that way very often. I'd say I'm highly receptive.

Available zone

Some people are happy to be sexually available if their partner is keen to have sex. Available people are quite capable of arousal and sexual fulfilment under the right conditions, although their sexual arousal may be somewhat slower.

> **Roslyn:** I never initiate sex with Nathan, but I'm happy to 'play' most of the time when he wants to. He is usually ready for sex long before I am, but he's patient and takes his time. As long as I don't have to hurry I can get aroused, and I usually have an orgasm if I want to.

Neutral zone

In the neutral zone the attitude to sex is, 'I can take it or leave it.' Neutral people rarely think about sex and might fail to recognise nonverbal messages that indicate sexual interest from others. They don't send out sexual vibes themselves. Arousal is more difficult for this group but is still possible if they are willing to get sexually involved.

Disinterested zone

Disinterested people find it difficult to understand all the fuss about sex. They don't miss sex if they don't have it. Disinterested people may never think about sex, are often unaware of sexual behaviours in others and rarely if ever experience raw sexual desire. These people are currently regarded as completely abnormal.

It takes more time and effort for disinterested people to become sexually aroused, and they may choose not to some, or most of the time. However, this group can also participate in sex and enjoy fulfilling and pleasurable intimate experiences.

> **Roger:** Sex has never been high on the list of priorities for me. I didn't date until I was 33 and married late. Stephanie enjoys sex and is disappointed that it's not a bigger part of our relationship, but she's coming to terms with that. The

biggest problem is the effort and time it takes for me to get turned on. As long as she gives me enough time and the right stimulation, I can respond to her in my own quiet fashion. I have no trouble giving her an orgasm one way or another. We are coping with the differences and we are both happy.

DESIRE BEHAVIOUR ZONES

Initiatory:	Mm — sex ... I love it — how about it?
Receptive:	Mm — sex. That'd be nice!
Available:	Sex? Sure, if you want to.
Neutral:	Sex? I can take it or leave it.
Disinterested:	Sex — why bother?

Most people experience a range of desire behaviours over time. Men are often more familiar with the desire zones of initiatory, receptive and available behaviour. However, there are many men who fall into the neutral and disinterested zones some, if not all, of the time. Although women generally relate more to the range of zones from receptive to disinterested, there are many women who are initiatory, especially during the stages of early sexual courtship.

Not on the list?

If you have been caught up in the DD cycle as the lower drive partner, you may not find your current desire behaviour zone on this list. Pressure to be more sexually interested and active usually alters desire behaviours.

> **Alec:** I was never a sexual mover and shaker like other guys. I have always been happy for Sacha to make the sexual moves, but she has this idea that it's abnormal for men not to actively seek out sex. She gets very angry with me and it's affecting my sex drive. I've really gone off sex.

Like Alec you may have been receptive, available, neutral or disinterested in the past, but you now find yourself to be sexually reluctant, unavailable, avoidant or even aversive. We will look more closely at these desire zones in Chapter 10. However, you should be able to identify desire zones which you have experienced in the past.

The key to compatibility when you and your partner fall into differing desire zones is acceptance and adjustment, rather than trying to force either party to change.

Be your own sex therapist

Can you recognise which desire behaviour zone you currently fall into?

If you answered 'Usually' to most of the questions in the quiz on page 45, you are probably initiatory in your sexual behaviour. If your answers were mainly 'Frequently' you are receptive, 'Sometimes' = available, 'Rarely' = neutral, while a majority of 'Never' answers correlates with disinterested.

Do you move from zone to zone depending on your feelings, your circumstances and your relationship? Such fluctuations are perfectly normal as was demonstrated by the River of Desire.

What zone were you in six months ago? Two years ago? Early in your relationship? Can you guess why these changes occurred?

What desire zone does your partner fall into? Does your partner move from zone to zone as well?

Sex drive is defined as the 'motivation and inclination to be sexual'. The more sex drive we experience, the more willing we will be to participate in sexual activity and the easier it is to become sexually aroused.

It is more effective to measure sex drive by describing desire behaviours than by comparing one person's libido with another's.

There are a range of desire behaviours, including initiatory, receptive, available, neutral and disinterested. It is normal to move from one desire behaviour zone to another.

Is My Sex Drive Normal?

I f I had a dollar for every time I've been asked what a 'normal' sex drive is, I'd be lying beside my king-sized swimming pool right now — wearing diamonds, mind you! According to *Forum* magazine, four out of five people think that other people are having more sex than they do. In fact, research reveals that couples have a lot less sex than most people imagine. A study in the *New England Journal of Medicine* by Frank, Anderson and Rubinstein found that a third of married couples studied were having intercourse two to three times a month or less. Another survey found that one-third of married couples went for long periods without sexual intercourse, with the average being once every eight weeks. You might think these couples must be on their last legs, but more than three-quarters of those surveyed were under 38 years old!

RANGE OF NORMAL SEX DRIVE

Surely there must be a *normal* level of sex drive, some sort of standard we can compare ourselves with to find out if we make the grade? Consider for a moment how different every human being is. Each person is a complete individual in so many ways — in height, weight and appearance, just to name a few physical variables. Humans are unique creations. No two people are alike, sexually or otherwise.

If we measure any human characteristic — for example, height — we find that some people are very tall and some short, while the majority will be of average height. In research we call this a 'normal' distribution and it can be represented by the bell-shaped curve.

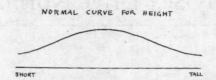

NORMAL CURVE FOR HEIGHT

SHORT   TALL

We can measure weight and plot it out using the same method. Some people will be skinny and some heavy, but most will be of average weight.

Human biological needs also exhibit a wide range of normal characteristics. For example, we all need sleep. Most people need around 6 to 8 hours of sleep. However, a few livewires can survive on 3 or 4 hours a night, and an equally small number of sleepy-heads need 10 hours of slumber or more.

What about our need for sex? Exactly the same principle applies, with a small group of people having a high interest in sex, a small group having a 'why bother' sex drive, and the majority of people grouped together in the middle range.

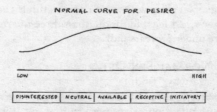

NORMAL CURVE FOR DESIRE

LOW   HIGH

DISINTERESTED	NEUTRAL	AVAILABLE	RECEPTIVE	INITIATORY

The desire behaviour zones fit snugly beneath the normal curve, just as you would expect.

WHAT'S NORMAL?

So what's normal — high, low or somewhere in the middle? The answer is, you guessed it — *all* are normal. Whether the thought of sex makes you horny or yawny, you're perfectly OK.

What if your partner has a different sex drive from yours? Surely one of you is normal while the other must be over- or undersexed? Compare sex and food. Do you expect your partner to always be hungry when you are, to want to eat the same kinds and quantities of food that you do? Do you feel unloved because you want a five-course meal and your lover prefers a pizza? Of course not. That would be ridiculous — just as ridiculous as expecting you to be a sexual mirror image of your partner.

The 'I'm OK, You're OK' attitude

Whether your sex drive is currently higher or lower, you and your partner are both normal — you are simply different, as you are in many other facets of your make-up. It can be difficult for partners to adopt this non-blaming 'I'm OK, You're OK' attitude when desire discrepancy has disrupted the relationship. Yet this is a vital step in overcoming the problems posed by DD.

Many couples with differing drives naturally arrive at this stance of acceptance and compromise, and work out the differences in a practical fashion.

Ken has always had a higher level of interest in sex than Jill, who goes through times when she doesn't give sex a second thought. 'It's never been a problem,' says Ken. 'We compromise — sometimes she will make love or help me out when she's not very interested, or I forgo sex and just enjoy the kisses and cuddles. She does for me and I do for her. We've never had a disagreement about sex.'

Not all couples are so understanding. Here's a typical story.

Adriana is always finding fault with Paul. 'He doesn't do enough around the house and he's a dismal failure in the bedroom. He just rolls over without even a goodnight kiss. In the beginning he was a pretty good lover. Now he's no use to me anywhere — not even in bed.'

Paul is hurt and angry. 'Nothing I ever do is enough. She's always nagging me and when she wants sex, she just demands it. I'm not a machine. I can't perform on call — and these days I just don't want to.'

This couple has a long way to go.

HOW LOW CAN YOU GO?

A low interest in sex is not an unusual phenomenon. Men and women who experience little or no sexual interest fall into two different groups. The first group never experience much interest in sex at any time in their lives. A low sex drive is natural for them. They fall into the *low sexual interest* group. The second group with low desire recall a much higher interest in sex in the past. They fall into the *inhibited sexual desire* group. Their natural sexual urges are being suppressed.

If your desire is currently on the lower side, which group do you fall into? To find out, let's review the quiz you completed in Chapter 4.

Be your own sex therapist

In Chapter 4 you answered this quiz with regard to your current level of sexual interest. Go through the quiz again and do a time warp. Take yourself to another time and/or situation. Answer the quiz several times as if:
- you are single and in your late teens
- you have just met your partner and fallen madly in love
- a miracle has occurred and today you woke up and all your worries had evaporated
- you are in a relationship with the 'partner of your dreams'.

Circle the appropriate answer.

Do you have pleasurable thoughts about sex during the day?
Usually/ Frequently/ Sometimes/ Rarely/ Never

Do you find it easy to get into the mood for sex?
Usually/ Frequently/ Sometimes/ Rarely/ Never

Do you ever initiate lovemaking?
Usually/ Frequently/ Sometimes/ Rarely/ Never

Do you find it easy to get aroused and to stay that way?
Usually/ Frequently/ Sometimes/ Rarely/ Never

Do you have sexual fantasies?
Usually/ Frequently/ Sometimes/ Rarely/ Never

Do you respond positively to your partner's sexual overtures?
Usually/ Frequently/ Sometimes/ Rarely/ Never

Do you masturbate?
Usually/ Frequently/ Sometimes/ Rarely/ Never

Do you miss sex if you haven't made love for a while?
Usually/ Frequently/ Sometimes/ Rarely/ Never

LOW SEXUAL INTEREST

If you found that your answers remained as 'Never' or 'Rarely', despite the changing sets of circumstances, then your usual range of sexual interest probably falls naturally at the lower end of the desire scale.

In Chapter 6 we will examine factors that can inhibit sex drive. If your sex drive remains low after these factors have been attended to, you have a low inbuilt sex drive or *low sexual interest*. Remember a low level of sex drive is perfectly normal.

Jo, a ballet teacher, met Mark, a university tutor, when she was 32. She was still a virgin, had never masturbated and never gave much thought to sex. Her passion was dancing. Mark was a caring man, but it soon became evident that they were mismatched in the sex drive department. Mark wasn't sure that under the circumstances they should make a serious commitment to each other, so they sought counselling.

When Jo did the desire quiz above, no matter what perspective she answered the questions from, her reply was always the same: 'Never'.

'Maybe I'm a freak?' Jo suggested. 'Everyone else has nothing but sex on their minds, but I just don't ever give it a second thought.'

Jo was not abnormal. She just had a low level of sex drive, evident from puberty. No magic spell, psychotherapy or medical treatment was going to dramatically increase her level of drive. It was just the way she was made. Counselling involved helping Mark and Jo to accept that their sex drives were different and neither of them was abnormal. They developed creative ways to deal with the difference so that both their needs could be met. They are now planning their wedding.

People with low sexual interest rarely think of sex or seek it out. Because of a combination of biological and social influences in their lives, sex is just not a high priority. They rarely fantasise sexually, nor do they make a habit of expressing sexual desire through masturbation or sexual initiation. They don't miss sex.

Low sexual interest is not in itself a problem. If two people with low sexual interest pair up, they will be a perfect sexual match. They might decide to make love on New Year's Eve and their anniversary, or not at all. Low sexual interest only becomes a problem:

- if you or your partner believe society's claptrap about how abnormal it is to have little interest in sex.
- if you pair up with a partner who has a higher interest in sex than you do and both of you lack the know-how to deal with DD. That's when the conflict and the blaming begins and the relationship starts to go downhill emotionally and sexually.

INHIBITED SEXUAL DESIRE

If you find that your answers in the exercise above change from 'Never' or 'Rarely' to 'Frequently' or 'Usually' under different circumstances, you probably have a reasonable inbuilt level of sex drive, but it is being inhibited by what is going on in your life and/or your relationship. This is known as *inhibited sexual desire*.

Your sexual interest is potentially there, but your current circumstances are preventing you from enjoying full and free expression of your sexual desire.

With inhibited sexual desire, your sexual interest has previously been higher and has now declined, or even disappeared. Although people who fall into this group may not currently desire sex, they often say they miss the excitement and fulfilment of passionate lovemaking. While low sexual interest is a lifelong situation, with inhibited sexual desire, the attention to the factors that are reducing sex drive will definitely help to improve your level of sexual interest. This was the case for my client Dorothy, who came to see me complaining about a total loss of interest in sex.

Dorothy, 31, a product manager for a large pharmaceutical firm, had plenty of boyfriends in her teenage years. She enjoyed sex, masturbated regularly, and really missed making love when she wasn't in a relationship. Dorothy married Simon, an accountant, and the relationship was a happy and passionate one. Things fell apart when they lost their first child, a son aged six months, to cot death.

Simon took to drink and Dorothy became a workaholic. Their sex life disintegrated rapidly — Dorothy found anything to do with sex repulsive, while Simon became sexually demanding and hostile. They argued constantly, and both became verbally and physically abusive. This miserable situation persisted for four years. The week before Dorothy came to counselling the neighbours had called the police during one of their fights.

This unfortunate couple needed many months of counselling and support to resurrect their relationship. The crux of the matter was that Dorothy was still grieving over the loss of their child. 'Why did God take our baby from us? He never hurt anyone,' she sobbed. Their relationship was in tatters.

Initially, Dorothy was treated for depression, and Simon attended Alcoholics Anonymous meetings. They worked hard together to re-establish the trust and intimacy in their relationship, and as they healed and reconnected, Dorothy's sex drive slowly returned to its former level.

Dorothy's story is a good example of how even the most robust sex drive can be brought to its knees by the trials and tribulations of life and love. Her sex drive was naturally on the high side, but it was completely inhibited by grief, depression and relationship problems.

Inhibited sexual desire can be *total* (affecting interest in all forms of sex) as in Dorothy's case — she not only lost interest in sex with Simon, she stopped masturbating, looking at other men and fantasising about sex. Or it may be *situational* (affecting desire for sex only in certain circumstances).

Situational inhibited sexual desire

For Dorothy, all forms of sex were a 'no no'. However, other people, while vehemently saying 'No' to sex with their partners, are quite happy to indulge in self-pleasuring or to seek out sex with someone other than their partner. This type of lowered drive is called *situational inhibition of desire*. It is only in certain situations that their desire is low. Often that 'situation' occurs with their long-term partner.

Holly and Michael lived together for four years before they married. It wasn't a happy relationship, as Michael was distant and unaffectionate and more involved with his drinking buddies than he was with Holly.

By the time they married, Holly had already lost interest in sex with Michael. However, she retained a rich fantasy life and masturbated regularly. Her interest in sexual contact with Michael returned briefly while they were trying to conceive. After several years and two babies, Holly began an affair. With her lover she enjoyed hot, passionate, frequent sex for two years. When the love affair ended, she entered therapy and eventually left Michael. She has since remarried and has a satisfying emotional and sexual relationship with her second husband.

Holly's sex drive never 'disappeared'. Her lack of interest was specific to Michael because their relationship was so poor. Holly had experienced situational inhibited sexual desire. She still fantasised and masturbated, and her interest in sex resumed with a vengeance in other relationships.

If you found that your sex drive was markedly increased by the thought of an 'ideal lover' in the exercise on page 56 it's an indication that you may have situational inhibited sexual desire. If you masturbate but steer away from sex with your partner, or if you enjoy sex with others but not with your partner, it's very likely that there are issues between you and your partner that need attention. If this is your experience, you will find Part 3, which focuses on relationship issues, very helpful.

Be your own sex therapist

If you have a problem with desire you can now recognise which category you fall into:

- Those with *low sexual interest* — people whose sexual desire is naturally low.
- Those with *inhibited sexual desire* — people whose inbuilt level of desire is being inhibited by various factors. The repression of sex drive may be total and affect all sexual activities, or it may be situational, related only to a particular partner or activity.

People with low sexual interest can still suffer from inhibited sexual desire. Under the influence of factors which negatively impact on their desire, their low level of interest in sex can become even lower.

Don't worry though — there are effective ways of coping, no matter what your situation is.

WHAT IS SEXUAL COMPATIBILITY?

Most people think that sexual compatibility means having the same level of sex drive as your partner. Yet we know that, in real life, this is a very rare occurrence. True sexual compatibility does not mean having perfectly matched sex drives; it means having the same sort of *expectations about sex drive* and *sharing a similar attitude about what is and isn't normal*. Your sex drives may differ widely, but as long as your expectations and your attitudes are similar you can overcome any degree of desire disparity. The exciting news is that just by reading this book and absorbing this new information about the true nature of sex drive, your attitudes will have already started to change. By now you are well on the way to learning how to overcome DD.

SEXUAL EXTREMES — AVERSION AND DEPENDENCY

We have spoken of the wide range of normal desires. However, two quite common sexual problems, which appear to be desire-related, are not desire problems at all but merit a brief mention. The first, sexual aversion, is a sexual phobia, while the second, sexual dependency, is classed as compulsive sexual behaviour.

Sexual phobia or aversion

A phobia is an irrational fear about something that most of us would find non-threatening. The most common phobias are claustrophobia (fear of confined spaces), agoraphobia (fear of open or public places) and social phobia (fear of being the centre of attention).

Sexual aversion is a phobia about sexual activity or the thought of sexual activity. This phobia is much more than a simple absence of desire. Sexual contact is feared and induces severe dread in the unfortunate sufferer. If a sufferer attempts sexual contact or even thinks about attempting sexual contact, symptoms ranging from intense fear to a full-blown panic attack may occur.

> **Janet:** Just the thought of sex makes me feel sick. I get dizzy, sweaty and feel like I'm going to throw up or faint. Sometimes I think I'm going to die when I have thoughts about sex.

Sexual aversion may be focused on the act of intercourse or anything to do with sex such as genitals, or body fluids and odours. The aversion usually occurs in adults aged between 20 and 40, and more women than men seek treatment for their fears. Some sexually aversive people cope with their fears by avoiding relationships and staying celibate. Or they may choose a mate who has a low interest in sex. A large group will go through the motions of sex, clenching their teeth and hating every moment of it.

Melissa, 28, has an aversion to the sight of male genitals. She had never seen a man's genitals until she married Stephen. Although intercourse is possible, she finds looking at or touching

Stephen's penis disgusting. Melissa anxiously reveals, 'I know it must upset him, but I can't bear the sight of it. It's better if it's soft, but when it's hard I feel like running away!'

Sexual aversion may be primary and affect the sufferer all his or her life, or secondary, occurring after a period of normal sexual functioning. The causes of sexual aversion are not yet fully known, but this phobia has been associated with traumatic sexual experiences such as a very strict upbringing, inadequate sexual education, sexual abuse, sexual assault or some other damaging experience. Sometimes it can be the cumulative result of years of sexual pressure and unwanted sexual activity.

Joanne, 48, was married to a bully. For 15 years he insisted on sex twice a day, dragging her off to bed any time he felt like it. He thought nothing of waking her in the middle of the night for sex. 'In the end, sex was like torture,' Joanne says. 'It was all I could do to stop from passing out while he did it to me.'

Fortunately, treatment for sexual aversion is simple and highly effective even if the phobic person is not in a relationship.

Sexual phobia or aversion is not a desire problem. It is a fear reaction to sex or some aspect of sex and requires special treatment. If you suspect that you or your partner have sexual phobia, then you will need the expert help of a sex therapist, psychiatrist or psychologist who is familiar with sexual problems.

Sexual dependency

A sexually dependent person, usually a man, is someone who never seems to be able to get enough sex. This is not a problem of having too much desire, despite sufferers' claims to the contrary. The sexual dependent, sometimes known as a sex addict, uses sex to avoid facing uncomfortable feelings and situations in his or her life.

Like drug or alcohol addicts, the sex addict is looking for an anaesthetic, something to numb his or her feelings of anger, grief, resentment or fear. The sex addict uses masturbation or sex with a partner the same way an alcoholic takes a drink — to escape reality. Unfortunately the relief is short-lived and the addict must continue to seek out sexual activity.

Henry, a successful entrepreneur aged 45, made love to his wife every day. He kept a mistress, and sought out casual sexual encounters with many other women. In addition, he visited brothels about twice a week. He also visited gay baths and saunas and had anonymous sexual contacts with men in parks and toilets. Henry came for counselling when he was advised by his GP to have a test for HIV. 'The first thing I think about when I wake up is "Where can I get sex today?" I feel uptight and tense until I score for the day, but then I start to think about the next one. At work, if I get stressed, I go into the toilet and masturbate.' Henry had all the signs of a sexual dependant. He pursued sexual activity even though he risked harmful, even life-threatening consequences. He was impulsive and had little control over his urges. As time went on, he needed more and more sex to satisfy his need for sexual euphoria.

Sexual dependants of both sexes have a core belief that they are worthless. They find temporary personal validation and emotional relief through sexual contact. They find it difficult to cope without regular sex or masturbation.

According to Sandra Pertot, in her excellent book *A Commonsense Guide to Sex*, a person is sexually dependent if he or she:

- 'experiences a regular, persistent sexual need that tends to be stronger when he or she is under emotional pressure;
- can't cope without sexual release and becomes agitated, tense or preoccupied with sexual feelings if there is no opportunity for orgasm when the need is there;
- finds that the sexual need sometimes interferes with daily life, that satisfying the sexual need can be more important than other things, such as getting to work on time, keeping up to date with regular chores;
- expects the partner to have sex based on his/her need with little or no consideration for the partner's feelings, and may use various types of manipulation to get those needs met.'

People who suffer from sexual dependency are usually in denial; they refuse to see they have a problem. Often they blame their partner, calling them frigid and unresponsive. They believe that if their partner would give them more sex, the problem would be solved.

Just as alcoholics often have to hit rock bottom before they will seek help, it may take a crisis such as a marital breakup or catching a sexually transmitted disease before a sex addict will seek help. Twelve Step programs have long been available to help with drug and alcohol addictions (Narcotics Anonymous and Alcoholics Anonymous, respectively), and similar groups have been set up for sexual dependency, called Sex and Love Addicts Anonymous (SLAA). If you suspect you or your partner have this problem, seek advice from your GP or your local Community Centre.

Key Points

A wide range of levels of sexual desire is considered to be perfectly normal. For this reason, DD should be approached with a non-blaming 'I'm OK, You're OK' attitude.

Low sexual interest is a lifelong experience of low sexual desire.

Inhibited sexual desire applies to people who have been more interested in sex in the past but currently experience reduced sexual desire.

Loss of desire can be total (reducing interest in any sort of sexual activity) or situational (sexual desire is reduced only under certain circumstances). Situational loss of interest in sex in respect to a partner is a strong indicator of relationship difficulties.

Sexual compatibility does not rely on equal levels of sex drive, but on similar attitudes towards sex drive.

Sexual phobia is a fear reaction to sex, while sexual dependency is a compulsive behaviour carried out to medicate painful feelings. Neither problem is classed as a disorder of sexual desire.

The Makings of a Mismatched Couple

Flames of Passion — The Highs and Lows of Sex Drive

Y ou don't have to have a medical degree to know that sex drive rises and falls. Some desire fluctuations can be anticipated or even predicted — for example, sex drive is generally highest early in a relationship; female sex drive commonly drops during pregnancy and after the birth of a baby; and unemployment, financial worries and stress can all take their toll on the sex drives of both men and women.

We can discover ways to cope more effectively with desire discrepancy by examining the factors that increase and reduce our sex drive. These factors can be employed to modulate not only *our own interest* in sex, but *our partner's interest* as well.

FLAMES OF PASSION

Imagine a flame, like a gas flame on a Bunsen burner in a laboratory. By turning the air inlet at the base of the burner, the flame can be made to burn low or high. Imagine that there is a similar 'control knob' on our flame of desire. Like a thermostat on a heater, or the dimmer switch on a light, this control knob can turn our desire flame up or down.

There are two types of factors that modulate sex drive — those that heat sex drive up, *desire enhancers*, and those that cool it down, *desire inhibitors*. An enhancer is any factor that increases sex drive. An inhibitor is any factor that turns sex drive down. The level of our sex drive is controlled minute by minute by the interplay between desire enhancers and inhibitors.

INHIBITORS AND ENHANCERS

Inhibitors and enhancers are often opposites, different sides of the same coin. For example, while fatigue is a real passion killer (inhibitor), adequate rest can help to stimulate desire (enhancer).

Be your own sex therapist

Examine the following list. Which factors do you think would increase your sex drive (enhancer) and which would decrease it (inhibitor)? Are there some factors listed that would have no effect on your sex drive?

A romantic dinner for two	Inhibitor/Enhancer
Fatigue	Inhibitor/Enhancer
Back pain	Inhibitor/Enhancer
Constant fighting	Inhibitor/Enhancer
Physical fitness	Inhibitor/Enhancer
Intimacy	Inhibitor/Enhancer
Acting out fantasies	Inhibitor/Enhancer
Plenty of hugs and kisses	Inhibitor/Enhancer
Pornography	Inhibitor/Enhancer
Poor body image	Inhibitor/Enhancer
Anxiety	Inhibitor/Enhancer
Having fun together	Inhibitor/Enhancer
Raunchy sex	Inhibitor/Enhancer

Repeat the exercise with reference to your partner's sex drive. How do you differ?

INHIBITORS OF SEXUAL DESIRE

Physical
- Fatigue
- Physical discomfort — pain (headache, backache, arthritis, painful intercourse), feeling unwell, nausea
- Poor general health
- Chronic illness
- Excess alcohol or drug abuse
- Some medications
- Hormonal changes — low testosterone, menopause, breast-feeding

Psychological
- Lack of emotional wellbeing — stress, guilt, frustration, anger, resentment, worry, sadness, depression, shame
- Poor self-esteem
- Poor sexual self-esteem — feelings of sexual inadequacy
- Poor sex education
- Negative sexual attitudes
- Poor body image
- Lack of pleasurable sexual fantasies
- Negative anticipation of sex — not looking forward to sex

Relationship
- Loss of loving feelings between partners
- Communication problems
- Lack of intimacy
- Lack of trust
- Insecurity — lack of commitment
- Unresolved jealousy
- Lack of respect
- Low attraction to partner
- Power struggles and inequality
- Intrusions to the boundaries of the relationship — e.g. interference by in-laws, demands of work, social activities, hobbies, children, etc.
- Tension in relationship — unresolved conflicts

- Lack of affection, companionship, fun, romance
- Sexual difficulties

Situational
- Unfavourable physical environment — e.g. lack of privacy, too hot or too cold
- Poor atmosphere for lovemaking — e.g. lack of time, distractions, phone, TV, kids

Be your own sex therapist

If you are experiencing a lowered interest in sex, run through the list of inhibitors and note any items that may currently be operating in your life. This will probably give you a good insight into why you are not ripping your partner's clothes off every night of the week.

Are there any inhibitors that you could minimise or eradicate? How could your partner help?

If your partner's desire is not burning brightly at this time, can this lack of sexual interest be explained by some of the factors on the inhibitors list?

Are there any inhibitors affecting your partner's desire that you could work together to minimise or eradicate?

ENHANCERS OF SEXUAL DESIRE

Physical
- Adequate rest
- Physical wellbeing
- Good health
- Fitness
- Normal hormone levels

Psychological
- Emotional wellbeing — contentment, happiness, relaxation
- Good self-esteem
- Good sexual self-esteem
- Good sex education

- Positive attitude to sex
- Healthy body image
- Positive sexual anticipation
- Pleasurable sexual thoughts and fantasies

Relationship
- Attraction between partners — sexual chemistry
- Satisfying sexual experiences — positive feedback will increase desire
- Frequent non-demand affectionate behaviour
- Enjoyable sensuality
- Acceptance — unconditional love
- Companionship, fun, romance
- Trust — fidelity issues and jealousy resolved
- Commitment to relationship — security
- Good communication and intimacy
- Respect
- Issues of power and control resolved
- Constructive conflict resolution
- Boundaries of relationship firm against intrusions

Situational
- Favourable environment — e.g. adequate privacy, minimal distractions
- Atmosphere conducive to lovemaking — e.g. adequate time

APHRODISIACS — FACT OR FICTION?

More than 900 supposed desire 'arousers' have been recorded. This enormous list of substances is a testament to human gullibility. The power of the aphrodisiac is in the mind — if you think it will work, it probably will. Remember how you can think yourself into and out of sex.

The origins of aphrodisiacs

Belief in the power of aphrodisiacs may arise from the fantasy that 'like produces like'. This is why the ingestion of animal penises and testes is often rumoured to increase sexual interest.

A substance's appearance can give rise to hopes that it will enhance desire — for example, the mandrake root mentioned in the Book of Genesis in the Bible resembles a man's legs with an appendage between. The bigger the appendage, the more prized the root. Ginseng root is probably prized for the same reason. The rhinoceros is also a victim of this idea — rhino horn is crushed into powder and mixed with liquid as a drink. It irritates the urethra but does not enhance desire. Spanish Fly, made from a dried extract of the bodies of green blister beetles which live in Southern Europe, also causes urethral irritation. It is a very dangerous drug because there is such a small margin between its irritant effect and its poisonous effect.

The only true aphrodisiac

Aphrodisiacs fall into the same category as love potions: a bit of fun without any basis. So forget about oysters, chocolate, the testes of an ass, the penis of a hedgehog or whatever else, and focus on the only true aphrodisiac — good loving. A fulfilling relationship is the only tried and true aphrodisiac available to men and women.

MINIMISING INHIBITORS, MAXIMISING ENHANCERS

For any individual to experience the full potential of his or her sex drive, inhibitors impacting on sex drive must be reduced and enhancers maximised. In healthy relationships where partners are working to meet each other's needs, desire enhancers are either freely provided or negotiated with regard to the feelings of both parties while desire inhibitors are kept under tight control.

Often this is easier to achieve in principle than it is in practice. There are many pitfalls. Even partners who are completely willing to provide each other with sexual enhancers can make mistakes.

Never assume

Response to enhancers and inhibitors is highly *individual*, and can never be predicted with certainty. For example, while one person may lose all interest in sex when they are stressed, another might seek sex out more keenly when they are uptight as a form of stress relief.

Men and women tend to respond to different enhancers and inhibitors. Take Jeannie and Peter, who have been married for four years. Jeannie is offended by enhancers that really turn Peter on.

> We boil at different degrees.
>
> RALPH WALDO EMERSON

> **Peter:** I bought Jeannie some sexy lingerie and she refused to wear it for me. I did it because I love her and love how she looks. I'm so sorry I upset her.
>
> **Jeannie:** If he thinks I'm going to wear that stuff, he's got another thing coming. Even the thought of it makes me feel like a prostitute.

It is unrealistic to expect that your partner will be affected by the same inhibitors and enhancers that affect you. Trouble erupts when one partner insists that the other should enjoy his or her turn-ons and ignores those factors that really do enhance sexual desire and arousal for their mate. This leads to conflict and resentment, resulting in either loss of desire or damage to the relationship.

> **Kevin:** Ailsa parades around naked and thinks nothing of wearing the shortest skirt she can find. I sometimes feel embarrassed when I'm out with her. I prefer women to act like ladies.
>
> **Ailsa:** Most men love a woman to dress up sexy. Kevin acts like an old woman when I get a bit raunchy. After all, if we weren't meant to enjoy sex, we wouldn't have genitals! His body really turns me on, so I'm just trying to return the compliment. I'm not going to change what I wear. He'll have to get used to it.

It worked on my previous partner

Steve was surprised when he married for the second time. What made his first wife Rita very receptive to sexual advances turned his second wife, Fiona, right off.

> **Steve:** Rita liked the light on, and loved to get naked and get right into sex. I'm lucky if I can get Fiona to change in front of me; and she wears a neck-to-knee nightie to bed every night.
>
> **Fiona:** I love Steve, but I think he takes this sex stuff too far. He watches me like a hawk when I get undressed. He comes into the bathroom when I'm having a shower. He touches my bum whenever I bend over. He seems to think that it's all normal behaviour. I think his first wife must have been a bit of a nymphomaniac, because apparently she loved all of that.

Building a satisfying sex life involves finding out specifically what works for your partner sexually and expanding your relationship to include at least some of your partner's enhancers, even if they do nothing for you at all. It also means avoiding or minimising elements that might turn your partner off sex.

For Steve and Fiona, this exercise meant respect for Fiona's privacy when she was changing and in the shower, but finding time when she was relaxed for Steve to admire and appreciate her body, either dressed or undressed. Steve liked the light on when they made love, but this made shy Fiona too uncomfortable to enjoy sex. A bedside night light turned down low or the occasional candle met both their needs. Like Steve and Fiona, couples must work together, compromising and negotiating until a mutually agreeable solution can be found.

Create safety in the relationship

Unless you are a mind reader, the only way to find out what works for your partner is for them to tell you, and vice versa. However, expressing sexual needs to a partner is not always an easy task.

When we open ourselves up in this way, we make ourselves vulnerable to rejection and criticism. In the sensitive area of sexuality, judgments tend to be the rule rather than the exception. Why would you take the risk, especially if in the past your partner has ignored or judged your sexual needs as irrelevant or unwholesome?

> **Martin:** When we first met, Sally found a raunchy magazine under my bed and she freaked out. Now she wants more sex from me, and expects me to be able to switch from the demands of work to sex in the blink of an eye. It would make it a lot easier for me to get in the mood for sex if I could have access to that sort of material. I wouldn't even mention it to Sally because she'd hit the roof. Yet it would help us through this rough patch if we were having a bit more sex and fewer hassles.

Before your partner can open his or her mouth, you must open your heart and your mind and be ready to accept their individual version of sexuality. In all likelihood it will not match perfectly with yours, and it may not even fit in with what you see as 'normal' or 'OK'. The reverse also applies. For you to open up to your partner, you need to negotiate a safe place to explore your needs together.

ENHANCERS AND INHIBITORS IN YOUR RELATIONSHIP

Differing enhancers and inhibitors need not cause conflict in your relationship if you develop:
- a thorough knowledge and acceptance of what turns *you* on and off
- an understanding and acceptance of what turns *your partner* on and off
- a safe space in your relationship to openly share this information and the willingness to act on it in a loving way.

Be your own sex therapist

Are there some enhancers that really turn you on, but leave your partner cold? Or vice versa?

If your desire is flagging, do you know what enhancers you could employ to turn up your sexual flame again? What inhibitors must be minimised to set your desire on fire again?

Is your partner aware of what you need to keep your sexual motor running high? Does your partner try to meet these needs?

Do you know how to turn up your partner's sexual heat? More to the point, if you know what to do, do you do it?

If you know what to do, do you do it?

Partners in a relationship are often aware of precisely what turns their 'other half' on, as well as what turns them off. However, they persist with behaviour that inhibits their partner's sex drive and actively withhold enhancers from their partners for a variety of reasons, including:

- to try to control their partner's sex drive
- to punish their partner
- because they can't be bothered
- because they judge their partner's enhancers negatively — they may judge the enhancers to be disgusting (e.g. erotica, nudity, varied lovemaking) or unimportant (e.g. romance and affection).

Then they wonder why their partner keeps saying 'No' to sex!

Frank was always complaining to Leonie that she didn't give him enough sex. Frank's frequent attempts to initiate sex were clumsy. At no particular time of the day or night, with no regard for how Leonie was feeling or what she was doing, he'd ask, 'What about some rumpy-pumpy tonight, love?' In bed he'd grab her breasts or roughly put his hand between her legs. When she did agree to sex, he jumped on top of her immediately and rolled off afterwards without a thought for Leonie's needs.

Leonie could hardly bear to lie beside Frank in bed some

nights, let alone have sex with him. When she did give in to him, it was because she felt guilty and couldn't stand the pressure of his constant nagging and complaints.

I asked Leonie what she would need to feel more inclined towards having sex with Frank. Leonie said that she would love more help around the house and with the kids. She felt totally unsupported by Frank, who seemed like just another big, demanding baby. She wanted him to spend some quality time with her, talking and listening, to help her get in the mood for sex. She wanted him to approach sex gradually, not blurt out requests for sex or intrude on her personal space too quickly. She wanted more time in loveplay, more affection and more sensuality when they did have sexual contact.

During counselling I explained to Frank that in order to improve Leonie's sexual interest, he would have to work harder in the relationship. When I mentioned helping with the kids or the housework, making time to talk to Leonie and being more affectionate during lovemaking, he looked at me as if I was suggesting he commit a crime.

'What's the housework got to do with sex?' Frank asked. 'Or the kids? And what does she need all that lovey dovey stuff for? You just fix Leonie up, give her some pills or something to get her going, and we'll be right as rain.'

Frank just couldn't see how his uncaring behaviour was inhibiting Leonie's sex drive. He wasn't prepared to be responsible for the consequences of his own actions. Nor was he willing to put in the minimal effort required to encourage Leonie to participate more willingly in the sexual side of their relationship.

In poor relationships like this, when he withholds her enhancers — 'Why should I tell her I love her? I'm married to her, aren't I?' — she will usually react by withholding his — 'If he thinks I'm ever going to let him see me naked again, he's got another thing coming.' Or vice versa. Often it's difficult to tell who took the first step, but regardless of how it started, most of these couples end up in a Mexican stand-off: 'If you won't give me my enhancers, then I won't give you yours.'

An opportunity for sexual growth

In any relationship, both parties have much to gain from reducing desire inhibitors and making each other's desire enhancers an integral part of the relationship. Couples often report that, with regular exposure to each other's enhancers, in time they begin to respond to their partner's enhancers as well as their own. Learning about your partner's enhancers and their inhibitors is an important step in creating sexual compatibility.

Sexual compatibility is created by finding ways to fit all the different pieces of the romantic jigsaw puzzle together in a comfortable way. The painful alternative is to lop off parts of your own or your partner's sexuality to make for a better 'sexual fit'.

There's an old saying: *Don't cut the man to fit the coat, cut the coat to fit the man.* The challenge in a long-term relationship is to fully embrace each other's sexuality, creating a safe and trusting space, within an 'I'm OK, You're OK' atmosphere. Developing this attitude of *acceptance, understanding* and *compromise* is a vital step for couples working to overcome DD.

Key Points ❦

Sex drive is modified by inhibitors which decrease desire, and enhancers which promote it. Response to these influencers is variable. It is impossible to accurately predict how any individual will respond to any particular factor.

To experience the full potential of sex drive, enhancers must be maximised and inhibitors minimised.

Couples may have differing inhibitors and enhancers, but this need not be a source of conflict if the relationship can be expanded so that both partners get their needs met.

The only way to find out what your partner's enhancers and inhibitors are is to make the relationship safe enough for your partner to express their needs openly, without fear of judgment or rejection.

In a healthy relationship, enhancers are provided freely or negotiated with regard to the feelings of both partners, while inhibitors are minimised.

7

His Desire, Her Desire — Bridging the Gap Between the Sexes

Although the sexual anatomy of men and women obviously differs, there is a widely held expectation that men and women should function like sexual Siamese twins, identical in every way. Yet each person's sexuality is unique and idiosyncratic, regardless of gender. I can guarantee that no two people reading this book have exactly the same sexual education, attitudes, experience, expectations, anxieties or needs. Our sexuality is as personal as our fingerprints. By looking closely at what makes the desire of men and women tick, we will bust the myth of perfect sexual compatibility.

THE GREAT DEBATE: WHO HAS THE HIGHER SEX DRIVE — MEN OR WOMEN?

It is generally accepted that men are more highly endowed with sexual interest than women. This is not necessarily true. Male sex drive is described as:

- more urgent
- less distractable
- more goal-directed
- more focused on intercourse and orgasm than female sex drive.

Female sex drive, on the other hand, is described as:
• more diffuse
• more distractable
• including an urge for connection and affection.
The difference between male and female sex drive lies not so much in the *quantity* of sex drive but in the *quality*.

Both sexes can enjoy equally high levels of sexual interest. However, men tend to have a *stronger* sex drive than women — it usually takes a lot more to turn a man off sex than a woman, because a man's River of Desire can always count on a helping hand from testosterone.

Biology or culture?

Is this difference between male and female sex drives due to our biology, or a result of the way society programs us to behave? The answer is that both our genes and our culture have a role to play.

Male sexual interest has been doubly assisted. As well as ample quantities of testosterone, male sex drive receives enthusiastic social encouragement. Take the famous double standard: men have always been expected to sow their wild oats, while women who slept around ran the risk of being labelled promiscuous. Only recently have women been permitted to freely express their sexual needs. As changes occur in sexual attitudes and gender roles in the future, the 'nature' of male and female desire could well change accordingly.

Testosterone — the major player in the desire game

Testosterone acts like a hand that turns the male desire thermostat up high, and holds it there, keeping the flame of desire burning bright.

Testosterone makes a man's thermostat *harder to turn down*. Women, by comparison, have only tiny amounts of testosterone in their bloodstreams — their thermostats are *easier to turn down*. As a result, a woman's sex drive is more easily turned off by the events of the day (week, month, year) than her partner's. Her sex drive is much more distractable and variable than his. This difference

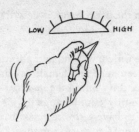

The 'HAND' OF TESTOSTERONE TURNS
UP MALE SEXUAL DESIRE

between the sexes is frequently misunderstood by couples. Take this scenario:

A couple goes out together on a picnic. Unfortunately, everything that could go wrong, does go wrong. They get lost, it pours with rain, the dog vomits in the car, they get a flat tyre, ants eat the picnic, they have a huge fight, etc.

When they eventually arrive home at midnight, the weary couple heads for the bedroom. When her head hits the pillow, all she can think of is 'Sleep, Sleep'.

Next minute, she feels a tap on her shoulder. She can't believe it! After all that's happened, how could he possibly be wanting sex? It's the last thing on her mind. She acts dead, thinking, 'What a selfish, inconsiderate bastard!'

Her man, on the other hand, is feeling pretty uptight after a long day and knows that a bit of slap and tickle will relax him and he'll drift off to sleep like a baby. When she doesn't respond to his overtures he turns his back to her and sulks, thinking, 'What's the matter with her? She must be frigid.'

Sound familiar? This couple are both victims of their primitive sexuality.

Cave Man/Cave Woman sexuality

Our sexuality is still very much a part of the Stone Age. Male human beings have been endowed with a strong, undistractable desire. Back then, a Cave Man's sex drive had to be strong enough to motivate him to mate under the most difficult of circumstances

— during famine, under threat of attack by ferocious animals or marauding neighbours, in a cave without privacy and often without shelter. A strong sex drive was a must to ensure the continuation of the human species.

So why not make Cave Woman into a raving nymphomaniac — then they could both be at it all the time, like bunnies?

The answer is survival.

> The rabbit has a charming face:
> Its private life is a disgrace.
> I really dare not name to you
> The awful things that rabbits do.
>
> ANONYMOUS

In reproductive terms, men are sperm donors while women are designed to look after babies. It has long been the woman's job to ensure that her infant is safe and well and grows up to reproduce. Cave Woman's biology dictates that nothing, not even a hot, passionate Cave Man breathing down her bearskin, can keep her from carrying out that job.

Imagine this scenario: Mr and Mrs Cave Dweller are in their cave making passionate love on a bearskin rug. Over in the corner is Junior, dreaming sweetly. A sabre-toothed tiger creeps into the cave and decides to have baby for lunch. Who is going to notice first, Mum or Dad?

Of course, Mum will be the first to raise the alarm. Women are hot-wired so that they will never be so overcome by lust and passion that they neglect their major responsibility — the wellbeing of their offspring.

Mother Nature has, in fact, made a perfect match — men with a strong, intense sex drive to ensure that pregnancies regularly occur, and women with more distractable desire who can nurture and raise children. Men with their high levels of testosterone have a much more focused, urgent and undistractable sex drive, perfect for the sperm donor role. Women's sexual drive and arousal is designed to be 'distractable' — having the heavy hand of testosterone on a woman's thermostat could potentially put her offspring at risk. Lower levels of testosterone ensure a woman is equipped to perform her mothering functions.

THE FANTASY OF THE SEXUALLY VORACIOUS WOMAN

We've come a long way from Cave Man times — perhaps too far when you examine modern attitudes to female sex drive. For centuries the comparative sexual reserve of women has been recognised and respected. The 1990s may well be remembered as the decade when, for the first time, women were made to feel abnormal if they didn't have a sex drive like a man's. Many men now expect women to have a high libido, and feel frustrated and disappointed when their partners don't initiate sex on a regular basis.

> **Jason:** My wife Martina is not a sexy woman. In the beginning it wasn't too bad, but once we married and the kids came along she turned off sex completely. She never approaches me for sex, and I'm sick of getting things going all the time. I never thought I would end up with a sexless woman in a sexless marriage.

Women, too, feel angry and cheated because their appetite for sex does not meet a certain standard.

> **Martina:** Jason thinks he's the only one missing out. What about me? Other women seem to be enjoying lots of passionate sex and I have no desire at all. I don't feel like a real woman and it's affecting our marriage in the worst possible way. I wish I was normal.

Men and women of all ages now seem to believe that if a woman doesn't lust after sex, she is abnormal. This pervasive myth has its origins in three main sources.

Erotica and pornography

Once hidden away, sexually explicit material is as close as your corner store these days, with adult magazines stacked in amongst the toilet rolls and dog food. R-rated videos are freely available, and X-rated material can be readily obtained through mail order.

The women portrayed in erotic magazines are often sexual 'greedy guts' — they are always ready and willing to participate in any sexual activity with anyone, anywhere! That's a hard act for a flesh-and-blood woman to follow, even if she wanted to. Many men and women are brainwashed into thinking that this is 'normal' sexual behaviour for women.

Glossy women's magazines

Glossy magazines provide a steady diet of sexual information — or, more likely, 'myth information' — to women of all ages. Articles like 'Multiply Your Orgasms', '10 Easy Steps to Sexual Ecstasy' and 'Hottest Holiday Sex Ever' promote a fantasy image of women who have nothing but sex on their minds.

Movies and books

Movies and books have jumped on the bandwagon, portraying women as lustful predators, looking for sex wherever they can get it. At the cinema, movies show women eager for sex, even with total strangers — without

> We live in a fantasy world, a world of illusion. The great task in life is to find reality.
> IRIS MURDOCH
> ENGLISH NOVELIST

so much as a 'How do you do' or an exchange of names, let alone any discussion about safe sex. Blockbuster novels and sophisticated soapies portray female sexual stereotypes, like the Super Bitch with no morals and an insatiable craving for sex.

These media images ignore the realities of female sexual functioning and sell us damaging mythology instead. Our expectations of female sex drive have changed in recent decades, and now we demand that female biology somehow comes up to scratch.

Women Who Rarely Experience Sexual Desire

Women who experience low or infrequent sexual desire are not sexually deficient. According to recent studies, a third of women rarely have enough spontaneous interest in sex to initiate lovemaking. Most women are not initiatory — they are more likely to fall into receptive, available, neutral and disinterested desire zones.

The Desire Threshold

The phenomenon of absent or infrequent female (and less commonly male) sex drive can best be understood by introducing the concept of the *desire threshold*. Imagine that we could graph a person's level of sex drive throughout their lifespan.

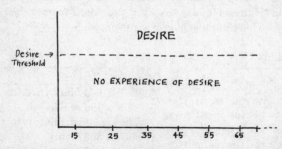

The desire threshold, shown as a dotted line, represents a cut-off point on the desire graph.

Above this desire threshold, a man or woman is aware of desire — they think about sex, they feel horny, they look for sexual opportunities and seek out sex.

Below the desire threshold, a man or woman has no experience of sexual interest. Sexual opportunities will be missed, ignored or even avoided. They don't think about sex, they don't miss it, they could go without it forever. It's like losing your appetite for food. Suddenly eating is not high on your list of priorities.

Sexual symphony

The best way to understand the desire threshold is to use the analogy of music from a radio. When volume on the radio is very low, we experience silence — the human ear is not capable of picking up such soft sounds. As the volume is turned up, a critical point is reached when we first become aware that music is playing. This is the *sound threshold*. Above it we hear music, and below it we don't.

Picture a similar threshold for desire. Below the cut-off point there is no experience of desire — there is 'sexual silence'. Above the threshold, there is an increasing experience of desire — people feel horny, lusty, randy, toey. They hear the 'sexual symphony'. Desire gets stronger and stronger as you move up away from the threshold, just as music gets louder and louder as you turn up the radio.

HIS TIME LINE

Here is a typical man's time line:

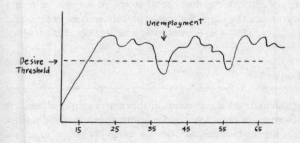

Puberty blues

Notice the dramatic rise in sexual interest as a boy enters puberty and testosterone surges through his system. Even if sex drive is on the low side in adult years, the majority of men can look back on these teen years and recall what it felt like to be horny.

> **Tony:** I haven't been interested in sex for some years now, but I can remember in my teenage years I had sex on the brain! I was randy morning, noon and night.

This flooding of the body with testosterone gives young boys a huge sexual advantage over teenage girls. Boys rapidly learn a great deal about their sexual desire and the very obvious changes of male sexual arousal. Boys become intensely aware of their sexual needs, often releasing sexual tension through masturbation or wet dreams. Girls, on the other hand, generally take much longer to get in touch with their more subtle sexual response.

A man's sexual peak

It is said that a man reaches his 'sexual peak' at 18. This gives the impression that a man's *sexual interest* is highest in his late teens. This is not strictly true. Men's interest in sex can remain high throughout their lives. Many a woman waits in vain for her partner's libido to taper off as his hair greys and his eyesight dims.

The term 'male sexual peak' refers to a young man's *sexual performance*, specifically the number of times he can perform in a row. The younger the man, the faster he can become erect again and re-ejaculate. This is not necessarily a reflection of his level of interest in sex.

Ups and downs

Note that fluctuations are present on this man's graph depending on the influences of enhancers and inhibitors, but desire does not fall to great depths because testosterone keeps its heavy 'hand' on his desire thermostat. Despite fluctuations, this man's sex drive rarely falls below the threshold. No matter how tough the going gets, he's almost always able to hear that sexual 'music'.

Men who fall towards the lower end of the normal curve will find that their sexual interest disappears more regularly under adverse conditions as it drops below the desire threshold.

HER TIME LINE

Here is a typical woman's time line:

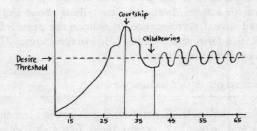

Slowed sexual awakening

While a teenage boy's sexuality wakes up with a start, teenage girls experience surges of the female hormones, oestrogen and progesterone, with only tiny amounts of testosterone. In the absence of high testosterone levels, sexual awakening for girls is often a slow process that lasts well into their twenties and thirties. First sexual experiences for girls are not usually motivated by uncontrolled lust but by other pressures: from the boyfriend or the peer group, out of curiosity, or even as an act of rebellion against parents. Early sexual experiences are frequently unsatisfying, with young girls asking, 'Is that all there is?'

A woman's sexual peak

This slow awakening accounts for the maxim that a *woman reaches her sexual peak in her mid-thirties*. Because women must learn about desire and arousal with minimal help from their hormones

> The appetite grows by eating.
>
> FRANÇOIS RABELAIS
> FRENCH PHYSICIAN

(in a society that still tends to discourage female sexual expression), full sexual awakening may be delayed for several decades.

By their mid-thirties, most women have learnt to achieve orgasm one way or another (with or without a partner) and their enjoyment of and interest in sex peaks. Some women in their late thirties and forties experience high levels of sex drive at a time when their partner's performance is starting to decline. This can be frustrating for both parties.

Comparing a man's sexual peak with a woman's is like comparing apples with oranges. In men we are talking about a capacity for repeated sexual performance; in women the peak refers to levels of sexual desire and capacity for sexual response. There is no comparison between the two.

Harder to turn up, easier to turn down

Note the peak in female sex drive during courtship, and fluctuations above and below the desire threshold. In the absence of high testosterone levels there is nothing to buoy up female sex drive against the assaults of everyday living. Most women, even women with sex drives on the higher side, will find that their sex drive falls below the threshold from time to time when the going gets tough.

However, there is a group of women whose level of sex drive rarely, if ever, rises above the desire threshold. Are you one of these women? Your desire time line would probably look something like this:

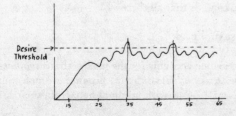

Note that your level of drive still fluctuates, but it rarely gets above the threshold. If it does, the rise is minimal and short-lived. You seldom, if ever, hear that 'sexual symphony' and if you do, it is only ever in soft and subtle strains. Most of the time you feel neutral or disinterested in sex.

Low desire and sexual fulfilment

It is vital for men and women with lower levels of desire or absent sex drive to realise that they are normal, despite society's current obsession with lust. If you have low or infrequent desire, arousal and sexual fulfilment are completely within your reach, as long as sex remains an attractive proposition for reasons other than sexual desire, and you are willing to be sexually intimate with your partner. This is discussed in Chapters 16–18.

NO SEXUAL DESIRE IN CHILDHOOD

You will note that no libido or sex drive is charted on these graphs before puberty. Parents often wrongly assume when their children are caught in sexual play such as 'Doctors and Nurses' or 'Mummies and Daddies', or even simulating intercourse, that they are driven by sexual desire. Childhood sexual rehearsal arises not from sexual desire as adults know it, but out of innocent sexual curiosity. Children are learning about their world all the time — they are inquisitive about their bodies in the same way that they want to know more about how a toy works.

> **Alicia, aged 5:** Mummy, where does the sun go at night? What's my belly button for? Who feeds the flowers?

From birth a child's body responds to sensual stimulation. Baby boys have been recorded on ultrasound as having erections while still inside the uterus. Girls under the age of five have been known to have orgasms through masturbation. Because these sensual feelings are pleasurable, children naturally seek them out — often not realising that what they are doing may be wrong in their parents' eyes, until they are caught and chastised. Children's motivation is sensual pleasure, just the same as they enjoy splashing in water and rolling in long grass. Once discovered in childhood, masturbatory activity continues not from sexual desire but from a desire to re-experience these pleasurable feelings. There is no sexual desire until puberty.

Childhood sexual activity must never be confused with adult sexual behaviour. It is completely different. If you discover young children engaged in sexual rehearsal, calmly distract them with another activity or game. You might say, 'It's time to have some afternoon tea now. Pop on your clothes and come into the kitchen.' On no account should children be shamed or punished. This can have harmful sexual repercussions when they are adults.

The same applies if you catch your child masturbating. Ignore self-stimulation if it is in private. If you feel comfortable enough, you might like to acknowledge the behaviour by saying, 'Most people enjoy touching themselves.' If the child is masturbating in a family or public situation, then point out to them that this is a private activity and is best carried out in their bedroom.

Use both these situations as opportunities to later bring up the topic of sex with your children; find out what they know and want to know, and give them sexual information relevant to their age group (see Resources).

Childhood sexual rehearsal is not acceptable when there is coercion involved (tricking, threatening, bribing of a child to participate) or where there is an age gap or power gradient between the children. I would be concerned if there was an age gap of four years or more between the children or if one child held excessive sway over the other, regardless of age. Parents must rely on their intuition in these cases to decide what is OK and what is not.

Of course, some parents may find that this sort of advice goes against their morality. Each of us has the right to bring up our children according to our values. However, shaming and punishment should be avoided at all costs, whatever your beliefs about masturbation or sexual rehearsal might be.

When Her Sex Drive is Stronger Than His

Although men generally are expected to have the higher desire, this does not always reflect what is happening in real-life relationships. Many women complain they would like more sex than their partners provide.

Janita and Terry have been married for 18 months. Janita complains, 'Before we were married, we had sex at every opportunity. It was exciting. Now Terry is happy with sex once a month and that's it. He's really focused on work most of the time. He accuses me of pressuring him to work harder because of the money I spend. We have goals and I am just making sure he meets them.'

Terry once had a higher level of interest in sex, but it has diminished under the pressure of Janita's sexual and financial demands. He is experiencing *inhibited sexual desire*.

Marcia, who has been living with David for three years, says, 'David was never very interested in sex but I thought it would get better when we were living together. In fact, it's got worse. Nothing I do changes things — and I've tried everything: new clothes, diet, exercise, even sex toys. I feel so desperate, I'm scared I might have an affair.'

David is a man with *low sexual interest*.

If men have a stronger sex drive, how can a female partner have more interest in sex? This apparent paradox can be easily explained by going back to the normal curve. There will be women at the upper end of the normal range who have a higher sex drive than their partners, although both are normal.

Janita and Terry's situation is a good example. Janita had a higher level of sexual interest, while Terry was about average. Neither was abnormal, just different. During courtship their opportunities to make love were limited and he was keen to make love whenever they had the chance. This sexual enthusiasm during courtship effectively masked his lower level of interest in sex compared with Janita. Due to conflict in the relationship over money, work and sex, Terry's interest in sex has dropped down even further.

David's sex drive was never at a high level, and Marcia was aware of this from the start. Let's see where these two couples sit on the normal curve.

For some men, low levels of interest in sex represent their lifelong level of libido — men like David, who fall towards the lower end of the normal curve. Other men may have experienced a higher level of interest in sex in the past, but this has dwindled. Their sex drive is being turned down by the presence of inhibitors.

Inhibitors of male desire

Both genders share a list of common inhibitors as described in Chapter 6. However, men are particularly sensitive to the inhibitors listed below.

- Sexual boredom
- Lack of spontaneity
- Unresponsive partner — feeling undesired and undesirable
- Overwhelming sexual demands of partner
- Sexual problems — male and female
- Feelings of sexual inadequacy — poor sexual self-esteem
- Discomfort with sexual repertoire
- Fear of sexual rejection — repeated sexual knockbacks
- Birth control anxieties and interruptions
- Safe sex issues
- Fear of intimacy
- Lack of partner appreciation and acceptance — frequent criticism
- Unresolved relationship conflict and partner hostility.

These inhibitors crop up time and time again in counselling sessions with men with lowered desire. They are discussed in Chapter 19.

Notice how many of the inhibitors relate to sexual activity. Male desire is deeply vulnerable to sexual rejection, sexual dissatisfaction and sexual problems. Repeated rejections, criticisms of

sexual technique, problems in performing, low or reluctant partner participation, or overwhelming sexual demands can all reduce
sex drive in men. The libidos of men with inhibited sexual desire
can be increased by minimising these inhibitors and maximising
their enhancers.

Men in this situation often feel inadequate, while their partners
become increasingly anxious and confused. Female partners are
baffled, especially when they get together with their friends and
hear about how *their* partners can't keep their hands to themselves. Feelings of female rejection and male inferiority are
aggravated because of society's assertion that 'All men should be
interested in sex'. The situation is not improved when she says to
him, 'Every other man wants sex whenever he can get it — what's
wrong with you?'

Getting passion into perspective

When a man's level of sexual interest is lower than his partner's, it
need not pose a problem. Like the sexual reverse, where a man
wants sex more often than his female partner, the differences can
be resolved with understanding, acceptance and compromise.

Be your own sex therapist

For Men: If your sex drive has fallen from a previously
higher level, pause for a moment and consider what factors
are contributing to this drop in sexual interest. You might
like to refer to the list of general inhibitors in Chapter 6
which affect both sexes, as well as looking at the list of
specific male inhibitors above. Add any inhibitors you can
identify that are not listed.
Once this list is complete, discuss it with your partner.

For Women: If your partner's level of sex drive has fallen,
follow the instructions above and make a list of any factors
that you think might be affecting him.
Compare your list with the one he makes for himself and
discuss your lists together.

The inevitability of desire mismatch

Just in case you have yet to be convinced that desire discrepancy is quite normal, let's play Cupid for a moment and bring together a typical male, Adam, and a typical female, Eve. Having plotted their levels of desire throughout the lifespan, we can get an overview of the couple's potential sexual compatibility by joining their graphs.

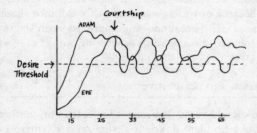

Adam experiences a constant sex drive, while Eve's interest tends to go up and down around the desire threshold depending on what's happening in her life. The period of most prolonged sexual compatibility occurs when they first fell in love. After that, they share the same level of desire from time to time. More often than not, when he's up, she's down, or vice versa.

If a couple like this has effective problem-solving and communication skills, they have a good chance of creating a hassle-free sexual relationship. If not, their relationship could go through some troubled times.

The point of playing this imaginary sexual mix-and-match is to demonstrate that couples cannot realistically expect to have the same level of interest in sex at the same time over the course of their relationship.

Be your own sex therapist

You might like to draw up your own desire time line. On a large sheet of paper draw a vertical axis to represent level of sexual desire. On the horizontal axis, mark out years in groups of 5.

Think back to when you first started to experience sexual desire. Childhood sexual rehearsal and childhood masturbation do not count. Teenage masturbation is one indicator of desire. Teenage sexual activity is another, but not necessarily so. Many teenagers engage in sexual activities for reasons other than sexual desire.

Note the effect when you fall in love — desire usually increases at this time. Think of life experiences that have influenced your desire and label them on your chart. Continue marking out the graph until you reach the present.

Have your partner map out his or her own desire time line.

Now superimpose one onto the other. This exercise will prove the inevitability of DD in long-term relationships.

If you experience situational inhibited desire — that is, your desire level is low for one sexual outlet (e.g. your long-term partner) but not for another — you might like to mark out two lines on your personal graph. For example, your desire for masturbation or for sex outside the relationship may not vary much, while your level of interest in sex with your partner fluctuates. You may or may not choose to share this information with your partner at this time.

Men's sex drive differs from women's sex drive in quality rather than quantity. This difference is due to both social and biological factors.

Women's sex drive is more likely to be turned down by the stresses and strains of everyday life and love than men's. This gender difference in sex drives is based on primitive reproductive needs.

These days, women are expected to express a high level of interest in sex. However, many women experience little if any interest in sex on a regular basis.

Boys and girls growing up experience their sexuality differently. A woman's full sexual potential may not be experienced until she is in her twenties, thirties or even later.

It is especially difficult for couples where the man is the partner with the lower sex drive, although this is quite a normal and common occurrence. Regardless of who has the lower sex drive, sexual compatibility is still possible.

Her Enhancers — Sugar and Spice and All Things Nice

Although men and women share many desire enhancers, there are some enhancers that, as a broad generalisation, appeal more particularly to men than women, and vice versa. Put simply, what turns him on may be different from what turns her on.

Here is a list of enhancers that typically promote desire in women.

> Sugar and spice and all things nice
> That's what little girls are made of.
> Slugs and snails and puppy dogs' tails
> That's what little boys are made of.

TYPICAL FEMALE ENHANCERS

- Romantic gestures — cards, flowers, gifts, compliments
- Communication
- Intimacy
- Non-demanding affection
- Sensuality
- Quality time spent with partner
- Low level of conflict

The following is a list of enhancers that typically promote desire in men.

TYPICAL MALE ENHANCERS

- Varied lovemaking
- Novelty
- Spontaneity
- Nudity — the female form
- Lingerie
- Positive sexual responses in partner
- Erotica
- Pornography

ALL MEN LIKE PORNOGRAPHY?
ALL WOMEN CRAVE ROMANCE?

To experience robust sexual desire and fulfilment, women need their preferred enhancers, while men are most desirous and sexually satisfied when they have access to *their* preferred enhancers. It would be easy if every man was turned on by *Penthouse* magazine and every woman was ready for bed after a box of chocolates. Human beings are far too complicated for that. As one would expect, responses to gender-based enhancers vary. One man's meat may be another man's poison. Men do not universally respond to typical male enhancers and some may even find them offensive. Take workmates Hugh and Rod.

> **Hugh:** I love really explicit pornography. I know it's not politically correct, but it certainly gets me going.
> **Rod:** I think it's wrong when you're married to look at other women, especially naked ones, even in photos. It's just like being unfaithful.

Men may find themselves to be equally or more stimulated by traditional female enhancers. On the other hand, women may respond to enhancers that are thought of as typically male.

> **Sarah:** I get really hot when Barry talks dirty to me about the girls he's been with before me. I love to hear all the details.

MALE VS FEMALE TURN-ONS — NATURE OR NURTURE?

So why do men and women prefer different enhancers? Once again, it's due to both our genes and our culture. Biologically these preferences have their roots in our primitive past when they were designed to ensure the survival of the species. It was a Cave Man's job to fertilise the egg. The Cave Woman's role was to bear the resulting baby. Human children remain dependent longer than the offspring of any other species. The formation of an enduring human 'pair bond' was necessary so that two parents could be available to care for the child and maximise the chances of its survival.

To do her reproductive job effectively, Cave Woman needs a long-term mate, so it's no accident that she is turned on by men who display qualities of commitment, attention, affection, caring, and the like. As for Cave Man, he's a sperm donor so he's excited by the prospect of a sexually available fertile female who responds to his approaches. These long established (and very different) biological enhancers were originally designed so that humans would populate rather than perish.

These preferences are now obsolete as far as our survival is concerned, but we are stuck with making sense of them in our modern relationships. In this chapter we will look at female sexual programming and women's preferred enhancers; we'll do the same for men in the next chapter.

WOMEN'S SEXUAL PROGRAMMING

A woman's reproductive role is to bear and nurture children, so she is on the look-out for a suitable father and protector for her offspring. She will be attracted to characteristics in a man that demonstrate his willingness to stick around to protect her and her infant. A man who makes an emotional connection with her is a better choice of mate, because he is less likely to depart and leave her holding the baby (literally).

A woman's desire is excited by a man who appears willing to be emotionally involved and committed to her, because her primitive Cave Woman conditions for mating are fulfilled. For this reason, the emotional quality of the sexual relationship takes on deeper significance for women than men. She is looking for security and long-term safety, keeping in mind the wellbeing of her future children. For the same reason, women are drawn to men with status and power, and who are successful and prosperous, based on the notion that such a man is better placed to look after her and her tribe-to-be.

The typical female enhancers of romance, time spent together, communication and intimacy have a profound effect on female sexual interest, turning the desire thermostat up to a higher heat. You don't have to be Einstein to figure out that these female preferred enhancers are present in greatest intensity in the early months of any new courtship. When Cupid's arrow strikes, a woman usually finds her sex drive peaks for 12 months or more due to an abundance of female preferred enhancers. This period of time, known as *limerence*, deserves special mention because of its powerful effect on female sexual desire.

LIMERENCE — LOVE OR LUST?

'Limerence' is a term coined by American psychologist Dorothy Tennov to describe the fabulous feelings most of us experience in the early stages of a romantic relationship. It is a temporary phase marked by physical, intellectual and emotional changes. We can't eat, we can't sleep, we stay up all night talking, yet we feel full of energy the next day. Many people lose weight at this time. We feel euphoric and are convinced no-one else has ever felt the way we do. Emotionally our feet just don't touch the ground.

We experience an 'urge to merge'. Our interest is completely focused on our loved one. We forget important tasks, ignore our friends and families, and neglect our work or studies. When we are not in the company of our beloved, we spend most of our time daydreaming about them. We can't wait to see them and spend hours on the phone when we're apart. We hang off their every word and think they are the best thing since sliced bread.

Limerence is an artificial state of euphoria created when we show only the best side of ourselves to our partners and they do the same to us. Nasty habits or difficult feelings are hidden away or if they do arise, they are dismissed as quaint or idiosyncratic. Even behaviour that would normally offend or annoy us is passed over in the rosy glow of limerence. People who are limerent seldom get cross with their partners. Conflict is avoided at all costs. If our beloved arrives late or forgets an arrangement, they are adorably muddle-headed. We think their breath smells good in the morning (as do their socks in the evening), all their jokes are funny, and the way they leave their clothes lying about the bedroom is adorably bohemian.

However, limerence is a time-limited experience. Twelve to 18 months down the track, things have changed — we get furious when our partner turns up late, and we complain about the mess they've left in the bedroom. It's not the end of the relationship — it just means that limerence has begun to fade.

> **Sally:** The things that attracted me to James in the first place are the things that drive me crazy now. He was so laid back and carefree before we were married two years ago. I come from a really stitched-up family, so I enjoyed his relaxed attitude. Now it irritates me. He never takes anything seriously.
>
> **James:** Sally wants me to be punctual and tidy and to move ahead in my job. She knew what I was like and she used to love me for it. Anyway, I'm not so sure I like the way she wants everything organised all the time. She's so tidy and particular it gets on my nerves.

James and Sally are looking at each other without the benefit of limerence's rose-coloured glasses. In the cold light of day, James' relaxed approach to life is not as enchanting as it once was. Sally's need for order and control is now rubbing James the wrong way. This couple will need to work through these differences which were initially masked by the powerful effects of limerence.

Limerence and the 'love drugs'

George Bernard Shaw did not know about the phenomenon of limerence but described it perfectly when he said of marriage:

'When two people are under the most violent, most intense, most delusive and most transient of passions, they are required to swear that they will remain in that excited, abnormal and exhausting condition continuously until death do them part.'

The 'high' of limerence is due to arousing brain chemicals which are released when we meet someone we are attracted to. These neurotransmitters include:

- *Acetylcholine* — produces a feeling of excitement, a rush similar to that produced by amphetamines.
- *Dopamine* — induces a feeling of wellbeing.
- *Noradrenaline* — induces feelings of pleasure, of conquering the world, contentment, joy and love.
- *Phenylethylamine* — creates heightened excitement.
- *Serotonin* — maintains a generalised feeling of emotional security.

Under the barrage of all these feel-good chemicals, what chance do we mere mortals have!

Limerence is not love

In our society this altered state is regarded as LOVE. Limerence is *not* love — it is infatuation. The swirling chemical high of limerence is a little trick played by Mother Nature on human beings to get them together for the purposes of, you guessed it, reproduction. We are still Cave Men and Cave Women at heart (and hormone).

In primitive terms, limerence lasts just long enough for a couple to get together, for the woman to be impregnated and a baby to be born. Then, theoretically, the man can be off again to find another mate and, by doing what comes naturally, ensure diversity of the species.

Limerence is a wonderful experience, but the passionate feelings we experience are not an indication that this is a lasting relationship or even a functional or fulfilling one. Even the most unhappy love affairs start out with both partners feeling limerent and over the moon.

Limerence continues for a variable amount of time. For some people it lasts a week, others a month, but most people experience limerence in a new relationship for at least 6 to 12 months. The effects of limerence can last up to three years, although the intensity usually begins to decline after the first 12 months.

Limerence will last longer if obstructions are placed in the way of lovers — for example, if the couple must be separated for any length of time, or the love affair is long distance. If the family or community disapproves of the relationship, this will also extend the euphoric phase.

Extramarital affairs are real hotbeds of limerence. Although the intense excitement and prolonged passion of an extramarital affair can feel like love, it is usually a matter of extended limerence. Extramarital limerence can endure for years, as long as the straying couple don't spend too much time together. Long-term relationships find it hard to compete with the thrill of this type of forbidden limerence.

> **Jerome:** I lived with Phoebe and the kids, but for years Linda and I would get together once a week, have dinner, then go back to her place and make love for hours. Sex was incredibly passionate. We couldn't get enough of each other. Then I'd go home to Phoebe.
>
> Linda was always begging me to leave my marriage, but I guess you could say I was having my cake and eating it too. One day Linda rang my wife and told her what had been going on. That was the end of my marriage.
>
> Within weeks of moving in with Linda I knew it was the biggest mistake I had ever made. We fought like cat and dog. Sex with her was not so great after a day or so of 'no speakies' whenever she didn't get her way. All those years I thought we were in love, but it was just lust. I sacrificed so much and in the end it wasn't worth it.

In with conflict, out with limerence

After a variable amount of time, limerence always begins to fade. Although important, our partner is no longer the total focus of our life. We return to our friends, our hobbies and other interests. We get tired of always being the 'perfect' partner, totally flexible

> The love boat has
> crashed against the
> everyday.
> VLADIMIR MAYAKOVSKY
> RUSSIAN POET

and amazingly patient. Our tolerance drops dramatically and our lover's cute habits become annoying. We start to reveal those 'less attractive' parts of our personalities, kept carefully hidden up until now. As we both start to reveal ourselves in the relationship, little arguments and irritations begin and limerence starts to fade.

Conflicts are inevitable in any relationship and are not a sign that the relationship is flawed. The hallmark of a healthy relationship is that conflicts are dealt with fully whenever they arise.

Limerence and love

The good news is that real love can only start when limerence begins to fade, when we stop hiding from our partners and start to bring our real selves into the relationship. Happily, in good relationships, we can re-experience moments of limerence by re-creating courtship activities like going away together, having a romantic candlelit dinner, or a lazy breakfast in bed, or taking a walk together along the beach. The emotional function of limerence is to keep two people together so they can learn to truly fall in love. Limerence is not love, but hopefully it can lead to love.

Loving our partner deeply and truly may not cause our bodies to zing with surges of sexy neurotransmitters, but we are rewarded with nature's softer chemicals — the endorphins. Endorphins are the body's opiates, our natural source of 'heroin' or 'morphine' — they induce a relaxed, comfortable feeling of wellbeing. The romantic but transitory high of limerence mellows into something deeper and much more sustainable in a long-term relationship.

Limerence junkies

Many people believe that limerence is love. They are happy in each new relationship until limerence starts to fade, then they move on to re-create it in a new relationship. And so on. These people become limerence 'addicts' or 'junkies' moving from relationship to relationship looking for permanent limerence and blaming their partners for the fact that romantic bliss and sexual ecstasy do not persist for more than a few months. By continually searching for the 'perfect partner' they avoid becoming involved in the sort of lasting, committed relationship where true love can take seed and grow.

Be your own sex therapist

Can you think of past relationships when you thought you were in love but you were actually experiencing limerence?
Are you a limerence junkie going from relationship to relationship, looking for sustained passion and excitement, and leaving when the magic starts to fade?

Limerence and sexual desire

Both men and women experience an upsurge of sexual interest when they are limerant. After all, courting involves:
- plenty of time together and mutual attention
- the excitement of discovering each other
- novelty and fun
- being adventurous — trying new activities and interests
- plenty of affection and non-sexual contact
- romantic gestures
- frequent expressions of love and affection
- mutual self-disclosure
- growing intimacy and closeness
- low levels of criticism and conflict.

For women, these are the most potent enhancers of all. Limerence can (temporarily) transform a shrinking violet into a sexual huntress. Limerence works more indirectly on men — most men are turned on by the company of a limerent woman who is sexually interested and adventurous.

In the initial months of sexual activity most couples seem magically to possess a perfectly matched set of libidos. As limerence fades, desire discrepancy often emerges for the first time. Or a minor desire mismatch may turn into a major one. If we were to interview 100 couples who had been together for less than a year about their sexual compatibility, the majority would

> If you put a bean in a jar every time you make love during your first year of marriage, and take a bean out every time you make love in the years that follow, don't be surprised if you still have beans left in your jar ten years down the track.
>
> ADVICE ON SEX FROM A
> BASEBALL COACH TO HIS TEAM

report plain sailing. But repeat the interviews five years down the track, and many couples would be experiencing stormy weather because of differences in sex drive.

As time wears on and limerence wears off, sexual desire drops to its normal level and continues to fluctuate in the usual way. The drop for women is typically greater than the drop for men. Men often complain that their partner was a 'hot tamale' in the first year of the relationship, and then for no obvious reason she started to cool down.

Couples who expect the passion of limerence to persist forever, irrespective of the ups and downs of life and love, will be deeply disappointed. The good news is that by re-creating some of those courtship conditions, we can recapture similar feelings. This is why going away on holiday generally sparks up a couple's sex life.

WHY WOMEN NEED THEIR ENHANCERS

To experience interest in sex, most women need their preferred enhancers. A woman's River of Desire is not swollen by high levels of testosterone, so the contribution of her relationship tributary is vitally important. Most of these enhancers are elements of a healthy, intimate relationship. To maximise female libido, enhancers should be present in:

- *Quantity:* How much? As much as she needs.
- *Frequency:* Daily at least — don't miss a day, if possible.
- *Quality:* Make a good effort, not a half-hearted gesture.

Twenty-three-and-a-half-hour foreplay

If a man desires frequent sexual activity with his partner, it is in his best interest to maintain a sustained background of romance, affection and attention for his partner on a day-to-day basis.

Women experience 'twenty-three-and-a-half-hour foreplay' — everything that happens in a woman's day affects her capacity for desire and arousal.

> **Antionette:** We both work hard all day and after dinner we watch TV most nights. He sits in his favourite bean chair, while I lie on the couch. When we go to bed he expects me to turn on like a light switch, even though we have hardly spent a moment together. I resent his sexual demands, and he sulks.

Little gestures mean a lot — ask your partner about her day *and listen to the answer*; give her flowers occasionally; organise a night out together; give her a card or make an unexpected phone call to say 'I love you'. To men these gestures often appear irrelevant in a long-term relationship ('Of course I love her — I have sex with her, don't I?'). But to a woman these small efforts are the basic building blocks of a good relationship, both in and out of the bedroom.

A woman's daily bread

For a woman to experience a sustained enthusiasm for sex that lasts beyond limerence, her enhancers need to be present in the relationship on a regular basis. It's no good providing a woman with enhancers out of the blue and expecting her to respond because *you* happen to feel like sex.

> **Tony:** I brought her home some flowers and she still gave me the cold shoulder. What's the point of trying?
> **Maria:** He's been treating me like dirt for the last few months. He brings me home some flowers and expects me to welcome him with open arms and open who-knows-what-else. Does he think a few carnations can make up for months of abuse?

Instead of thanking Tony for the flowers, Maria is responding to Tony's one-off romantic gesture by expressing a high level of resentment.

> **Tony:** She put the flowers in the garbage. I couldn't believe it.
> There's no money to spare, and when I buy her flowers she
> throws them out. All I want is a little closeness and affection.

Have you ever responded to a loving gesture by your partner with
resentment and anger in this way? If you have, it is probably a
sign that your needs are not being met adequately or consistently
within your relationship. We are talking here about the quality,
quantity and frequency of enhancers.

When needs are not met in a relationship, resentment builds up
over time. Instead of expressing this resentment and hostility, we
tend to hold it in. Finally, our partner makes that gesture we have
been longing for. Perhaps, for a woman like Maria, it's a bunch of
flowers or Tony cooking the evening meal. For Tony, it might be
Maria initiating sex instead of avoiding him all the time.

> **Maria:** I'm not very physical with Tony and he's always
> asking for affection. Yet whenever I get in the mood to
> give him a cuddle, he makes a sarcastic comment. Last
> night when I put my arms around him, he said 'What do
> you want now?' in a really nasty voice.
> **Tony:** I know I shouldn't have said what I did, but she has
> no idea how much I hang out for even the smallest bit of
> affection from her. When she does touch me, all I feel is
> anger.

When that long-awaited gesture occurs, instead of the joy and
gratitude our partner expects, out comes all the anger and resentment that has been building up for months or even years.

The occasional effort to meet your partner's needs could well
have the opposite effect to the one you intended. Instead of getting
into your partner's good books, you may find yourself out on your
ear. By meeting your partner's needs on a *regular* basis, you will
keep your relationship healthy and avoid the build-up of resentment that can harm both you and your partner.

INCREASING FEMALE DESIRE

If you are a man and you want to increase your partner's level of sexual desire, make sure you meet her needs and supply her with desire enhancers on a *daily* basis. If you can't be bothered finding a few moments each day to talk to your partner, cuddle her tenderly, support her emotionally, and make her feel special and important, don't expect her to feel hot and horny when you climb into bed at night (or any other time!). The healthier and happier the relationship is, the more likely the female partner is to feel desire. Part 3 of this book will show you both how to inject more romance, companionship and passion into your relationship.

Be your own sex therapist

If you are a woman, what enhancers might improve your relationship and help to increase your level of sex drive?

Do your partner and your relationship provide you with these enhancers on a sustained and regular basis?

Was there a time in your relationship when your desire was higher? Were your enhancers being provided at that time?

If your partner makes a loving gesture, do you always respond positively or do you experience resentment and frustration? This is a sign that your needs are not being adequately met, either in quantity, quality or frequency.

THE WIDE ACCEPTANCE OF WOMEN'S ENHANCERS

Society validates and supports female preferred enhancers. For example, every second women's magazine includes articles with titles like 'Create More Romance in Your Relationship' or 'Put the Sizzle back in Your Sex Life'.

Women feel entitled to expect this input from their men and are vocal if their enhancer needs aren't met. 'You never buy me flowers, you never take me out to dinner, you never listen to me!' Women feel resentful and express righteous indignation when their partners fail to meet these significant emotional and sexual needs.

Unfortunately, society's view of men's sexual enhancers is not so encouraging, as we shall see in the next chapter. If the sexes are to be truly equal, we need to develop the same sort of supportive attitude towards men's enhancers as we already hold for female enhancers.

Key Points ◄〜❤〜►

To experience optimal levels of desire, arousal and sexual fulfilment, men and women need their preferred enhancers in the relationship.

Men respond to anything that denotes fertility, sexual availability and novelty. A woman's desire is excited by elements of affection, commitment and security in the relationship.

Female enhancers are present most intensively in the courtship phase of relationships, known as limerence. Female sexual desire is usually highest in this early phase of a romantic relationship.

Limerence junkies are people who go from relationship to relationship looking for the emotional and sexual high of early courtship.

For a woman to have a sustained and enthusiastic interest in sex, her enhancer needs must be met on a daily basis. Sporadic romantic or emotional gestures are useless and may serve to increase resentment.

Women are supported by society in their demands for female-based enhancers. Men's enhancers are not viewed with the same enthusiasm by women or society in general.

His Enhancers — Slugs and Snails and Puppy Dogs' Tails?

Men's list of preferred desire enhancers differs greatly from the 'sugar and spice' list of typical enhancers for women. Emotional connection, romance, affection or closeness don't figure so highly. Men's enhancers are largely related to sexual activity and many rely on visual stimulation, a sensual enhancer that tends to have a much greater impact on men than on women.

TYPICAL MALE ENHANCERS OF DESIRE

- Varied lovemaking
- Novelty
- Spontaneity
- Nudity — the female form
- Lingerie
- Positive sexual response in partner
- Erotica
- Pornography

Be your own sex therapist

If you are a woman, take a look at the list of male enhancers.
How do you feel about the different enhancers? Rate them as
positive, neutral or negative.
Do any of these enhancers work for your partner?
Which enhancers are currently acceptable to you within your
relationship?
Do any of these typically male enhancers work for you?

Women who are educated to understand why men are attracted to
erotic material and explicit sexuality often exhibit greater tolerance because they don't take male enhancers personally and
nor do they misinterpret them as a threat to themselves or the
relationship.

MAKING MEN'S ENHANCERS WRONG

> Is sex dirty?
> Only if it's done right.
> WOODY ALLEN

Compared with women's typical
enhancers of romance, intimacy and
affection, it is much more difficult
to sell the idea that men's enhancers
also have a place in relationships.
Men's enhancers are seen by many as dirty and degrading, unwholesome and sometimes unacceptable. Compare this attitude
with that of the Ancient Greeks who had explicit sexual scenes
depicted on everyday household items like plates, serving dishes
and vases.

When men and women both understand men's enhancers, they
often come to regard them in a more positive light.

THE EYES HAVE IT

Men's enhancers rely strongly on visual elements. This natural male
inclination to look at the female form often gets men into trouble,
trouble which can be easily avoided with a little cooperation between
the sexes.

Have you ever wondered what draws a man's eyes to skimpy

outfits, miniskirts and the flash of female flesh under a see-through shirt? While a woman's sexual programming prepares her to be the bearer and nurturer of children if she chooses, men have been given the simpler reproductive role of 'sperm donor'. Men are programmed to be on the look-out for the best 'soil' in which to plant their seed and constantly search for signs of female sexual availability, good health and abundant fertility. This usually means a young woman with curves in all the right places and an outfit that shows them off.

Men who look — biology and society at work

They say that *women fall in love with their ears, men fall in love with their eyes*. Men are much more visually responsive than women are. Centuries of exposure to erotic images have conditioned men to respond to explicit sexual scenes, nudity, lingerie and the like. Daily exposure to the charms of the female form continues today, with suggestive images of women bombarding men from TV, movies, magazines and advertising.

This socialisation of men to respond to the sight of the female form builds on male biology. Back in the Stone Age, it was often necessary for Cave Man to become rapidly aroused with very little stimulation: Cave Man beholds Cave Woman beckoning seductively from the bushes. Out of the corner of his eye he also sees a hairy mammoth rounding the top of the hill, bearing down on both of them.

Cave Man is designed so that, by the time he reaches Cave Woman, his eyes have done all the necessary work to get him fully aroused and ready for action. After all, he has to be able to:

- get it up ...
- get it in ...
- get it off ...
- and get it out ...

before the mammoth stomps them both to death. In a nutshell, Cave Man's survival and the future of the human race depends on his ability to get visually turned on. No wonder men feel compelled to look!

I saw you looking at her! Don't deny it!

Cave Man was always on the look-out for a potential mate. Modern men are still blessed with this primitive facility to appraise all women, forever seeking out females with characteristics of fertility and youth (as if you hadn't noticed!).

> Dear Dr Rosie,
> My husband always looks at other women. He makes comments and his jaw drops whenever an attractive young girl goes by. Worst of all, he denies that he does it. We end up having a huge blow-up because I want him to stop.

> Love's tongue is in the eyes.
> PHINEAS FLETCHER
> ENGLISH CLERGYMAN
> AND POET

Now isn't that a familiar female complaint! This bloke is doing his Cave Man thing (a little too enthusiastically, I might add). His partner feels hurt and threatened. Her solution is simple — he should simply stop looking. However, to solve this problem *both* parties need to change their attitudes and behaviour.

Who's looking?

Girls, if we faced facts, men aren't the only ones doing the looking. Both men and women constantly look at individuals of both sexes. It is our natural scanning ability, installed as a protective mechanism. Humans are herd animals (like wolves and horses) and we must be able to decide in an instant who is 'of the herd', and thus a friend, and who is a potential foe.

However, there is a difference: *women are much more subtle about the way they look than men are.* Women and men have different sorts of eyesight — women have much better *scanning vision* than men. Any woman worth her salt can spot the competition in a miniskirt 100 metres away. They will look the competition up and down, make comparisons (usually unfavourable to herself), chew her up and spit her out (mentally) long before her man spots those long legs coming towards him.

Now that she has finished with Miss Miniskirt, she waits for the inevitable — her man to notice, ogle, swivel and drool. Then she pounces on him — for doing exactly what *she* was doing only a minute before — checking out Miss Miniskirt!

> Looking at cleavage is like looking at the sun. You don't stare. It's too dangerous.
>
> JERRY SEINFELD

Men's contribution

Many men look at women other than their partners in a very unsubtle and offensive way. If a man has to look (and most men do), he should follow these rules.

Rule 1: If you must look, then try to look in a subtle, restrained way. Mentally undressing the female competition garment by garment in front of your partner is not very smart. Don't ogle, don't swivel and, whatever you do, don't drool. Be respectful of your partner and every other woman you encounter.

Rule 2: Use every lovely girl you see as a prompt to remind you to pay your partner yet another compliment. Many women complain that their partners gush over the competition, but never bother to praise the woman they are with. Praising your partner will reassure her so that even when you *do* look, she feels secure in your affections and not threatened by your wandering eye.

Rule 3: Pay your partner compliments on a regular basis — not just when she's dressed up to go out (or, worse still, when she has to ask for it!). Compliments are strong enhancers for women, and they need them in order to feel acknowledged and appreciated. Some compliments are worth bottling, like the time my husband woke up beside me and said, 'I've just been sleeping with Miss World!' Boy, did I start that day on the right side of the bed — *his* side!

Rule 4: Never deny that you were looking — it infuriates a woman beyond all measure. She's not an idiot. If you were looking, admit it — and then reassure her.

Women's contribution

Like it or not, men can't take all the blame for this problem. Women need to get their man's behaviour into perspective; certainly he shouldn't ogle outrageously, deny what he was doing, or compliment strangers and ignore you — but women, too, have a part to play in this little drama.

Girls, stop for a moment and think about what you are doing when you 'check out' the competition. Admit it — *you are comparing yourself with her*. Notice how you only compare yourself with women you consider to be more attractive than you are. By comparing yourself with her (she's younger, prettier, slimmer, or just different), you make yourself feel bad. If you have great legs, then you compare her waist or her breasts with yours. If you have gorgeous hair and a great body, you envy her outfit or jewellery. When women play the comparison game they select the aspects of other women that are guaranteed to make them feel bad and filter out any positive comparisons. Talk about being your own worst enemy!

It doesn't take long before our men bear the brunt of our appalling habit of comparing ourselves negatively with other women:

- You've caught him looking at some 'piece of fluff' in the street.
- You've made yourself feel bad by comparing yourself unfavourably with this other woman.
- When you catch your mate giving her the once over, you feel even more insecure, more threatened, more unlovely.
- You assume that his looking is a sign that you must be unattractive to him. You feel threatened.

All this happens in a matter of seconds. The next step is: *you dump all your bad feelings onto him*. You accuse him, get angry with him, give him the old silent treatment, or sulk. You act as if he is insulting you by looking at other women — in reality, he doesn't have to insult you, because you *have* already seen to that yourself!

Comparisons are odious

Women need to stop comparing themselves adversely with other women. It is an abusive habit destined to crack a woman's self-esteem so that all her self-confidence seeps away. If you are feeling threatened by your partner's visual callisthenics, don't jump up and down and dump on him. The next time you catch him looking, be responsible for your own uncomfortable feelings. Soothe yourself by rejecting those nasty negative comparisons. Remind yourself of your own special loveliness. This soothing self-talk may be all you need to put this experience into perspective. If you cannot reassure yourself adequately, then ask your man to help you out.

In a calm moment tell him that you feel insecure when he ogles other women and negotiate with him that he will mind his manners around you and other women. Explain that when it next happens you will ask him for reassurance, instead of reacting angrily.

'I noticed you looking at that girl and I felt threatened. Could you reassure me that:

- You love me.
- You think I'm pretty/desirable/sexy.
- You're not thinking of leaving me for her (or anyone else).
- I'm the only woman in your life, etc.

In return for your honesty and brave self-disclosure, he should give you the loving reassurance you need then and there.

For girls only

One paradoxical trick that seems to work is to point out attractive women to your man before he sees them. Being a woman, you will always spot her first and you can say, 'Look at that attractive woman over there. Isn't she gorgeous!' Women who have tried this say they feel more in control and it seems to damp down men's natural inclination to stare. (Perhaps because if we give them permission to do so, it seems less tantalising!)

A CLOSER LOOK AT MEN'S ENHANCERS

There are very good reasons for taking a closer look at male enhancers, even if your man has a higher interest in sex than you do.

- Inclusion of your man's enhancers will improve the quality of his (and therefore your) sex life.
- Inclusion of a variety of male enhancers in a long-term relationship helps to keep both partners sexually active and interested.
- Male desire enhancers become more important as men age and their sexual response slows.
- There are an increasing number of couples where the man's sex drive is lower than his partner's. For these couples, male enhancers can be a real boon.

Varied lovemaking/novelty/spontaneity

> Variety is the soul of pleasure.
> APHRA BEHN
> ENGLISH POET

There's nothing quite like the feel of a brand new outfit the very first time you wear it. Seeing a movie for the first time is more exciting than seeing a rerun on TV at home. It is human nature to seek out variety and novelty, and sex is no exception.

Rex: My wife Rita is happy with the same old routine twice a week. We get into bed, we turn out the light, we kiss for a while and stroke each other, and then we have intercourse. There's nothing new or exciting. I'd love to leave the light on, or sit up and face each other for a while. I'd like to give her oral sex and, if she wants to, she could return the favour like she used to. If the truth be known, it's boring. I'd like just once to get into bed and wonder what's going to happen next.

Our senses delight in new sights, sounds, smells, tastes and touches. Newness can be injected into relationships by using a little

> The real voyage of discovery consists not in seeking new landscapes, but in having new eyes.
> MARCEL PROUST

imagination. Rex does not hanker after the novelty of another partner — he simply wants to experience his sexual relationship with Rita in different ways.

Routine and habit help to keep us feeling comfortable and safe, but they also dull our senses. We become blind to the view we see every day, no matter how wonderful it is, and deaf to glorious music played over and over again as background noise.

Novelty and variety can be introduced into long-term sexual relationships in many different ways. You can alter what you do, when you do it and how you do it. Place of lovemaking, time, style and duration can all be varied. Strategies to expand your sexual repertoire will be looked at more closely in Chapter 17.

> Habit is a great deadener.
> SAMUEL BECKETT

Nudity — the female form

Men love to see their partners naked. They happily label themselves 'breast', 'bum' or 'leg men' (or all three). Many women shy away from nudity out of a poor regard for their bodies. They find men's fascination with their body parts, especially the more intimate zones, rather confronting.

Most men would much rather look at their flesh-and-blood disrobed partner than some airbrushed image in a girlie magazine. When a man loves you, although time, children and gravity may have taken hold of your body and refuse to let go, he still sees *you* as the fulfilment of his dreams.

> If nobody had learned to undress, very few people would be in love.
> DOROTHY PARKER

Josie: I'll never forget the time I stepped on the scales and found that my diet was really working. Over a few days I had lost 4 kilograms and I was looking hot! I decided to give Sebastian a treat. After dinner I went into the bedroom and changed into a sexy lace teddy. Sebastian was watching TV, but I soon got his attention when I put on some music and started dancing about the room flashing my body. I was feeling really raunchy and kept bending over showing him my backside. He was loving it. We had a great night of sex and woke up next morning on the couch with our clothes all over the living room.

Now this is the funny part. I stepped back on the scales the next morning and was horrified to find that I had put all the weight back on! I couldn't believe it. Then I realised that the day before, the zero reading on the scale must have been altered to minus 4 kilograms — so much for my weight loss! The curious thing was that, in my mind's eye, I was skinny so I acted sexy and proud of my body. I hadn't lost a gram, but I thought I looked great and so did Sebastian. I realised how much I let my fears about my body get in the way of expressing my sexuality.

A healthy body image is a powerful sexual enhancer for both men and women, no matter what shape your body is in. Nudity and sexy lingerie are both strong visual stimulators for men. Women love pretty lingerie for themselves, but many sacrifice this luxury in case it gives their partners ideas about sex. If you are avoiding nudity in front of your partner, it may be a symptom of desire discrepancy. Lower drive partners often avoid nudity or a semiclothed state in the presence of their mates just in case it promotes sexual desire or is seen as a sexual invitation.

Greta: Hans' needs for sex are greater than mine, and seeing me naked gets him in the mood when I'm not. These days I change in the bathroom. I know he feels shut out, but I don't want to lead him on. I gave up wearing revealing clothes because he would always grab me or make unseemly comments. This problem with sex has caused us to drift apart.

Hans: Greta is as beautiful to me as the day we married 22 years ago. In the early years she was proud of her body and would flaunt it in front of me. These days she hides it away from me. If I walk in on her half dressed she acts as if she has been caught by a stranger, not her husband. I miss her lovely shape. And she never dresses sexy any more. More like an old woman.

Modesty is one thing, but covering up to avoid your partner is another. Both parties suffer. The one who covers up must remain ever-vigilant in case they are discovered in a state of undress. The other partner often feels shut out, physically and emotionally. When nudity becomes an issue between partners, there is constant tension in the bedroom and bathroom. Sharing these restricted territories becomes an uneasy contest for two people who should at least be able to relax in the privacy of their own home.

Positive sexual response in partner

Men are widely regarded as selfish beings when it comes to sex, solely interested in their own satisfaction. My clinical experience of men does not confirm this assumption. Certainly it is easier for men to want sex, to get turned on and to climax, but this rapid romp through the male sexual response cycle does not necessarily provide men with sexual and personal fulfilment.

> She: We had really great sex last night. He did everything I wanted and I had one orgasm after another. It was the best sex I ever had.
> He: We had really great sex last night. I did everything to her she wanted and she had one orgasm after another. It was the best sex I ever had.

This is a more accurate reflection of the truth.

Truly fulfilling sex for a man cannot occur unless he has an interested, willing partner who enjoys making love with him. Many a man's favourite sexual fantasy is based on a sexually available woman eagerly coming on to him. When they make love she has a really good time. He knows how to please her and ends up feeling that he is 'good in bed'. Notice how much the fantasy focus is on *her* response, *her* pleasure, her satisfaction. *Men get to feel 'good in bed' by making women feel good in bed.*

> Joe: My first wife, Delphine, would let me have sex once a month. She would lie there like a log, rigid and unmoving. She always told me to hurry up and not to ruin her

hairstyle. I felt lower than a snake having sex like this, but it was my only chance until next month and I didn't dare refuse. Having sex like that was worse than no sex at all. And Delphine thought she was doing me a big favour.

When women can't get satisfying sex, they will usually try to avoid sexual activity if possible. Men, on the other hand, will accept poor quality sex if the alternative is no sex at all. Because women avoid sex if it doesn't fulfil them, a man's choice to continue sexual activity is often seen by his partner as an indication of sexual satisfaction. This is not necessarily the case.

If your man seems to be a selfish lover, he may be just that — or he may not know how to make love to you the way you like. He may be aware that he fails to ignite your desire, to turn you on, to sexually satisfy you. Feeling sexually inadequate and bad about himself, he gives up on the idea of having pleasing sex for himself as well. If you are not enjoying sex, your man may be going through the sexual motions but that doesn't necessarily mean he is sexually fulfilled.

For both your sakes, it is vitally important to let your man know what turns you on and what turns you off. The best sex for a man occurs when his partner is thoroughly enjoying herself.

Erotica/pornography

People often ask, 'What is the definition of pornography?' Just as beauty is in the eye of the beholder, the decision as to whether sexually explicit material is offensive or not is a personal judgment. There is a saying: *'What turns me on is erotic, what turns me off is pornographic.'*

This is a difficult and sensitive topic to explore because people have such strong views. To discuss this issue runs the risk of offending, which is not my intention. However, it is important that this topic is raised so that both sexes can come to a better understanding of male enhancers and put them into a more realistic perspective.

Women's tolerance of explicit sexual material varies. There is a large group of women (you may be one of them) who finds any sort of erotica or pornography unacceptable in the context of a relationship, or even outside it. Some women will accept erotica as long as it is not too explicit, while others enjoy a wide range of sexually explicit material.

When a woman condemns pornography or erotica, she is not being difficult or flighty. Erotic material may unearth deep fears for her — fears about her man's attitudes to women, to her and to sex, and concerns about his sexual needs, just to name a few.

Women decry pornography for a range of reasons.

1. *Pornography depicts male domination plus the submission and objectification of women.* This argument against pornography is a valid one — it regularly depicts male dominance and female subordination. Many women find these stereotypes of disempowered women in erotic material offensive. However, pornography is not alone in depicting women as inferior. We are surrounded by images that portray women in one-down positions. From Renaissance paintings to the stick thin models in fashion magazines, we see images that reflect the male-dominated culture in which we live. The nature of erotica could well change as the balance of power between the sexes evens out.

Women rightly complain that in pornography men treat women as objects. In fact, pornography objectifies and degrades *both* men and women. Men objectify most things in their lives — personal relationships are more difficult for men than women. Men relate to and value a range of objects in their lives, including their cars, their boats, their football teams. Even in kindergarten, boys will seek out 'things' to play with rather than relationships with other children.

Despite any feminine wishes to the contrary, sex for men tends to be more impersonal. As a result, men's preferred enhancers do not centre on the relationship but on 'things' — lingerie, naked bodies, erotica, varied lovemaking positions and activities, sex toys and the like. We cannot make a man respond to a woman's enhancers, just as we cannot force a woman to respond to a man's.

Contrary to popular opinion, men are not necessarily gaining erotic pleasure from this objectification of women. A man and a woman viewing the same erotic video will, more often than not, have completely different perspectives on the content because they respond to different elements in the material. Most men are so busy getting turned on by what they are seeing, that they are not consciously aware of the politics of the material. Women are not sidetracked by rapid sexual arousal, so they retain the capacity to experience the material intellectually, politically and personally.

However, the problem with men's 'unconscious' viewing lies in the fact that, arousal or none, the politics of pornography are still present and can have an impact even if it is subliminal. For that reason, men (and women) should be highly selective about the sort of erotic material they expose themselves to.

Men who keep the politics of pornography in mind when selecting erotic material for themselves or to share with a partner are not only more likely to gain partner acceptance, but they also avoid exposure to unhelpful sexual and emotional attitudes to women. The sexual politics in an erotic video may not matter to him, but they could certainly matter to her.

Another common fear is that pornography incites violence. Although there has been a lot of media hype about this issue, no solid proof of a link between explicit sexual material and violence has been found.

I am not saying that pornography is right or wrong — only you can decide that for yourself. Nor do I contend that women should include anything in their relationships that they find offensive. I am saying that we are surrounded by distasteful images of women similar to the ones found in pornography wherever we turn. Women should speak up about images they find to be exploitative wherever they find them, but the way to deal with these issues is not to ignore erotic material or ban it through censorship. We need more open debate about all areas of sex, better sex education in our primary and secondary schools, and a more tolerant, informed and responsible attitude to expressions of both male and female sexuality.

2. *Women feel threatened by their partner's 'need' for such material, fearing it signifies lack of satisfaction within the relationship.* Most women can accept that men enjoy sexy lingerie and varied lovemaking without feeling threatened by this interest. However, the moment the image of *another woman* is introduced,

her fears and insecurities can erupt. She worries: He's not happy with my body; he wants to have sex with someone else; he likes her body better than he likes mine; he's not satisfied with our sex life just the way it is.

Women who are secure in themselves, and emotionally and sexually secure in the relationship, are much more tolerant of the inclusion of erotic material.

Men: If your partner responds negatively to erotic material and seems threatened, it could well be a sign that she feels insecure emotionally and physically and sexually inadequate. Before you attempt to introduce any erotic material into the relationship, put time and effort into making your partner feel good about herself, her body and her sexuality. Tell her how much you like her and her body; how much she pleases you; how you like her better than any other woman; how you enjoy kissing, touching and making love to her. Be consistent and persistent with your praise until she really believes that she is special to you. This should reduce or eliminate her anxieties about erotic material.

3. *Women believe that in the context of a committed relationship, a man who resorts to erotica or pornography is being 'unfaithful' to his partner.* For some couples, even fantasising about someone else constitutes infidelity and a breach of relationship boundaries. This is an issue that couples must decide for themselves.

Women: If you feel that erotica intrudes on the boundaries of your relationship and leaves you feeling betrayed, you need to talk to your partner about these feelings. Strong and consistent reassurance may be all that is needed to resolve your anxieties. However, if you still find erotic material unacceptable, you have the right to state this and to expect your partner to respect your wishes. You might like to discuss with your partner which of the other male enhancers are acceptable to you.

4. *Many women worry that their partners will negatively compare their flesh-and-blood bodies with the airbrushed 10 out of 10s in magazines and movies.* Women who fear comparison of their bodies with erotic images may be comforted to know that men are far less judgmental about female bodies than women are. While women constantly compare their own bodies with others',

men's eyes are more likely to be drawn to the areas of their partners' bodies that they find pleasurable and focus on them.

> **Cherie:** When I was in my early forties I fell in love with a man who was ten years younger than I was. I wasn't in the best shape and I felt really uncomfortable when I caught him looking at my body, especially when I was undressed. When I looked in the mirror all I could see were the stretch marks and a tummy that looked like a spaniel's who'd had too many litters. I often hid behind a robe or a towel and avoided being naked around him. I thought he must be comparing me to girls his own age.
>
> One day he sat me down and looked me straight in the eye. He told me how attracted he was to me, all of me, including my body. He told me how much pleasure it gave him to see my bum and my breasts, and yes, my stomach. He told me that, to him, I was better than Elle Macpherson. I finally accepted what he said and stopped letting my shame about my body come between us.

Men are not as fickle about the female body as women are. Men don't compare, but women do. If women could learn to love their bodies more, they would not be so threatened by their men looking at other women in the street, on TV, at the beach or in erotica.

Pornography and sexual mythology

Although pornography is offensive to women for its obviously sexist attitudes, viewing of pornography can be damaging to both sexes in more subtle ways. Erotica presents many false premises to viewers about men, about women and about sexuality. It creates a harmful set of unrealistic expectations about sexual performance that mere mortals cannot hope to reach.

By showing 'fantasy sex' masquerading as 'reality sex', pornography adds to sexual anxiety and lack of understanding between the sexes. A man guided by this material could turn his partner off by employing the techniques he sees in pornography — limited foreplay, rough handling, prolonged vigorous thrusting. When his partner doesn't respond, he may think there is something wrong with her.

Women, too, can gain false messages about sexual activity from erotica. Not only can the antics of fantasy women make a real woman feel inadequate, but the images of fantasy men, hung like horses, performing under any conditions and prolonging intercourse for hours, can give a woman totally unrealistic expectations of sexual performance from her man.

Both men and women need to keep these facts in mind when they view erotic material. People are generally able to separate fact from fantasy — for example, in a science fiction movie about aliens, people know they are seeing a make-believe world. We need to practise this same sort of scepticism when we view erotic material, to ensure that we separate what is real sex from what is fantasy sex. Individuals who are unable to make this clear separation between fantasy and reality in their own minds would be strongly advised to avoid any sort of explicit erotic material.

Women, erotica and pornography

Some women do enjoy pornography and explicit sexual displays just as much as men do. But most women have a hard time admitting this material turns them on. One study into pornography showed both male and female subjects erotic material and scientifically measured their levels of sexual arousal. Subjects were then asked about their level of sexual response. The men reported being sexually aroused by the material, and this corresponded to the physical measurements obtained by the researchers. The women reported a lower or total lack of arousal response. However, physical measurements demonstrated that the women definitely experienced a physical response to the material that they were either unaware of, or they denied because it was socially unacceptable.

In general, women's erotic preferences differ from those of men. While men show a preference for viewing nameless, faceless female body parts and a series of anonymous sexual encounters, many women prefer a romantic storyline suggestive of a relationship between a couple in their erotica. Recently, R-rated videos with a storyline attractive to women have been made under the Femme label. They may be available in your local video store.

While most men respond rapidly to the sight of female genitals, women are rarely aroused by the sight of male genitals unless they can call on fantasy to facilitate their response. Research has shown that those women who do respond to nudity are likely to be stimulated to the same extent by either the naked male or the female body. Many women feel anxious about this response to female nudity because they wrongly assume it must be a sign of homosexuality.

A negative reaction to erotica has been socially programmed into women over centuries to repress full and free expression of female sexuality. Sex has been for 'Boys Only' for too long. Fortunately, times are changing — women and men are seen as sexual equals in Western cultures, with women now starting to explore their sexuality to its fullest. More women are beginning to enjoy enhancers seen in the past as typically male. Women are now asking for nudity, sex toys, erotica and male strip shows, while erotic videos and magazines for women are increasing in popularity. As a result, a burgeoning industry has been established to provide erotica specifically for women and couples (see Resources).

WHAT'S GOOD FOR THE GOOSE IS GOOD FOR THE GANDER

Women now feel more empowered to insist that their partners supply their 'female' enhancers and feel resentful if these demands are not met. However, if a man gets upset when his enhancers are not accepted, he is often seen as sexually demanding, unreasonable or even perverted. It is not unusual for women to shame and deride their partners for enjoying specific enhancers.

Dear Dr Rosie,
Some years ago I found some *Playboy* magazines in our garage. I made my husband apologise to me for having this filth near our house and had him burn them all while I watched. I lost all respect for him and told him so. We have a regular sex life, so I can't understand why he would want this sort of material. He promised never to look at another one again. Recently I found one in the boot of his car. I think I should pack up the children and leave.

To me this is a form of sexual discrimination. If women are entitled to benefit from their enhancers, why should men go without simply because of the widespread negative perception of men's sexual needs? A couple who wishes to achieve their full sexual potential together should look at ways to regularly include a range of both male and female enhancers in their relationship.

You scratch my back and I'll scratch yours

A relationship is a two-way street — give and take. Many men don't need extra stimulation to have a healthy sex drive, but men's quality of sexual experience will be improved by inclusion of their male enhancers in the relationship.

A man whose sexual needs are being met is more likely to be willing to meet his partner's needs, both sexual and nonsexual. It's a case of 'you scratch my back and I'll scratch yours'. It is common to find that when a woman refuses a man his enhancers, he will be less willing to make the effort to meet her sexual and emotional needs, and less keen to provide her with her particular desire enhancers.

> **Stella:** For years I wouldn't let Norm see me naked, touch my body or try anything apart from basic sex. I even turned off anything too sexy on the TV. Yet I knew something was missing from our relationship. I wanted more time with Norm, to enjoy activities together — just the two of us — but he never seemed to have the time or energy for me.
>
> We went through a rough patch 10 years ago, had counselling and I began to see the light. I realised that you have to give if you want to get. Norm and I talked about it and I began to change my old habits little by little. It wasn't easy for me, but I knew our marriage was worth it. I became more sexually adventurous, thought up sexual surprises, and dressed the part for him. At first it wasn't comfortable, but I soon began to enjoy the effect I was having on him.
>
> Norm's response was wonderful. As I began to give to

him in ways that were meaningful to him, he rewarded me with love and attention I never thought possible. He was so grateful for the little things I was doing. After all these years of marriage, we are closer than ever.

Norm: When Stella started to change I got in touch with feelings of love for her that had slipped away from me years ago. At a very deep level I felt more connected to her than ever. I didn't know that sexual intimacy was so important to me. In fact, I didn't realise what was wrong with our relationship, just that I wasn't happy. She gave us a new lease of life and love, and I will never be able to thank her enough for her gift to me and to us.

> If you don't risk anything, you risk even more.
> ERICA JONG

The goodwill that flows when partners stretch to understand and accept each other's individual sexual needs spills in every direction and improves the relationship for both parties.

GUIDELINES FOR INTRODUCING MALE ENHANCERS

Couples will find they get more intense excitement from male enhancers if they have a wide variety to choose from and they don't do or look at the same thing over and over again. For example, if the man enjoys lingerie, have several garments to wear in rotation. Even if he loves a specific outfit, don't wear it over and over again or it will lose its appeal. For reading and visual material, purchase a generous supply over time and look at each one in turn. Once you have viewed the material put it away for a while and the next time you use it it will work almost as well as the first time.

If you use a male enhancer every night of the week (lingerie, striptease, sex toys, erotic material) you will soon find a need developing for more powerful or more explicit enhancers because of a phenomenon called 'habituation'. For this reason it is often a good idea to restrict the use of male enhancers to specific times — such as a weekend sex session or after a special night out. They should be regarded as a treat rather than as a necessity.

Having a wide variety of erotic activities and stimulants, and restricting the use of male enhancers to special occasions, reduces the need to progress to the sort of highly explicit material that may offend some women. Regular or frequent use of hard-core pornography is unhealthy. The key to enjoying erotic material is *moderation in quantity, quality and frequency*.

Use erotic material sparingly to enhance arousal from time to time, not to create it on a regular basis. However, in some cases, especially as men age, the inclusion of enhancers may be the only way to achieve a high enough level of arousal to overcome diminished erectile function with age. In such cases, enhancers may be required most of the time.

Keep in mind that the images and activities shown in pornography are unrealistic representations of human sexual activity. If you have difficulty separating fact from fantasy, it is best to avoid explicit pornography.

The covert or hidden messages in explicit pornography are politically, emotionally and sexually unhelpful to both men and women. Choose your material with this in mind.

Material or activities should only be included in the relationship by mutual consent. No person should be forced to participate or experience sexual activities that they find unacceptable.

Advice for women

Try to see your man's enhancers as a product of his sexual programming, rather than as an insult to you and every other woman on earth! Ask yourself what male enhancers you might be willing to include. You may have to move out of your comfort zone to try something new. Make a list of things you would be willing to try. Regard this experimentation as sexual personal growth.

Take small steps at a time. Don't move too far, too fast, or you may get out of your depth. Over time, even new experiences should become comfortable. If not, you might be best to abandon uncomfortable activities and try something else.

What if your partner enjoys explicit erotica that you find deeply offensive? This is a problem faced by many couples. Be clear in your own mind about what is acceptable and what is unacceptable, and communicate this to your partner. *You don't have to participate in any activity you find offensive.* Instead, look for alternative enhancers that excite your partner but don't offend you.

Advice for men

Your partner's negative reaction to your enhancers is socially programmed, so she will need time and your patience to explore and possibly accept some of your enhancers. Start out with something tame — the aim is not for you to get excited, but for her to learn to be comfortable with a range of new sexual activities.

Be creative — the easier you make it for her to explore your enhancers, the more progress she will make. Encourage her and praise her efforts.

If you want *your* needs to be met, make sure she is getting *her* needs, both sexual and nonsexual, met. If she is unwilling to try something new, discuss what you could do for her to increase her willingness to experiment. Maybe if you helped more around the house or with the kids she would be less tired and more enthusiastic about meeting your sexual needs.

Some material that arouses you may not be healthy for you or your relationship. Material that degrades, harms, abuses or humiliates women can affect your attitudes to your partner. Material that includes children, incest, violence and extreme sexual activities can have a detrimental effect on you. Avoid this sort of material.

Don't expect to include your enhancers every time you make love. One reason women avoid the introduction of male enhancers is the fear that once the floodgates are open, sexy videos, lingerie, erotic acts and bondage will be on the menu every night. Enhancers are an exciting *addition* to a couple's sex life, but they cannot take the place of the closeness and connection generated by loving partner-focused sex. The emotional content of the sexual relationship has enormous significance for women, and constant use of enhancers can detract from the more spiritual aspects of sex when two hearts, rather than just two bodies, join as one.

There may be activities or experiences that you enjoy that are just too uncomfortable for your partner to share with you. Accept these limitations with good grace and focus on the enjoyment you can both share, not on what you are missing out on.

Men who can't get their enhancer needs accepted by mutual discussion will often make a unilateral decision to secretly enjoy these materials or activities. The moment this happens, there is deceit and distancing in the relationship. Keeping printed matter, videos or sex toys hidden from a woman is a demanding task. Women have better noses than bloodhounds when it comes to male contraband. A duped woman's hurt and loss of trust when her man is caught out can permanently damage even the happiest relationship. Women are not in a position to introduce their enhancers in this unnegotiated fashion, because they must rely on positive interaction with their partners to get their enhancer needs met. Men's enhancers should only be introduced into the relationship after negotiation and with mutual consent. There is no place for trying to force a partner to accept something they don't feel comfortable with.

Be your own sex therapist

For women: Has your view of male enhancers changed at all after reading this chapter?

Do you know what sort of enhancers work for your partner? Can you make a list? Can you rate them from most exciting to least exciting?

Are any of these enhancers acceptable to you within your relationship?

For men: What enhancers work for you? Make a list and rate them from most exciting to least exciting.

Can you think of ways to encourage and support your partner to include some of your favourite sexual enhancers into the relationship?

If you have tried to introduce enhancers in the past and failed, do you have some idea why you were unsuccessful? What would you do differently if you tried again?

Perhaps you might like to think about sharing this list with your partner, or at least discuss some of the items.

INCREASING UNDERSTANDING THROUGH OPEN DISCUSSION

My approach to men's enhancers is obviously more liberal and broad-minded than most, and results from my many years of clinical work with men. This very practical approach is based on accepting men's sexuality and trying to encompass their needs within relationships, rather than trying to alter age-old male patterns of sexual response. Couples need *open discussion* and *mutual decision making* about the needs for *both* male and female preferred enhancers.

In addition to the lists we have seen in the last couple of chapters, we all have our own individual turn-ons that may not necessarily be sexual. When my husband does the ironing, especially when he irons his stepsons' (my sons') school shirts with utmost care, that works as an enhancer for me. When I am relaxed and happy, that works as an enhancer for him.

All couples will benefit from the inclusion of their own personally preferred enhancers into the relationship. Finding out your partner's top 10 enhancers will not only improve your sex life but will also help you to learn more about the special person you share your life with.

Key Points ~ ♥ ~

Men's enhancers are related to signs of fertility, youth, good health and female sexual availability.

Men's response to visual stimulation is biologically engineered to promote rapid arousal. Centuries of social conditioning with erotic stimulation have built on this biological basis. Women who understand the biological and social conditioning behind men's enhancers will be more accepting of them.

Women react poorly to men's need for enhancers because they feel personally and sexually threatened. Men make matters worse by forcing the introduction of enhancers or enjoying them in secret.

Pornography is *politically* threatening to some women because it objectifies and subjugates them. Pornography is *personally* threatening to some women because it sparks feelings of sexual and physical inadequacy.

Covert messages in pornography require men and women to be highly selective about the erotic material they expose themselves to. These messages promote negative attitudes between men and women and unrealistic sexual expectations.

The introduction of male enhancers into a relationship should be based on open discussion, negotiation and mutual consent.

Inclusion of a range of male enhancers in a relationship can benefit both partners. The quality of sex for men is improved, and their willingness to contribute to the relationship both emotionally and sensually may well be increased by higher levels of mutual goodwill.

Pursuer/Distancer —
A Vicious Cycle in Action

Differences in desire have the capacity to shatter goodwill, trust and love between partners. This chapter looks at how Romeo and Juliet can progress from loving each other to fighting over who gets the furniture and photographs, with a little help from desire discrepancy.

A VICIOUS CYCLE

When a couple with differing desires begins to run into trouble, a vicious cycle is set up. The higher drive partner becomes the *sexual pursuer*, chasing the lower drive partner for sex. Pursuing may take the form of frequent initiation, complaints about lack of sex, sulking or arguments.

The lower drive partner becomes the sexual distancer, trying to avoid sexual contact. Distancing may involve going to bed early, reluctance to hug and kiss in case it leads to sex, or refusal to undress in front of the partner. This distancing behaviour provokes the pursuer to chase even more. This cycle is called the PURSUER/DISTANCER CYCLE, or P/D cycle.

> ### Be your own sex therapist
>
> Do you think that you and your partner might be caught up in the pursuer/distancer cycle?
> Are you a sexual pursuer or a sexual distancer? What about your partner?
> Have you played different roles in this or previous relationships?

THE SEXUAL PURSUER

The sexual pursuer takes on the role of 'chasing' the distancer for sex. Pursuers may exhibit one or all of these behaviours over time:

- The pursuer initially may be *patient*, thinking that in time or with the 'right handling' the distancer's interest in sex will be increased or rekindled. This patient phase may be long or short-lived.
- The pursuer often becomes *upset*, expressing resentment about the infrequency of sexual activity in the relationship. Complaints of sexual frustration and rejection start to surface. Tantrums and sulking are common reactions at this stage. Or the pursuer may just act depressed, give the silent treatment, or be difficult and uncooperative outside the bedroom.
- The pursuer may become *demanding*, initiating sex frequently and reacting badly when sex is not forthcoming. The pursuer may blame the distancer and make him or her wrong.
- If the pursuing behaviour escalates, it can really start to damage the relationship. The pursuer becomes *angry*, and may heap abuse on the distancer or make threats ('Give me sex or I'll have an affair!').
- The pursuer eventually *withdraws* and disconnects from the partner.

These behaviours are actually the pursuer's attempt to express interest in sex. As expressions of sexual desire, these pursuer desire behaviours go with the list of desire behaviours described in Chapter 4. Unfortunately, from the distancer's perspective, these behaviours don't appear to be expressing sexual desire. Quite the opposite. They seem more like expectations, demands, or at worst, abuse.

Escalating pursuer desire behaviour can be summarised like this:
- **Patient:** It'll work out ...
- **Upset:** Why can't I have more sex?
- **Demanding:** Sex is my right — give it to me!
- **Angry:** Give me sex or else!
- **Withdrawal**

> What mad pursuit? What struggle to escape?
> JOHN KEATS

These behaviours don't necessarily follow in a step-wise sequence. A pursuer can exhibit several behaviours at one time or move rapidly from one behaviour to another.

The pursuer's merry-go-round

The P/D cycle is self-perpetuating. The more the pursuer pursues, the more the distancer distances. The more the distancer distances, the more the pursuer pursues.

The P/D cycle looks like this.

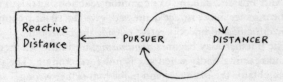

The pursuer pursues for sex, initiating sex frequently, complaining, or being resentful and acting hurt. After a while, when these strategies don't have the desired effect, the pursuer tries another tack. They back right off, withdrawing into reactive distance.

Reactive distance

When pursuers are in reactive distance, they cease initiation and stop hassling for sex; instead they sulk, radiate hostility or give the distancer the silent treatment. For many distancers, reactive distance can be a relief because sexual harassment temporarily stops.

However, the sulky manipulation and emotional withdrawal of their partner's can be very distressing for them.

Before very long, pursuers come out of reactive distance and begin pursuing, and round and round they both go again.

The pursuer and sexual desire

A side effect of the P/D cycle is that it emphasises the pursuer's needs for sex and makes him or her feel more horny and needy for sex than ever! Often the pursuer firmly believes that the distancer is *withholding* sex — that the distancer really wants sex but is not 'letting' the pursuer have it. This is not usually true — in the P/D cycle, the distancer rapidly loses interest in sex with the partner.

The pursuer may also equate sex with love — not only does the pursuer feel sexually rejected but often feels unloved as well. These feelings of sexual and emotional rejection cause the pursuer to act in a hostile, resentful and aggressive way towards their partner.

Why do pursuers act in this destructive way? *Because they don't know what else to do.* Lacking the skills for negotiating mutually agreeable sexual activity, the pursuer has no other option but to try to manipulate his or her way into sex by making the distancer feel obligated, guilty or just plain bad.

Pursuers often believe that:
* there is a 'normal' level of sexual frequency (usually determined by their own level of sexual need)
* saying 'No' to sex is a personal rejection
* in a relationship, all sexual needs should be enthusiastically met by the partner on demand.

The important message for pursuers is that, although your aim is to express sexual interest in your partner and to persuade them to connect sexually with you, your behaviour has the opposite effect. Instead of furthering your cause, these behaviours push the distancer away and actively reduce their sexual desire for you.

What distancers need to realise is that the pursuer's irritating and often offensive behaviour is a clumsy attempt to get their needs met. Unhelpful, yes, distressing, yes, but it doesn't mean that pursuers are terrible people for behaving in this fashion. The P/D cycle gains momentum because pursuers and distancers don't know what else to do, not necessarily because they want to make each other miserable.

Be your own sex therapist

Pursuers: How has the P/D cycle affected you emotionally? The following feelings are very common ones for pursuers. Have you felt: hurt, rejected, anxious, depressed, guilty or self-blaming? Resentful, angry, cheated, envious, alone, defeated, sad or embarrassed? Insecure, frustrated, confused, inadequate, abandoned, undesirable, disappointed, dissatisfied, tormented, desperate, panicky or vulnerable?

Have you engaged in any of the pursuer behaviours listed below?

- Nagging your partner about the problem.
- Getting resentful and/or expressing anger to your partner.
- Blaming your partner for the problem and attacking his or her sexuality.
- Acting depressed around your partner.
- Withholding affection and disconnecting from your partner.
- Demanding sex.
- Using affectionate contact as an opportunity to press for sex.
- Abusing your partner emotionally or physically.
- Accusing your partner of having an affair.
- Making sarcastic comments or mentioning your lack of sexual satisfaction to others in front of your partner.
- Refusing to meet your partner's needs in other ways.
- Having sex with people outside your relationship.
- Allowing your hurt and anger to damage your relationship.
- Permitting your hurt and anger to reduce your enjoyment of life generally.
- Talking about divorce or separation.

List any other strategies you have tried.

Have any of these strategies improved the DD situation in the long term? In my experience, these behaviours are ineffective and often make the situation worse.

Do you feel that your partner is withholding sex from you?

Have you and your partner attempted to discuss in a rational way both of your sexual needs?

Do you miss affectionate and other nonsexual contact with your partner?

THE PURSUER/DISTANCER CYCLE IN ACTION

The P/D cycle can start even when there is a minimal difference in levels of sex drive. Let's look at Phillipe and Celeste, who came for counselling after six years of marriage.

When they first married, Phillipe was initiatory and Celeste was receptive. They both enjoyed sex and their relationship was generally good. Although in practical terms this combination made for a good sexual match, Phillipe expected that Celeste should be expressing interest in sex by initiating as often as he did. He was disappointed when Celeste failed to express what was, to him, a 'normal' level of sexual interest. He felt hurt and rejected.

Phillipe started putting pressure on Celeste, putting her in the role of sexual distancer while he took on the role of sexual pursuer.

Celeste's reaction to her husband's sexual demands shows typical distancer behaviour.

Celeste, who started out as sexually *receptive*, soon found herself less interested in sex. Initially she was still *available* if Phillipe wanted to make love and she continued to enjoy sex with him. As his badgering continued, she began to turn off him and off sex, developing a *neutral*, take-it-or-leave-it attitude. As the conflict wore on, she became sexually *disinterested* and matters deteriorated even more.

Phillipe was worse off than he was at the start. He didn't know what to do except to keep pursuing Celeste for sex. He nagged her for sex, sulked and became increasingly angry.

As Phillipe's hostility increased, Celeste found herself *reluctant* to be involved sexually with her husband. Before too long she became sexually *unavailable*, preferring not to participate. As his pursuing of her continued she rapidly became sexually *avoidant*, steering away from sex or anything that might lead to sex.

Finally, in response to his continuing pressure and personal attacks, she became sexually *aversive*, where even the thought of sex was a turn-off. By this stage she had withdrawn emotionally and sexually from the relationship and sex was a total 'No Go' area.

Escalating distancer behaviour can be summarised like this:

- *Reluctant:* Do I have to?
- *Unavailable:* Not tonight ... I've got a headache.
- *Avoidant:* Not if I can help it.
- *Aversive:* No way!
- *Withdrawal*

THE SEXUAL DISTANCER

Very early in the P/D cycle, distancers become wary of physical contact and affection, just in case it is seen as a sexual invitation or an agreement to go further. Passionate hugs and open-mouthed kisses stop first, then holding hands, then sitting or lying together. Couples may end up in separate beds on one pretext or another (he snores, she's a light sleeper), or a child may be brought into the parents' bed to limit opportunities for sexual activity.

Eventually you end up with two people who keep a metre or two of space between them at all times — they walk around each other in the kitchen, taking care not to brush too close; they sit on opposite ends of the couch to watch TV (or watch sets in different rooms); they go to bed at differing times — a distancer may stay up late hoping their partner will fall asleep, or go to bed early and pretend to be asleep when the partner comes in.

Maintaining distance

There are many ways to sexually avoid your partner. You can immerse yourself in work, the children, the newspaper, the TV, good works or any other activity. You can avoid being affectionate, walking about semi-naked or getting changed around your partner in case it promotes sexual ideas. Talk about sex can be sidestepped.

Another powerful way to maintain distance is to get hostile. Distancers also become reactive, getting annoyed or angry at their partners, attacking their sexuality or shaming them for their sexual interest. They may see their partners' desire for sex as base and animalistic, and their expression of sexual needs as evidence of neediness and weakness. They often assume that all their partner wants them for is sex.

Cool, calm and collected

On the outside, the distancer usually looks cool, calm and collected. While the pursuer is jumping up and down, criticising, harassing or just plain sulking, the composed distancer serenely looks across at the pursuer as if to say, 'What's your problem?'

However, underneath, the distancer typically feels under pressure, inadequate, anxious, obligated, fearful, full of self-blame and, above all, guilty.

Mercy sex

When the P/D cycle is in full flight, distancers feel little or no desire but they are likely to agree to sex whenever their guilt mounts up or to avoid an argument. Guilt-motivated sex, or *mercy sex*, is pleasureless and does nothing for either party in the long run.

Distancers who engage in mercy sex develop a strong sense of being used for sex. Distancer loss of self-esteem and feelings of worthlessness are the end result. Each time the distancer gives in to keep the peace, his or her desire will be turned down another notch.

> **Celeste:** After a couple of weeks I feel so guilty about Phillipe's sexual frustration that I eventually initiate sex. I don't want it, I don't get turned on and I certainly don't enjoy it, but it reduces the tension for a few more weeks.
> **Phillipe:** She's got me on this 'sexual diet'. Once every couple of weeks she lets me have sex, but she just goes through the motions. I don't say no, because there's nothing else on offer. Sometimes it feels like she rewards me with sex. If I've been a 'good boy' she lets me have sex, but if I step out of line, you can forget it. Most of the time she just stays out of my way.

The distancer merry-go-round

In response to the pursuer's pressure to perform sexually, distancers forget that sex is something we gain from, not something we give. The effect of the P/D cycle on the distancer is to consistently reduce both sexual interest and sexual arousal.

Distancers are caught between a rock and a hard place. They often long for sensual activities like hugging, cuddling and affectionate kissing, but they can't get too close to their lovers in case it is misread as an invitation to sexual activity. In fact, the very activities that could reignite the distancer's desire, such as non-demand affection, intimacy and closeness, are muscled out of the relationship by the P/D cycle.

Be your own sex therapist

Distancers: How has the P/D cycle affected you emotionally? The following feelings are very common ones for distancers. Have you felt under pressure, pursued, smothered or suffocated by your partner's sexual needs? Resentful or angry, hurt, anxious, depressed, guilty or self-blaming? Unappreciated, miserable, alone, intimidated, defeated, sad or helpless? Insecure, frustrated, confused, panicky or vulnerable? Mocked, inferior, inadequate, worthless?

Have you worried about your sexuality and felt ashamed or abnormal?

Have you tried dealing with DD by:

- Ignoring the problem?
- Withholding affection and disconnecting from your partner?
- Avoiding any contact that might lead to sex?
- Avoiding letting your partner see you undressed?
- Going to bed and getting up in a way that avoids sex?
- Reducing sexual contact, when it happens, to a minimal activity?
- Getting resentful and/or expressing anger towards your partner?

- Blaming your partner for the problem and attacking their sexuality?
- Pushing your partner away by focusing on other matters, e.g. family, work, hobbies?
- Abusing your partner emotionally or physically?
- Having sex with people outside your relationship?
- Allowing your hurt and anger to damage your relationship?
- Permitting your hurt and anger to reduce your enjoyment of life generally?
- Talking about divorce or separation?

List any other strategies you have tried.

Have any of these strategies improved the DD situation in the long term? In my experience these behaviours are ineffective and often make the situation worse.

Do you feel that your partner is only interested in you for one thing — sex? Have you ever felt offended or disgusted by your partner's needs for sex?

Have you been afraid that your partner will look for sex outside your relationship? Do you sometimes *wish* your partner would look for sex outside your relationship?

Do you feel obligated to give your partner sex? Does having sex with your partner feel like 'giving in'? Do you engage in mercy sex out of guilt or to avoid arguments?

Do you miss affectionate and other nonsexual contact with your partner?

Do you ever feel like sex but refrain from telling your partner?

WHO'S TO BLAME?

There are no good guys or bad guys here, just two people trying to get their needs met. Both the pursuer and the distancer are suffering — both are missing out on a satisfying hassle-free sex life. Consider the P/D cycle a relationship merry-go-round where both parties hop on at the same time. Problems with DD are the only ticket required for couples to hop on the carousel. One thing can be guaranteed — once the P/D cycle starts, the problem of DD will always get worse.

To recap

The desire behaviours model has proved to be very useful in helping couples to understand the normal range of desire behaviours and to demonstrate how conflict over DD can alter desire behaviours dramatically.

Desire Behaviours

Withdrawal	**Escalating**
Angry: Give me sex or else!	**Pursuer**
Demanding: Sex is my right — give it to me!	**Behaviour**
Upset: Why can't I have more sex?	
Patient: It'll work out ...	
Initiatory: Mm — sex ... I love it — how about it?	
Receptive: Mm — sex. That'd be nice!	
Available: Sex? Sure, if you want to.	**Normal Range**
Neutral: Sex? I can take it or leave it.	**of Desire**
Disinterested: Sex — why bother?	
Reluctant: Do I have to?	**Escalating**
Unavailable: Not tonight.	**Distancer**
Avoidant: Not if I can help it.	**Behaviour**
Aversive: No way!	
Withdrawal	

The Makings of a Mismatched Couple

The pursuer/distancer cycle has the potential to turn even the smallest desire mismatch into an ever widening breach between two partners. Any chance of the lower drive partner resurrecting his or her libido is lost as long as the P/D cycle persists. Obviously the first step in dealing with desire discrepancy is to interrupt the P/D cycle so that couples can begin to negotiate sexual compromises that meet the needs of both parties. This will be dealt with in Chapter 16.

The pursuer/distancer cycle begins when a couple does not know how to handle differing levels of sexual interest.

Under the influence of this vicious cycle, the desire behaviours of both the pursuer and the distancer change, only serving to make the problem worse.

The cycle enhances the pursuer's sexual desire and inhibits that of the distancer, making the initial DD even worse.

Neither partner is to blame for the situation and both are suffering equally.

The P/D cycle must be interrupted for DD to be resolved.

Healing Your Relationship

11

Good Loving —
Caring and Communication

In this section you will learn about improving your relationship to improve your sex life. Whether you like it or not, what goes on in your relationship on a day-to-day basis will dictate the quality of your sex life.

A good relationship is the foundation stone for a mutually satisfying sexual relationship. A good relationship is one that makes both partners happy. A bad relationship is destructive to one or both partners. It is impossible to have good sex in a bad relationship in the long term.

How is your relationship? Is it running smoothly on all cylinders? Or is the ride becoming more bumpy every day? Loss of goodwill between couples is a common side effect of desire discrepancy. To overcome DD, mutual positive regard and warm feelings between partners often need to be patiently rebuilt.

> **Cheryl:** When I first met Leon I was in my early twenties and he hung around with a very sophisticated crowd. What I didn't realise then was that Leon had problems with alcohol. The relationship never worked well, but I was young and foolish and married him anyway.

When I tackled him on his drinking, he would lash out at me. Later he'd explain that 'attack was the best form of defence', but his belittling comments and criticisms ate away at me. I loved Leon for a long time and tried my best to make things work but gradually my interest in sex, which had been very high in the beginning, faded away. It took many years for my sexuality to fully recover after I left him.

As Cheryl discovered, it is very difficult to desire your partner when they are not meeting your emotional needs. *A poor relationship will reduce desire, especially in female partners.* Unlike men, women don't have help from testosterone to buoy up desire when their relationships run into trouble.

In Chapter 6 the following list of desire inhibitors relating to the wellbeing of the relationship was introduced. To maximise sexual desire, these factors must be minimised or eradicated.

RELATIONSHIP-BASED DESIRE INHIBITORS

- Loss of loving feelings between partners
- Communication problems
- Lack of intimacy
- Lack of trust
- Insecurity — lack of commitment
- Unresolved jealousy
- Lack of respect
- Low attraction to partner
- Power struggles and inequality
- Intrusions to the boundaries of the relationship — e.g. in-laws, work, social activities, hobbies, children, etc.
- Tension in relationship — unresolved conflicts
- Lack of affection, companionship, fun, romance
- Sexual difficulties

TROUBLESHOOTING

Couples need to be able to identify which areas of their partnerships need renovation. Regard the following suggestions as signposts to areas in your relationship that might need tender loving care (TLC).

Be your own sex therapist

How does your relationship rate?

Do the following quiz. Rate each item on the sliding scale from 1 (unsatisfactory) to 5 (satisfactory). Your partner should do the same.

How do you feel about the following?

- How you talk together.
- How you listen to each other.
- How you take notice of what the other says.
- Your respect for your partner.
- Your partner's respect for you.
- The amount of affection in the relationship.
- How your partner touches you.
- Your partner's consideration for you.
- Your partner's attitude to you.
- The amount of time you spend just with your partner.
- How much time you both spend pursuing separate interests.
- How much independence you have.
- How much independence your partner has.
- How much fun you have together.
- Yourselves as a couple in company.
- How you make decisions together.
- Who takes control in the relationship.
- How you resolve conflicts and handle problems.
- How you share household tasks.
- How you share responsibilities.
- How you raise your children together.
- How you handle money issues.
- How you handle your in-laws and extended family.

- How you handle the demands of outside friendships.
- Your partner's working habits.
- How much you have in common.
- Your partner's importance to you.
- Your importance to your partner.
- The level of trust in your relationship.
- The level of honesty in your relationship.
- The level of commitment in your relationship.
- About your relationship generally.
- About the future of your relationship.
- About yourself.

This exercise can help to pinpoint areas of your relationship that need attention. Any areas that score 2 or less need urgent attention.

Total your scores. A score of 170 means that your relationship is in excellent shape. If the two of you agree that you are generally satisfied with your relationship, concentrate on the practical strategies described in the next section for overcoming DD.

Over 135 means your relationship is in pretty good shape, but it could probably do with some work.

Between 85 and 135 means you definitely have some areas that need TLC.

A score of less than 85 signals a relationship in dire need of attention.

Compare answers with your partner and discuss them together.

Do you need counselling?

You may need professional help to get your relationship back on track. Relationship counselling is necessary for relationships which exhibit any of the following:

- 'No go' areas that cannot be discussed.
- Issues that are argued over again and again or remain unresolved.
- Emotional and verbal abuse such as constant criticism and putting down, either publicly or privately, shouting, name

calling, withdrawal and the silent treatment, sarcasm, intense jealousy, constant come backs and explosive anger.

- Sexual or physical abuse (either actual or threatened).
- Addictions to drugs, alcohol, shopping and spending, gambling, sex, dieting, exercise or work.
- One partner exercises excessive control over the other.
- A previous affair remains an open wound for one or both partners.

For relationship counselling ask your GP about local resources (counsellors, psychologists, psychiatrists), contact your local Community Health Centre or call Relationships Australia (see Resources).

Can you salvage your relationship?

There are some signs that suggest it just may not be possible to salvage your relationship. You are much less likely to have a positive outcome from DD if:

- Your relationship has never, even when things were at their very best, worked well and made you happy.
- You no longer enjoy any recreational activity with your partner.
- One partner refuses to work on the relationship. This could be manifested in a refusal to discuss important issues, or making fun of or ignoring issues. Or it could take the form of one partner blaming the other for problems and refusing to take any responsibility for the difficulties.

> Cheryl: I'd seesawed for years, thinking of leaving Leon one moment and deciding to stay the next. I'll never forget the night I confronted him and pleaded with him to save our marriage. He turned to me and said, 'It's not my problem' and he walked away. I knew at that moment that our marriage was over. Without his help, I knew I was flogging a dead horse. We separated within six months.

Having a partner who won't work on the relationship signals the death knell of love. It's like a two-seater canoe, where one person is busy paddling while the other sits back for a rest — all the canoe does is go around in circles.

LOSS OF LOVING FEELINGS BETWEEN PARTNERS

Love is the most potent desire enhancer of them all. To have great sex in your relationship you must have good loving. Lose your loving feelings for your partner and your arousal and desire will soon follow.

Erich Fromm, author of *The Art of Loving*, says: 'Love is the active concern for the life and growth of that which we love.' 'Active' means that love is a *doing* thing. Love is not an experience, it is an activity. Most of us take love for granted. We expect to be able to abuse it, to ignore it, to neglect it and somehow love will still be there like a shining beacon in the night to guide us to one another.

My definition of love is a simple one: 'unconditional positive regard'. In my own relationship that means that whatever my husband says or does, I try my very best to view his words and behaviour in the most positive light possible.

To maintain unconditional positive regard requires a lot of mature self talk and 'self soothing'. It is very easy to judge, blame and become self-righteous or irritable, especially when there is a high level of stress in your lives. It requires hard work to make love last. You need to:

- Focus on your partner's positive traits.
- Find activities you enjoy and do them together.
- Act in loving ways like you did during courtship.
- Say 'I love you' every day (at least).
- Thank your partner.
- Reduce criticism and increase praise.
- Treat your partner with consideration. Find out what he or she likes — activities, outings, food, music — and be willing to share these pleasures with them.
- Do caring things for your partner.
- Reminisce about good times together to refresh your tender and caring feelings for each other.
- Carefully monitor and moderate your feelings of boredom,

resentment, irritation and frustration with your partner.
- Bite your tongue unless it is really important to speak up.
- Try to put yourself in your partner's shoes.
- Keep a sense of humour.

If you don't *actively* pursue these qualities in your relationship *every day*, reduced or absent sexual desire and loss of sexual chemistry will be the end result.

We should consider our love to be like a rare tropical plant that needs lots of TLC to survive. If you fail to feed and water a plant it won't grow and thrive, and eventually, it will die. Most of us take great care not to neglect our children, our pets, our homes and our work. But we often neglect ourselves and our relationships.

POOR COMMUNICATION

Some people say 'We don't communicate.' There is no such thing as *no communication*. We are communicating with each other all the time, both verbally and nonverbally.

Research tells us that 90% of human communication is nonverbal. What we say is less important than *how we say it* or *what we are doing with our bodies while we say it*.

> Married couples ... tell each other a thousand things without talking.
>
> CHINESE PROVERB

For example, Manfred might *say* to Nicole that he has plenty of time to chat about the kids' problems at school. However, the moment he looks at his watch, turns his body away from hers, drops eye contact or moves towards the door, his body sends her a completely different message.

Getting your message across means more than just saying what's on your mind — good communication involves talking clearly, listening carefully and fully understanding each other. It means making sure that your body language and your words match each other so the message is not confusing.

'I' messages

The first step in communication is sending a clear message. This is not always easy, especially when you feel upset. Communication experts recommend the use of 'I' messages which *focus on the experience of the sender rather than on the character or behaviour of the receiver*. An 'I' message is a simple way of taking responsibility for your feelings and talking about the problem in a way that doesn't cause your partner to become defensive. To formulate 'I' messages, ask yourself:

- What specific behaviour is my partner engaged in that I have feelings about? (*behaviour*)
- How do I feel about my partner's behaviour? (*emotion*)
- What are the consequences of this behaviour for me? (*consequences*)

   Begin by saying:

   'I have something I'd like to talk to you about. Is now a good time?' If it's not a good time, make a commitment to speak to each other soon.

   State your concern in the form: 'When you ....
(behaviour), I feel .... *(emotion)* because
.... *(consequences)*. Then request a specific change in partner behaviour. The partner should reflect back to you what you have said and then respond. You can also use this method to effectively praise or communicate pleasant feelings towards one another.

   Let's look at what *not* to do. This is a typical message focusing on the character and behaviour of a partner:

> **Freda:** You always initiate sex when you're in the mood and you never stop to think about what sort of day I've had. You grab my boobs before we've had a chance to talk. How about thinking about me for a change, Stan? Don't I matter, too? You're so selfish.

Now here is an 'I' message with a clear request for behaviour change:

> **Freda:** Stan, I get upset when you initiate sex without first talking to me and checking to see how I'm feeling. When you grab for my boobs before talking to me, it's like my feelings and needs aren't important to you. I'd like you to find out how I'm feeling first, before you touch me like that.

Even when the sender gets the message right, most receivers are too busy thinking about what they are going to say next, looking for danger signals, judging or spacing out, to truly listen to what their partner has to say. People are even less likely to hear what is being said when they don't particularly like what their partner is saying.

Instead of listening to what their partner is trying to communicate, poor communicators interpret the sender's words and add their own meaning, mangling the sender's message in the process.

Active listening

To ensure good communication, the receiver should give the sender feedback about what was said, in case there is need for clarification. This is called *active listening*.

> Give your partner the priceless gift of being heard and acknowledged.
> MATTHEW MCKAY
> AMERICAN AUTHOR

Sender's 'I' message:

> **Freda:** I get upset when you initiate sex without first talking to me and checking to see how I'm feeling. When you grab for my boobs before talking to me, it's like my feelings and needs aren't important to you. I'd like you to find out how I'm feeling first, before you touch me like that.

Receiver's feedback:

> **Stan:** You're saying that you feel upset when I approach you for sex without checking to see how you are feeling

first. When I do this, it makes you feel like you're not important to me. You'd like me to talk to you before I touch you.

This careful talking and hearing process ensures that messages are sent and received as they are intended. When a couple fail to communicate, they experience misunderstandings, conflicts and withdrawal — definitely not a good basis for a passionate sexual relationship. (See the Resources section for further reading.)

Key Points ❦

Good loving is the key to great sex. Loss of loving feelings results in loss of sexual desire and arousal.

Sustaining love is an active process that requires daily effort.

Communication involves careful speaking and thoughtful listening. It is impossible to resolve conflicts and negotiate with each other if you cannot communicate effectively.

12

Up Close and Personal — Intimacy and Trust

Intimacy is a sharing of ourselves, a letting down of our guard to reveal our true selves. In simplest terms, intimacy is 'in-to-me-see'.

PROBLEMS WITH INTIMACY

True intimacy means stripping away your mask, and sharing, through honest conversation and shared experiences, who you really are. It means moving through your individual anxieties and fears and coming in close. It means sharing differences as well

> Intimacy is when I invite you to tell me exactly who you are on the inside and you do the same.
>
> TOBY GREEN
> PSYCHOLOGIST

as similarities. It means taking the risk of telling your partner information about yourself that they may not approve of or that they may have trouble accepting. This level of self-disclosure requires a high level of trust. *True intimacy is the key to ongoing sexual passion within a relationship.*

Selective vs total intimacy

Most couples wrongly think that intimacy is sharing what you think and feel and having the other person not only *agreeing* with what you say, but *approving* of it completely. This *selective intimacy* means sharing only what you know your partner will concur with and keeping back any matters that might cause disapproval, disagreement or conflict. This is not true intimacy.

When a couple engages in selective intimacy, they are seeking each other's approval rather than attempting to be real. Thoughts, feelings, experiences and needs that might rock the boat are carefully hidden away, for years, for decades or forever.

Maurie and Leonora have been together for seven years and believe that in a good relationship a couple should be everything to each other. To keep the peace and live up to this expectation, they only share themselves selectively.

> **Maurie:** I feel so alone so much of the time. Thank goodness I have you to help me feel better.
> **Leonora:** I feel the same way, Maurie. You're my best friend.

What Maurie really wants to say is that he feels alone even when Leonora is there. He feels a deep emptiness much of the time. These feelings have been present since Maurie's parents were killed in a car accident when he was 12. He worries that if he tells Leonora the truth, she will think he is weak and not happy with her. After all, how can he be married and still feel lonely?

Leonora is also being less than truthful. Although she really loves Maurie, her best friend for years has been her girlfriend Helen, because she can tell her anything at all. Maurie is often distant and preoccupied with his feelings but won't talk about them, so Leonora backs off. She can't tell him the truth about how she feels shut out by him — friends don't do that.

Genuine intimacy is not dependent on another's approval. We should not expect another person to totally approve of us — instead, we should both honestly express who we are even if the other person doesn't necessarily see things the same way we do.

Maurie: I get it — false intimacy is when I only say what I think you want me to say.

Leonora: And true intimacy is when we say what we really think and feel, even if it feels uncomfortable for both of us.

Couples who complain they have nothing left to talk about often practise selective intimacy. They have exhausted all the topics that are mutually OK for them. They have plenty left to say, but

> I will have no locked cupboards in my life.
>
> GERTRUDE BELL
> ENGLISH PAINTER

further chat means delving into those difficult areas where they may not agree with, like or approve of what their partner thinks, feels and needs.

Re-creating intimacy

Over the years, many couples lose touch with each other. Intimate feelings become nothing more than a romantic memory. They live under the same roof but not together.

The first step to re-creating closeness in your relationship is to restore good times together. The regular sharing of pleasurable, enjoyable activities, known as 'recreational intimacy', is crucial for couples to re-establish their love. This process is described in full in Chapter 15.

At the same time, any ongoing conflicts in the relationship that might be forcing the couple apart should be resolved (see Chapter 14). If this proves difficult, counselling will help. Once the level of hostility drops in the relationship, trust can begin to thrive and grow. The process of trust building is described later in this chapter.

When regular shared activities are under way, trust has been re-established and the couple is feeling less alienated, intimacy is the next step. Start to speak from the heart to your partner, tell the truth about who you are, how you think and feel, and what you want. Just be honest.

As one speaks, the other simply listens and gives feedback that shows that the speaker has been heard. No judging, no arguments, no rejection. There is no debate about who you both are. You may not necessarily like or approve of everything your partner reveals

> It takes two to speak the truth — one to speak, and another to hear.
>
> HENRY DAVID THOREAU
> AMERICAN AUTHOR

to you, but you can try to accept them for who they are, using compassion and understanding to make sense of the different ways your partner thinks, feels and behaves. Total intimacy is the hallmark of a courageous couple.

Differing intimacy needs

Just as individuals can have differing needs for sex, so too can there be differing needs for emotional and physical intimacy. *Emotional intimacy* is expressed through verbal communication, tender words, loving talk and emotional sharing. *Physical intimacy* means nonverbal contact — attention, eye contact, gentle touch, hugging, kissing and low-grade affection that doesn't necessarily lead to sex.

The amount of physical and emotional closeness you need or can tolerate is mainly determined by your family environment. If your parents weren't physically or emotionally close with each other or with you, you are unlikely to experience a need for, or perhaps even enjoy, emotional or physical closeness with others.

Boy touching, girl touching

Women tend to exhibit a greater need for nonsexual forms of intimacy, probably due to the differing ways we bring up our boys and girls. Our touching of boys differs from our touching of girls. From birth, parents touch girls more tenderly and more often than boys. One survey found that during their stay in a maternity hospital, mothers with newborn infants touched their girl babies an average of 23.7 times, while boy babies were touched only 16.2 times, only two-thirds as much. Boys are much more likely to be treated to rough and tumble play, such as being thrown up into the air or roughly tickled, than girls. As they grow up, boys' physical contact with others is often limited to playground and sporting activities, while little girls enjoy gentle, affectionate touch with friends and parents throughout childhood.

By the time puberty arrives, parents have often reduced touching of boys to minimal levels. Boys are taught to shake hands with adults, while girls are still permitted to clamber onto Daddy's knee or get a good long hug from Mum well into their teen years.

Little boys are taught very early to suppress their emotions. While emotions like anger and competitiveness are encouraged in boys, they are actively taught not to be sad, not to cry and not to care. Boys soon learn to be tough, resilient and emotionally independent. By the time most men reach adulthood they have lost touch with their needs for intimacy, closeness and affection. These needs are present, but they are often distilled down to a need for sexual contact. For many men this is the only legitimate way they can ask for closeness without betraying the macho myth that real men don't need affection, intimacy and sensuality.

Unfortunately, this approach can make women feel that all men are after is sex. In the final section of the book we will explore ways of teaching men and women to recognise and look after their nonsexual needs in appropriate nonsexual ways.

Emotional pursuer/distancer

When one person wants more intimacy than the other, a pursuer/distancer cycle is set in motion, similar to the vicious cycle experienced with desire discrepancy. One partner becomes the emotional pursuer, pressuring for more emotional closeness and affection, while the other partner distances themself, withdraws and shuts down.

The situation gets worse and worse with the distancer (the partner who needs less intimacy) increasingly shutting down emotionally and physically. This shutdown panics the pursuer, who hounds the distancer even more. In this cycle, one or both parties typically lose interest in sex.

A double whammy

Emotional and sexual P/D cycles often operate simultaneously. Frequently it is the woman who takes the roles of emotional pursuer and the sexual distancer. While she craves emotional closeness, she draws away from sexual encounters, wanting her emotional needs to be met first. In this scenario the man plays the simultaneous roles of sexual pursuer and emotional distancer, pushing for sex which fulfils his needs for closeness but avoiding connection, which threatens him.

Sadly neither party gets their needs met and their relationship deteriorates both emotionally and sexually.

Be your own sex therapist

Do you and your partner share total intimacy? Could you be more open and honest about yourself in your relationship? Could your partner?

How did your parents express their feelings for each other? Did they show affection to each other?

How did your parents show affection to you? Did you receive enough affection and attention from them?

Did your parents subject you to physical punishment of any sort (slaps, beating, pinching, hitting)? Did you suffer from sexual abuse? How has this affected your feelings about being touched?

Do you have higher or lower needs for emotional and physical closeness than your partner does?

Are you an emotional pursuer? Is your partner?

Are you an emotional distancer? Is your partner?

How do these cycles affect your relationship?

Discuss this with your partner.

LACK OF TRUST

We all start out as trusting individuals — it is life that teaches us not to trust. The shattering of trust can take place at any time — in infancy or childhood, during teenage years, in adult relationships. As a result, many of us come to our adult relationships with less than optimal ability to build trust in others. Let's go back to Cheryl, married to Leon, the problem drinker.

Cheryl: I wanted to trust Leon but it was impossible, mainly due to his drinking activities. I soon learnt not to believe him when he said he'd call if he was going to be late. Or he'd call from the pub and tell me to have dinner ready in half an hour. Hours later he still wasn't home. After a while I stopped making dinner for him at all. It got to a stage when I knew if I asked him a question about where he'd been, he'd lie to me — so I stopped asking.

After we married he didn't encourage trust in other ways. He never told me much about his day — where he'd been or who he'd seen. He told me nothing about his business and never let me know how we stood financially. He made important decisions without consulting me. He even put our house on the market without telling me until later.

The sandcastle of trust

When you enter into a relationship you enter into an agreement, or more correctly, a long list of agreements. Agreements may be simple everyday expectations, such as an undertaking to talk to each other in a pleasant way; or they may be agreements that are major cornerstones of the relationship, such as telling the truth or being faithful to each other. Infidelity, lying, breaking of promises and other agreements are common examples of breaches of contract. It doesn't matter if the broken agreement is big or small, negotiated or unnegotiated, the price of betrayal is loss of trust.

In clinical practice I use the sandcastle model of trust to explain to couples how trust can be built and destroyed in a relationship. Imagine that your trust in your partner is built like a sandcastle on the seashore, using beach sand and a spade. Trusting types possess first-class equipment to rapidly build a sizeable sandcastle — a good sized emotional spade and firm damp sand to work with. Each time your partner turns up at the agreed time, you pile sand on your castle. Each time your partner is there for you, each occasion your partner tells you the truth, each time your partner places commitment to the relationship over attraction to another — on goes another spadeful of sand.

A person who is trusting not only builds trust rapidly, but they

> Learning to trust is one of
> life's most difficult tasks.
>
> ISAAC WATTS
> ENGLISH HYMN WRITER

construct a solid sandcastle that can withstand quite a bit of battering from the elements. Problems within relationships are inevitable, but they need not necessarily damage trust if it has been strongly built. The wind may blow and the rain may fall, but a trusting person's sandcastle is sturdy enough to survive. Trusting people probably have a little cement mixed through the sand so that their castle can easily brave the wind and waves without crumbling.

The effects of betrayal

Most healthy people start their relationships with a willingness to trust. When an affair, lies, or other breach of trust is discovered, the original sandcastle of trust is demolished and must be rebuilt. A major betrayal is like a wave that surges up the beach and washes the sandcastle of trust completely away. Smaller betrayals act like kicks here and there, damaging the sandcastle and weakening it, so that eventually it topples to the ground.

Betrayal not only destroys trust, it also *damages the ability to build trust*. Imagine that instead of a spade to build your castle, thanks to betrayal you have traded in your spade for a teaspoon! And instead of coarse, firm sand, all you have to work with is the finest, driest, whitest sand you can imagine, as easily blown away as talcum powder. This makes building the sandcastle for the second time, third time or more, much slower and increasingly more difficult.

After a serious betrayal, many people have nothing to rebuild trust with except teaspoons. In severe cases the teaspoons have holes in them like sieves.

> **Darren:** My ability to trust was never very good. In childhood I soon learnt not to trust anyone. My mother emotionally and physically abused me, and my father stood by and did nothing. Others may be building trust with teaspoons, but all I've ever had to work with is a fork. And my sand is as fine and dry as a desert dune.

Imagine building a sandcastle under these conditions. Not only would the going be slow and tedious but the slightest breeze, the slightest uncertainty or fear, would whisk away your sandcastle in an instant. So it is with betrayal. After the affair, or the lie, or the letting down, the betrayed partner finds trust building a painfully slow process, often to the frustration of the betrayer.

Rebuilding trust

> **Dan:** I know I did the dirty on Barbara. I cheated on her more than once, but that's all behind me now. I want to make a fresh start and be a really good husband and father now. But she keeps dragging up the past. She wants to know where I am every minute of the day. She sniffs my clothes and goes through my pockets. She freaks out if I'm home 10 minutes later than I said I'd be. I just wish she'd get over it so we could get on with our lives. After all, it's been two months!

Dan doesn't realise that a mere two months or even two years down the track, he can't force Barbara to trust him. Trust, like love, comes unbidden in its own time. Just as you cannot make yourself love someone, you cannot make yourself trust someone. Trust is something that must be earned.

After a breach of trust has been discovered, the betrayer wants all the guilt, blame and sadness left in the past. Once the decision to recommit to the relationship is made, the betrayer becomes impatient for the relationship to be back on track, preferably in the shortest time frame possible.

Meanwhile the betrayed partner can't cooperate. He or she keeps asking questions, getting anxious, wanting to know who was on the phone, long after the 'recovery' time allotted by the betrayer has run out. The moment the betrayer expresses anger or frustration, any gains in trust are immediately lost, blown away like a fragile pile of dust in a tornado. And the process has to start all over again.

> We have to distrust each other. It's our only defence against betrayal.
>
> TENNESSEE WILLIAMS
> AMERICAN PLAYWRIGHT

The price of betrayal

After any betrayal, big or small, it can take months or years of hard work from both partners to rebuild trust. It's a process that can't be hurried. The price the betrayer has to pay for breaching trust in the relationship is diligent attention to supporting the betrayed in re-establishing trust. For the betrayer, and depending on the issues involved, this can mean months and months of:

- telling your partner where you are, what you are doing, who you are with and what you talked about — all day, every day in the beginning!
- volunteering information rather than waiting to be asked — if your partner has to ask, then you're not doing your job well enough
- dealing with your partner's anxieties with warm and freely given reassurance
- being open to requests from your partner for reassurance, requests that in the beginning might be almost constant
- dealing with your partner's suspicions in a loving manner
- sharing your thoughts and your life more openly with your partner
- forgoing activities initially that might cause your partner overwhelming anxiety, such as going away on a trip alone, even if it is for business
- being patient, patient, patient.

Using the sandcastle analogy, for trust to be rebuilt the betrayer has to provide a shelter, a safe and untroubled environment for healing to take place. This is like building a wall around a budding sandcastle to protect it from the elements. This shelter is created by the betrayer acting in a consistent, trustworthy and comforting fashion aimed at reducing insecurity on the part of the betrayed for *as long as it takes*. In this fashion, trust can be rebuilt and trust-building mechanisms can eventually be healed. This work is the price the betrayer must pay to get the relationship back on track.

Be your own sex therapist

Do you trust your partner? Always? Sometimes? Rarely?
Never?

Does your partner trust you?

Has either of you breached the trust in the relationship?

Has the relationship recovered from this?

Has the betrayer (you or your partner) done the work necessary to regenerate trust within the relationship as outlined
above?

Sex and trust

Lawrence put it very well. He is
saying that in order to *want to have
sex*, to desire sex, *you must feel
safe*, you must trust your partner.
Without trust, the idea of letting
down your guard and getting close
emotionally or sexually is very

> If you want to have sex,
> you've got to trust,
> at the core of your heart,
> the other creature.
>
> D. H. LAWRENCE

frightening indeed. A person who continually lets their partner
down cannot expect them to feel safe enough to experience sexual
desire. The shutting down of desire in this situation is a protective
mechanism. Loss of trust inevitably means loss of sexual desire, if
not immediately then sometime in the future.

Key Points ❧

Intimacy means disclosing to each other who you really are. This degree of vulnerability requires a high level of trust.

True intimacy is total — it embraces the thinking and feeling realities of both partners completely, without regard for approval or agreement. True intimacy celebrates our differences as well as our similarities.

Couples may experience differing needs for emotional and physical intimacy. To experience maximum desire, emotional and physical intimacy needs must be negotiated and met to the satisfaction of both partners.

Trust is the fuel of desire. Once trust is damaged in a relationship, it may take years of hard work by both partners to rebuild it.

13

Maintaining Love — Commitment, Respect and Equality

LACK OF COMMITMENT

What is commitment? Commitment is a conscious decision to enter into an intensive, exclusive, extensive relationship with another. In practical terms, commitment means putting the welfare of your relationship above the welfare of either partner — being prepared to do whatever it takes to keep your partnership healthy and thriving.

Close off all exits

Like pregnancy, there are no degrees of commitment — you cannot be a little bit pregnant, nor can you be a little bit committed — it's 100% or nothing. To achieve the healthy, happy sex life you want, you must stop camping on the outskirts of your relationship, waiting for signs that it will work out (or not).

You can't be like an absentee landlord, expecting to collect the rent but not putting any effort into caring for the property. Lack of

> Be a resident in your love life, not a tourist.
>
> DR LLOYD WAGNER
> AMERICAN SOMATIC THERAPIST

commitment produces insecurity, loss of trust and distancing, all of which can negatively affect sexual desire.

Commitment phobia

For some men and women the idea of commitment is like having a pillow put over their faces for the rest of their life. They feel terrified and suffocated at the thought. People who have trouble with commitment in relationships often have problems with commitment in other areas of their lives. Some people have difficulty committing to anything — a home, a job, possessions, friends, even family.

A person with commitment problems may have unrealistic expectations. They may believe that there is a 'perfect partner' out there who will fit exactly into the place in their heart, like a missing piece from a jigsaw puzzle. As a result they keep on moving on, forever looking for perfect fulfilment. Yet fulfilment comes from committing, not the other way round.

The origin of a person's commitment phobia may be found in negative experiences in past romantic relationships or even in their own parents' troubled relationship. They may think all relationships are somehow threatening and dangerous. They must realise that they have the power to create their relationship any way they want — that history doesn't need to repeat itself.

Defining the relationship

People get confused about the difference between *defining* the relationship and *committing* to it. Defining the relationship means stating that we are (in no particular order):

- friends
- dating
- lovers
- living together
- engaged
- married

Many people hurry to define their relationship. They assume that defining the partnership automatically means equal commitment from both parties. This is not necessarily true. Research has shown that, for women, a de facto living arrangement is a much greater commitment, usually entered into with a view to building a long-term future together. Men are more likely to see a de facto situation as a convenience and a way of maintaining their own freedom.

Commitment and 'defining the relationship' are separate issues. Partners need to discuss their personal ideas about what commitment means, so that each clearly understands what this pledge means to the other. Many couples entering marriage take the attitude that, if it doesn't work out, 'we can just get a divorce'. This is not commitment.

Baby steps

Couples should first commit to *ways of being in the relationship together*. You can commit to always being honest with each other, to supporting each other emotionally, to listening to each other, to being faithful to each other. These small commitments can pave the way for deeper commitments as the relationship grows and develops. A person who has difficulty making small commitments is likely to let his or her partner down on the bigger issues.

More extensive commitments should only be negotiated when it has been proven that smaller commitments can be kept. How can someone be expected to keep a major commitment like marriage vows when they cannot be relied on for small things on a daily basis? *Commitment is the grown up way to say 'I love you'.*

Be your own sex therapist

Are you truly committed to your relationship now? Have you ever been 100% committed to your relationship? What about your partner's level of commitment?

Take a sheet of paper and make a list of the usual ways in which you exit from your relationship, avoid intimacy and shut your partner out. Ask your partner to do the same. Partners exit the relationship by:

- working long hours
- obsessing about housework or sport

- spending all their spare time with the kids
- filling their life with social engagements
- always having their head in a newspaper or book
- drinking, drug taking, gambling and other compulsive behaviour
- using pornography and solo sex (masturbation) to excess
- being tense and uptight all the time
- always working on the car, bike, etc.
- fighting constantly
- any other exits you might use.

On a second sheet write down how you perceive your partner abandons the relationship.

In a non-threatening way, go through these lists with your partner, taking great care to listen to what your partner has to say. For your relationship to work, these 'exits' must be reduced and preferably closed off permanently.

Mark off which exits you are willing to eliminate or reduce.

To maximise your relationship's emotional and sexual potential, you must close off all exits and commit. With a relationship, you're either in or you're out — there are no halfway measures.

INSECURITY

Insecurity in a relationship can sometimes be a symptom of low levels of trust and/or lack of commitment by one or other partner. This is described as *relationship insecurity* and the only solution is to make sure that both of you not only *talk the talk* of commitment, but *walk the walk* of commitment as well.

> **Desiree:** I feel really insecure with Miguel. He claims he loves me but he lets me down so often. He can fly into a rage over nothing and he doesn't turn up when he says he will. A few times he's left me waiting for him for hours in town at night. It's nothing major, just one little thing after another. He wants to get married, but I really don't feel safe with him.

Miguel says he is committed, but his actions send Desiree a very different message. He says one thing, but does another.

Personal insecurities also show up in relationships. No matter how committed you and your partner are, if you don't manage your personal insecurities the relationship can be destabilised.

> **Julian:** I know Katie loves me, but I get really scared when I see her talking with other men. She works in an office full of them and I often pop in there just to check on her. She's completely committed to me, but I can't shake these feelings. She could have anyone — why should she be interested in a nobody like me?

No amount of commitment or reassurance from Katie will make Julian feel secure. He sees himself as worthless and inadequate and doubts that he is lovable.

Personal insecurities grow like weeds in the manure of poor self-esteem and manifest as feelings of worthlessness, feeling unlovable, fearing abandonment, and irrational jealousies. Insecurity is often experienced in other areas of life, such as at work, in studies, or with friends and family, as well as in romantic relationships.

You cannot expect your partner to make up for your personal insecurities. Certainly a solid relationship and plenty of loving reassurance will temporarily boost a flagging self-esteem, but the resolution of the problem lies within you, not from your partner or your relationship. If you have personal insecurities I recommend you read *Self Esteem* by Fanning and McKay (see Resources).

UNRESOLVED JEALOUSY — CONQUERING THE GREEN-EYED MONSTER

Show me a man or woman who has never been jealous and it's odds on they've never been in love. Marriage counsellors report that jealousy is a major factor for 30% of couples seeking counselling.

Many people think that jealousy is an expression of love, but it is more an expression of our fear than our love: our fear that we are not attractive enough, that we might not be able to meet our partner's needs and, most importantly, our fear that we may lose the one we love.

Jealousy can be positive

Jealousy has very little to do with our partner's love for us and a lot to do with how we think and feel.

Helen has convinced herself that Bill is seeing another woman because he stays late at work. She searches her husband's pockets and lifts the extension on the phone whenever he makes calls. She tortures herself, imagining him with other women.

Then there's Bill, who has been sulking for days since Helen listened attentively to his mate at a barbecue on the weekend. He's hurt because he believes she enjoys his mate's company more than his.

Through feeling jealous, both Bill and Helen are getting important information, but it concerns how they feel themselves and has very little to do with their partner's feelings. If the truth be known, Helen and Bill are deeply in love with each other and neither would dream of being unfaithful. However, Helen has never believed that anyone could really love and care for her. When Bill works late, she feels insecure and jealous. What her jealousy is actually telling her is that she needs to improve her self-esteem and organise more time with Bill in order to feel important and secure.

On the other hand, Bill is getting the message from his jealous feelings that he would dearly love his wife to give him her undivided attention when he speaks to her. A more constructive approach by this couple would be for them to bring their fears out in the open, state their needs, and ask each other for more time, attention, reassurance and affection.

> For love is strong as death; jealousy is cruel as the grave.
> SONG OF SOLOMON

Jealousy out of control

It has been estimated that 1 in 5,000 people has a real problem with jealousy. Severe or 'pathological' jealousy occurs more often in men and is linked with heavy drinking patterns. Sufferers feel compelled to check up on their partners, worrying about what they are up to every minute of the day. They examine clothing and bedsheets, note down car mileage or make surprise visits to their partner's work. Each day is an endless stream of interrogations and accusations. The sufferers become so obsessed with imagined infidelity that they make life a misery for all concerned. These people need psychiatric help to cope with their underlying problems of low self-esteem and irrational thinking.

Making friends with jealousy

Most of us try to deal with our jealous feelings by acting angry and putting pressure on our partners to change *their* behaviour. The insecurity and inadequacy *we* feel is never mentioned. Jealousy is often a sign that we need to work on ourselves, increasing our self-esteem and confidence. Instead of labelling jealousy as a personal failing, try to see it as a friend that is telling you how to create a happier relationship with yourself as well as your partner.

Jealousy is nothing to be ashamed of. It is a natural emotion that can guide us along the path to happiness if we will only listen to what it is trying to tell us.

Be your own sex therapist

Is jealousy a problem in your relationship? If you or your partner wish to overcome jealous feelings, follow the steps set out below.

1. When you feel jealous, calmly admit your feelings to yourself and to your partner.
2. Ask your partner to reassure you that he or she loves you and is committed to the relationship. Don't feel ashamed if you need to do this every day, or even every hour.

3. Be patient with each other. Some people need a lot more reassurance than others and this can be tiresome. However, if you give reassurance freely every time it is requested, the jealous partner will eventually begin to feel more secure and ask less often.

4. Use your jealousy to pinpoint your own attitudes and behaviours that may need attention and suggest ways that your relationship could be changed for the better.

LACK OF RESPECT

Respect comes from the Latin word *respicere*, meaning 'to look at'. It means seeing a person as they truly are, being aware of their unique individuality and valuing that. Respect involves a desire for that person to grow and unfold, not in a way that you see fit or to serve you, but to fulfil their true potential. Respect means giving the other person the freedom to be who they truly are.

Most of us are too self-interested, too keen to get our needs met and too eager to 'improve' our partner, to give each other total respect. The familiarity and wear and tear of long-term couplings (plus a shared bathroom!) leads to a low background level of disrespect in most relationships. Disrespect is shown by occasional criticism and lack of support; through unkind comments and put-downs; through negative attitudes, blaming and making wrong.

Toxic disrespect

There is a line, albeit a fine one, between *normal disrespect* and *toxic disrespect*. Normal disrespect does not significantly damage self-respect. When you are suffering at the hands of toxic disrespect, your partner's comments and behaviour are not something you can just shrug off or forget a few moments later. They really hurt.

Disrespect may be toxic in both its quality and quantity. The target partner may be subjected to *quantity disrespect* — a barrage of little comments and criticisms all day, every day. Or it may be the *quality* of the comments that do the harm — infrequent comments that go right to the bone, catching the target off guard like a sniper's bullet. Criticisms are aimed at you personally, rather than at your behaviour. Not 'That was a really silly thing to do', but: 'You're such an idiot. Anyone with half a brain could have coped with that.'

With toxic disrespect the target begins to believe that the partner's view of them is correct. 'You're out of your mind. How could anybody believe that?' The target thinks: 'Well, maybe I am a little crazy after all.' The disrespectful comments have begun to eat away at the target's self-respect.

If you think you may be a victim of toxic disrespect, Patricia Evans' book, *The Verbally Abusive Relationship*, will help (see Resources).

Healthy respect

Respect means treating your partner with positive regard that embraces their flaws, rather than pointing them out or harping on them. Respect means accepting the differences between the two of you and not making the other person wrong. Respect means rejoicing in your partner's triumphs and commiserating with their mishaps. Respect means giving your partner consideration for their thoughts, feelings and needs, and empathy about how they experience the world. Mutual respect is the fertile ground in which love and passion can take seed and grow.

> Love is the extremely difficult realisation that something other than oneself is real.
>
> IRIS MURDOCH
> ENGLISH NOVELIST

LACK OF CHEMISTRY

Chemistry is a complex recipe that relies on physical and emotional attraction to each other, courting and romantic rituals, flirtation, and the capacity to generate feelings of being desired and being desirable.

Chemistry is present in abundance during the limerence phase of relationships. Once limerence fades, chemistry requires effort. Chemistry grows out of attention to a range of attributes — your hygiene, your dress, your manners, your habits. It means seeing your partner with new eyes every day and treating them in that special way that shows love, respect and appreciation.

It's hard to feel chemistry for someone who bathes once a week, hangs out in baggy old clothes and passes wind loudly at the dinner table. It's hard to feel chemistry for someone who fails to say 'please' or 'thank you', who never brushes their teeth or combs their hair. Chemistry will plunge if you reek of garlic, beer or cigarettes, and pick your nose continually. It's hard to feel chemistry for someone who only talks to you when the ads are on TV, who pays more attention to the dog and who never has a nice word for you.

Chemistry is based on paying attention to the way you present yourself and behave around your partner. Chemistry peaks when you make the effort to make each other feel special every single day.

Be your own sex therapist

Do you find your partner attractive? Was there more chemistry in your relationship in the past? What has changed?

Each make a list of three things you can do to increase the chemistry in your relationship. Do them for two weeks and see if they make a difference. After two weeks, keep doing the ones that make a difference and add three more. Keep adding to your list.

Each make a list of three things your partner could do to increase the chemistry in your relationship. Show your partner the list and ask him or her to do them for two weeks and see if they make a difference. Thank your partner for his or her effort. Keep the ones that work and add three more. Keep adding to the list.

INTRUSIONS

Imagine that your relationship is like a ball of plasticine or putty — smooth, round and pliable. Intrusions act like fingers poking deep into the ball of plasticine, distorting it and altering its shape.

Examples of common intrusions include in-laws and other family members, children, work, recreational pursuits and hobbies, religious activities, friends or past lovers. It could be your preoccupation with shopping, sport, drinking, gambling or drug taking. Perhaps you are overcommitted to community activities or just to helping others in distress. All intrusions have the potential to cause relationship stress and conflict.

> **Ken:** From the beginning it was a struggle between Sofia and myself. My parents lived in another state and I was an only child. She came from a traditional background where family is everything. Her mother and father were always at our place, so were her sisters.
>
> Her parents are old now and take up lots of her time. Her sisters all have children and because we have no children, we are unofficial babysitters for the lot. Sofia loves it, but it puts a big strain on our relationship. Some days I just want to scream 'What about me!'

Whatever your outside focus is, if your partner feels left out, the relationship will suffer and so will your sex life.

Boundary riders

From time to time we need to be able to make the rest of the world go away so that we can truly be together. Unless you make your relationship a high priority, other elements in your life will continue to intrude on it, taking time, energy and attention away from it. Often this priority shift requires a major change of attitude and behaviour. It may mean leaving the mobile phone or the bleeper at home and ignoring the email. It means talking about 'we' and 'us', not 'them'. These changes may affect your or your partner's relationship with others.

Couples need to see themselves as boundary riders, ever watchful for violations of the fences around their relationship and chasing away intruders. This patrolling exercise requires cooperation and vigilance.

> ### Be your own sex therapist
>
> What major intrusions are currently imposing on your relationship?
> How can you work together to protect your relationship from these pressures?

POWER STRUGGLES AND INEQUALITY

When couples engage in power struggles, they fight over who is going to run the show. Common areas for power struggles are money management, domestic chores, decision making and raising of children.

Sex role stereotypes

Power struggles are made more difficult by the shifts in sex roles experienced in the last few decades. Traditionally it was accepted that men exercised power both in the outside world and within the family, while women took a submissive role. Everyone knew what they had to do and most of them did it, even if it didn't make them happy. At least men and women knew their 'rightful' places.

These days men are expected to be involved with domestic chores and children, while women are now expected to operate in the world of business and commerce. Although these changes are beneficial to both (research has found that men who share the housework enjoy better health in the long term and their partners experience more marital satisfaction), gender role shifts still require a lot of adjustment.

More often than not it will be the woman who is pushing for more equality in the relationship, while the man is more comfortable maintaining the old status quo. This sets up a vicious cycle where the woman pushes for equality and change and the man withdraws. In response the woman pushes harder, becoming louder and more critical,

> Love is the child of freedom, never that of domination.
>
> ERICH FROMM
> AMERICAN PSYCHOLOGIST

while he removes himself and won't negotiate. In this situation, women often feel hostile and helpless and men feel less attracted to their partners.

Corporate relationships

Some couples resolve the problem of power and control by dividing their relationship up into separate areas of responsibility for each partner — they develop *corporate relationships*. For example, she makes the money decisions and he makes the decisions about the house and children. He organises their holidays and she organises their social life. Each goes along with the decisions of the other.

Corporate couples don't have conflict over who is the boss, but they also miss out on the closeness and intimacy of making joint decisions about their life together. These relationships tend to be long on personal space and autonomy, but short on passion and desire.

There's nothing wrong with divvying up some of the responsibilities between partners, but when there are no opportunities for regular shared decision making, the relationship is denied an important avenue for mutual exchange and growth.

Be your own sex therapist

Do you feel equal, superior or inferior to your partner in terms of how much power and influence you have in your relationship?

Do you share important decisions?

Are you happy with the distribution of chores and responsibilities within the home? What needs to change?

Do you have a corporate relationship with totally separate areas of decision-making responsibility?

For the higher drive partner: Is it possible that, by imposing your will on your partner in the relationship, you might be reducing their level of sexual interest?

For the lower drive partner: Do you think that lack of control, submission and surrender in your relationship could be reducing your sex drive?

To enjoy a healthy relationship and a healthy sex life, you *must* resolve issues of power and control. The sexual side of a relationship is a sacred and spiritual connection and can only thrive on equality and shared responsibility. Where there is dominance and control, there is no equality.

Key Points ·❦·

Commitment to the relationship must be total for desire to thrive.

Insecurity is a sign of lack of commitment, low levels of trust or personal insecurities. A person who is uncertain in the relationship will also be uncertain about sex.

Jealousy can give us important information about ourselves and our relationships.

Lack of respect between partners will eat away at sexual desire. Respect allows each partner to blossom and grow as individuals.

Chemistry dies in relationships because partners stop making the effort to make each other feel special and important every day.

A healthy relationship has boundaries strong enough to repel even the strongest intrusions.

When you dominate and control your partner, you might gain power, but your partner will lose desire for you.

14

Problem Solving — Conflict and Negotiation

Like desire discrepancy, conflict in long-term relationships is inevitable. He wants this and she wants that. He thinks this and she thinks that. She needs this and he needs that. Effective conflict resolution is a key factor in creating and maintaining sexual passion within a relationship.

UNRESOLVED CONFLICT

You may already recognise areas in which your partnership is strained and conflicted. If so, you will need to do some work on your love relationship before you can get your sexual relationship back on track. *Ongoing conflict in any area of the relationship will impinge on sexual desire, more especially on the desire of the lower drive partner.*

Conflict up = desire down

During limerence, couples display an artificially high level of tolerance and conflict avoidance which cannot be sustained in the long term. When we let our true feelings, needs and habits show, limerence fades and conflict begins.

She prefers to see a 'chick flick' and enjoy a good cry, while he wants to see a 'guy' movie with chase scenes and submachine guns.

He's an early riser and she likes to stay up late. He likes sex in the morning before work and she can't open her eyes before 9 a.m., let alone anything else.

She doesn't approve of his friend with the body piercing and tats, and he can't stand her gossipy workmates.

On the positive side, once couples emerge from limerence and strip off their masks, they can truly fall in love. To keep that love alive and kicking, partners need to learn the skills of effective conflict resolution.

On the negative side, the waning of limerence and the emergence of conflict can seriously reduce levels of sexual desire, especially in women. Not only are those powerful female desire enhancers (intimacy, affection, time spent together, romance and communication) dwindling, but conflicting needs and expectations result in little skirmishes, arguments and even out-and-out fights — all powerful passion killers.

How do YOU deal with conflict?

Couples deal with conflict in a variety of ways. Some people avoid strife (conflict avoiders), while others are only too keen to face up to conflict (conflict confronters). Let's take a look at a range of strategies for coping with conflict. These different strategies are set out in the diagram on page 195.

Conflict avoiders
There are three types of conflict avoiders.
1. **Separators.** When the conflict phase emerges, some couples cope by simply calling it quits. Certainly, ending the relationship is a very effective way of terminating conflict!

> **Glen:** I've only had one long-term relationship and never again! These days, the first sign of a drama, I'm out of there. Life's too short to waste time going over your relationship with a fine-tooth comb.

2. **Distancers**. Some partners stay together and avoid conflict by leading separate lives. Partners create parallel compartmentalised lives, avoiding intimate contact that might evoke conflict. Over the years the relationship develops into a minefield of unresolved issues, with partners skirting around the perimeters to avoid setting off explosions.

> Evelyn: Walter and I have a good life. He has his work and I have my charity interests. In the beginning we were very much in love, but he wanted to live and work in the country. I grew up in a small country town and there was no way I was going back.
>
> I don't think Walter could stand the arguments, so he just gave in. We couldn't find a middle ground so we just drifted apart. We go away for a holiday once a year, but apart from that we don't spend much time together. We've slept in separate beds for years. Our relationship isn't too bad. At least we don't fight, like some couples do.

Men are more likely to withdraw from conflict and difficult discussions than women. Despite the 'hysterical female' label slapped onto women, research has shown that men tolerate stress less well than women, become more emotionally aroused during conflict and have more difficulty controlling their feelings. When faced with an unpleasant overload of emotions, men will often withdraw and avoid conflict. Their female partners in turn become more demanding, emotional and critical in an effort to get them to engage and sort matters out. It's not just the romantic relationship that suffers. Studies have found that women whose husbands withdraw and avoid conflicted discussion show a decrease in immune function after several years.

3. **Truce Makers**. Others agree to disagree. They don't actively resolve issues but call a truce on most areas of conflict. These couples avoid fighting and can achieve a high level of companionate love, living together like two best friends or brother and sister. However, such companionate love is usually associated with a low level of sexual passion.

Prue: Gareth is arrogant, racist and thinks nothing of being rude to people. He especially treats my close friends with disdain. I have asked him to be more gracious, but he ignores me. Gareth wants me to be more organised and run the house like an army barracks. I don't mind a bit of chaos, but it puts him off completely. For many years now we have been at a stalemate. I don't bring up his appalling manners and he doesn't bring up my style of housekeeping. But we both niggle underneath. We're good friends, but I must say it's more like living with my brother than a lover.

Conflict confronters

There are two types of conflict confronters.

1. **Fighters.** Some partners choose to slog it out, day in, day out, bickering and sniping over every issue that raises its thorny head. Sexual chemistry is rapidly eaten away by harsh words and angry, sarcastic voices.

   Shirley: Bruce is the most pig-headed man you could ever meet. And with me he's met his match. We fight a lot and most of it's old ground — the same thing over and over again. He's very cruel if he wants to be, but I just walk away and ignore him. It's funny — we fight a lot, but we never resolve anything.

2. **Resolvers.** These couples exercise their problem-solving skills, working together to negotiate solutions and compromises. They derive a huge benefit from their hard work. They return again and again to the 'in love' phase of the relationship, deepening their connection and affection with every problem solved. These relationships enjoy a high level of passion and sexual chemistry.

   Winona: It's a second marriage for both Tom and myself. We agreed early on that we wouldn't let any issues 'slip by the keeper'. There's an old saying — 'Don't let the sun go down on a disagreement' — that's our motto. We stay calm, talk quietly and listen to each other until we find a way to work things out. It's not always easy, especially with a blended family like ours, but the rewards are great. We've been married for five years now and we just can't get enough of each other.

These different styles of dealing with conflict are set out in the diagram below.

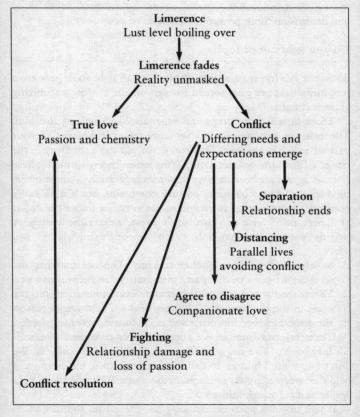

Notice that conflict resolution feeds back into the 'true love' phase with its ongoing passion and chemistry. Every other method of dealing with conflict takes a couple away from their passionate feelings.

UNRESOLVED CONFLICT — THE PASSION KILLER

When conflicts remain unresolved, love and chemistry get squashed by the growing burden of resentment and disappointment in the relationship. Unresolved marital conflict leads to anger and depression, both powerful inhibitors of desire.

Do you fight fair or foul?

All is *not* fair in love and war. If you wish to fight foul, here are a few hints that are guaranteed to turn up the thermostat during your next fight.

Those little words *always* and *never* are like a red rag to a bull. The moment you use one in a sentence, you can be assured your partner will take the bait. Try 'You *never* put the milk away in the fridge'; 'You *always* run late'; 'You *never* listen to me.' These phrases aggravate because they are an exaggeration — most of the time he or she may be guilty of your complaint, but not on *every* occasion. Your partner is certain to get very hot under the collar and become defensive. Just for interest, next time you have 'words' with your other half, catch yourself using *always* and *never*.

Another dirty trick is 'kitchen sinking'. This occurs when the disagreement begins over a particular matter but before long you both start throwing every misdemeanour ever committed into the fray (including the proverbial kitchen sink). The original reason for the dispute is long forgotten and is, of course, never resolved.

Character assassination is a popular family favourite. 'You selfish lazy slob', 'You nagging fat witch' — the list is endless. We don't allow our children to call each other names, but we have a field day when it comes to domestic disputes. We exaggerate, generalise and say hurtful things.

If you or your partner regularly use these foul fighting techniques, you will be richly rewarded with years of misery and bickering.

Can fights be good?

Many people claim that arguments are healthy for a relationship, that they enable us to let off steam and clear the air. Fighting is simply an excuse to vent anger towards our partner and it is destructive. There is a huge difference between maturely expressing your feelings and acting them out like a child. Although we might kiss and make up later, we can't take back all the hurtful things said or repair the damage done. Sharing feelings is best done by talking and listening. Let's face it, no-one really listens during an argument — we are too busy thinking of the next thing to say!

Cuddles after conflict?

What about those couples who say they enjoy their most passionate lovemaking after a violent argument? Anger is a stimulant and can be arousing, but so can watching an exciting game of tennis or even a horror movie on TV. This sort of arousal has nothing to do with mutual attraction and appeal.

When a couple ends up making love during or after a disagreement, nothing is lost as long as the experience renews their efforts to resolve the original conflict. However, sex is a powerful way to prevent discussion of difficult issues, and love play can be used to silence a complaining partner. The one who initiates lovemaking usually forgets the angry incident, but the other remembers and stores the resentment in their 'Hurt Museum' until the next argument.

While it is normal for couples to disagree and get angry, it is *not* normal or helpful for couples to fight. Fighting is a very ineffective way of resolving conflict. Each cycle of fighting leaves the relationship weaker than before and there is always enough heat in the embers of yesterday's argument to start tomorrow's.

Be your own sex therapist

Controlling fighting behaviour:
Avoid the words 'always' and 'never' and stick to the issue — no 'kitchen sinking' or name calling.

Never walk out without explanation — it is aggressive and says, 'You're not worth talking to.'

If things are getting out of hand, say: 'I'm getting angry — let's stop now and discuss this in two hours' time when we've cooled down.'

If you cannot resolve problems with your partner, seek counselling, preferably together.

Violence is a signal that outside help is needed immediately.

CONFLICT RESOLUTION — NEGOTIATION SKILLS

The difference between *conflict* and *negotiation* is that in conflict two parties take an opposing stance and come at each other head on, both determined to get their own way. One person 'wins', while the other is either manipulated or alienated and 'loses'.

In negotiation, both partners take responsibility for the problem and its solution. They join forces to look for ways to resolve the issue that are agreeable to both of them. They attack the problem, not each other.

In conflict, one person maintains that they are right and the other is wrong, and vice versa. In negotiation, both parties are seen to have legitimate, reasonable ideas and needs that are simply in opposition to each other. Neither is right or wrong. Negotiation stops couples taking an adversarial stance by focusing on the issues, not on defending positions.

Conflict involves the venting of feelings, often in an out-of-control and unhelpful way. Negotiation keeps your feelings separate from the situation, while still giving you a chance to acknowledge them.

Conflict is uncomfortable and therefore there is pressure to deal with it urgently before it polarises and damages the relationship. This urgency leads to hasty and often inappropriate decisions. Negotiation is something that can take days, weeks or even months because it is a process where you are both on the same side dealing with a problem, not fighting against each other.

Negotiation is aimed at finding a number of solutions that will benefit both parties, then working together to decide which one to implement. In negotiation you don't have to find the 'perfect' solution first time — you can always come back and fine-tune your solution through negotiation.

Negotiation theory accepts that conflicts are an inevitable part of relationships, not a deficiency or a failing, but an opportunity to grow and change. Negotiation is based on seeing things from your partner's point of view, and vice versa. The goal of negotiation is a mutually agreeable outcome — not of getting your own way, winning, punishing or getting revenge on your partner.

Negotiation skills

The goal of negotiation is to find a fair, mutually agreeable solution. McKay, Fanning and Paleg in their book *Couple Skills* describe these steps: preparation, discussion, suggestions/counter-suggestions and agreement.

Preparation
Sit down with a pen and paper and follow this outline. Putting your thoughts down on paper will help to make the process clearer and more structured.

Describe

The situation: What I think
Simply state the facts as you see them, without describing your feelings or making any judgments.

My feelings: What I feel
This is where you can ventilate how you feel about the situation. Make a list of words that describe how you feel. Writing down the situation and your feelings independently keeps the feelings separate from the facts as you see them. It is the out-of-control feelings that escalate conflict.

Our interests and needs: What we want and need
This involves making three columns.

- In the first column, write down what *you* ideally want — the interests, actions and outcomes that you assume your partner may not readily agree to.
- In the second column, make a list of what you think your partner wants that opposes your interests.
- In the third column, list the interests that you share — things that you and your partner both agree on and want.

Tentative solutions: Perhaps we could ...
This also has three parts.
1. *My ideal solution*: What you would want to happen if things could go completely your way.
2. *What I could live with*: Solutions you could tolerate.
3. *Unacceptable solutions*: Outcomes that, no matter what, you could not tolerate.

Let's try an example: Kip and Netty have been married for three years. Early in their relationship they had an enthusiastic and energetic sex life with plenty of variety and frequency. Since their first child was born, Netty has been tired and less interested in sex. Not only is she less interested in sex, but she is not keen to do anything other than basic foreplay and missionary position intercourse. Kip misses the variety and enthusiasm she once showed and is feeling sexually frustrated. He wants sex to happen at least twice a week and to once again enjoy activities such as mutual oral sex.

This is how Kip would go about negotiating his needs with Netty. The first step is preparation.

The situation:
Netty and I are having sex about once a month. She only enjoys very basic sex. I would like to have more frequent sex. I would like to have mutual oral sex with her again, like we used to.

My feelings:
Sexual frustration
Anxiety that it's never going to change
Rejection when Netty says 'No'

Worry that I might be attracted to someone else
Fear that I don't please her
Longing for the sort of sex we used to have
Resentment at Netty for refusing to have sex
Fear that she doesn't really care for me.

Our interests and needs:

My interests	My partner's interests	Our shared interests
Have more sex	To get more sleep	To find a solution
Have more regular sex	To feel relaxed	To prevent bad feelings between us
Have more varied sex	To take a break from the baby	
Give oral sex	To have more 'me' time	To both enjoy sex when it happens
Receive oral sex	To conserve energy and not use it up through energetic late-night sex.	To get our sexual needs met
Feel good about myself as a man		For sex not to be a hassle
Feel that Netty cares for me		To feel close and secure
Feel more secure in the relationship		To feel OK about our relationship.
Show Netty how much I fancy her.		

Tentative solutions
Kip's tentative solutions:

1. *My ideal solution:* Have sex that is raunchy, hot and varied, including occasional mutual oral sex twice a week or more.

2. *What I could live with:* Sexual contact once or twice a week with occasional mutual oral sex.

3. *Unacceptable solution:* The way it is now.

Netty was also completing her side of the process.

Netty's tentative solutions:

1. *My ideal solution:* Have sex when I feel in the mood.

2. *What I could live with:* Sexual contact once a week with occasional mutual oral sex, say once a month when I feel like it.

3. *Unacceptable:* Have sex that is raunchy, hot and varied, including mutual oral sex twice a week or more.

Discussion, suggestions/counter-suggestions and agreement
Once Netty and Kip have completed their preparation, they are ready for discussion of the issue, which basically involves learning to see the problem from each other's point of view by listening. After discussion they can make suggestions and counter-suggestions to each other about what they can do.

Some of the strategies for making compromises are:
- *Taking turns* — You have it your way for a while, then I'll have it mine and then we swap.
- *Tit for tat* — If you do this, I'll do that. This strategy is widely known as *behaviour exchange*, where people give mutually in order to get.
- *Part of what you want and part of what I want* — A compromise.
- *Trial period* — Let's try this compromise for a month and if it doesn't work out we'll negotiate again.

In Netty and Kip's case they first used *tit for tat*. She wanted to feel more relaxed and less tired, so Kip offered to take the baby off her hands completely for a couple of hours each week so she could have a little 'me' time. She suggested that he get up to the baby in the morning and change him and give him his bottle, and she would consider making love when he got back into bed to avoid the demands of late-night sex.

They also used part of *what you want* and *part of what I want*. Netty agreed to participate more enthusiastically in sex when it was happening, with occasional oral sex but only if she felt like it.

They agreed to make love twice a week, but it didn't always have to be intercourse — as long as Kip had an orgasm when he wanted to, it didn't really matter what they did. This added a little more variety to their lovemaking and took the pressure off Netty, who no longer had to get aroused enough every time they had sexual contact to enjoy intercourse.

Netty also gave Kip permission to masturbate if he felt horny. Kip had been doing this secretly and felt very ashamed, but now that it was brought out into the open they both felt much better.

This is a summary of what Kip and Netty negotiated:

- Sex about twice a week that doesn't necessarily involve intercourse in which Netty can participate up to the level of her own comfort.
- Permission for Kip to masturbate any time he needed to.
- Oral sex when Netty was in the mood.
- Kip was to take the baby for two hours a week to give Netty free time. He was also to take care of the baby in the morning. Netty was to consider early morning sexual activity.

> Netty: I have to admit that when I saw what Kip wanted and what I wanted, I never thought we could work out a compromise. But we did. Negotiation does work. If we'd tried any other way to solve our dilemma, I think we would have ended up fighting about it. We feel really excited at what we have achieved.

Negotiation works

The aim of negotiation is to find a solution that gives you both the maximum of what you do want and the minimum of what you don't want. These negotiation skills can be learnt either through reading books or through couple counselling, or both. In *Couple Skills* this process is set out in full and gives practical ideas about how to deal with hostility, stalemates and dirty tricks (see Resources).

Failure to confront problems

> There is no way to peace. Peace is the way.
>
> A. J. MUSTE
> AMERICAN PACIFIST

leads to distance in the relationship — *to get closer to each other, confront your problems*. Confronting doesn't mean fighting — it means hearing each other out, understanding each other and negotiating a compromise.

Key Points ·❦·

The more conflict you have in your relationship, the less desire you are likely to experience. The only effective way to deal with conflict is to learn to negotiate with your partner.

Negotiation works because it doesn't set partners up as adversaries. It brings partners together on the same side and pits them against the problem, rather than against each other.

Fighting doesn't resolve conflicts and both parties lose. A more effective solution is to confront problems and reach compromises where both parties can be winners.

15

Creating Passion — Friends and Lovers

T he ability to be friends as well as lovers is a much more effective recipe for good loving and great sex than trying every position in the *Kama Sutra*. Passion soon dies unless there is energy injected into the relationship through play, pleasurable shared experiences, hugs and kisses, and romance.

FUN AND COMPANIONSHIP — BEST FRIENDS AND LOVERS

We have learned that intimacy is a major component of a fulfilling, committed, sexually vibrant relationship. There are different sorts of intimacy.
* *Emotional intimacy* — the sharing of feelings.
* *Intellectual intimacy* — the sharing of thoughts and ideas.
* *Physical intimacy* — affection and physical closeness.
* *Spiritual intimacy* — the sharing of ideals, beliefs and values.
* *Sexual intimacy* — the sexual sharing of two bodies.

The final one is *recreational intimacy*, which is a sharing of enjoyable activities together. Research recently undertaken in Australia has shown that *couples who share a high level of recreational intimacy have the most desire*.

Colin: Trina and I work together, live together, sleep together. You couldn't get much more togetherness than that. If spending time together is so important, why isn't our sex life better?

Being together is not the same as enjoying yourself together. If you spend all day, every day with your partner but you bicker and squabble or ignore each other, it won't help your relationship — quite the opposite. Recreational intimacy refers to the sharing of a range of enjoyable activities together with a view to deepening your love connection.

Bad habits

Paul Reisner, actor and author of *Couplehood*, gives a perfect example of how, as relationships mature, unhelpful habits take the romance out of outings. During courtship if you and your loved one are going to see a movie, you do everything together. You walk to the cinema together, stand in the queue together, buy your tickets together and go into the movie together.

A few years down the track, going to the movies becomes like a military manoeuvre. I know this because my husband and I got into the habit of going to the movies in this regimented way until I read Reisner's book and was reminded of what a relaxed, fun date should be like.

It went like this: My husband dropped me off at the cinema and he drove off to find a parking place. Meanwhile I stood in the queue and got the tickets. Next he arrived at the cinema and bought the goodies to eat and drink at the candy counter. We met breathlessly on the stairs and marched into the movie. All over in a matter of minutes with inflexible precision. It was more like an invasion than a date.

Now that we have adopted our former laidback courtship approach to going to the movies, our nights out are infinitely more pleasurable. We try to have dinner before or go out for a coffee afterwards so that we can have time to talk.

Whatever makes YOU happy, darling

During courtship we are much more experimental and more agreeable to doing something just because our partner wants to do it. As a result, we engage in a wider range of activities outside our normal routine.

> Eric: I love going to the football and cricket, and in the beginning Geraldine would come to all the games with me, paying attention and getting excited about the play. I had a great time. These days she won't come to a game. It's too hot or too cold. It's too far or too late. It takes too long or it's too crowded. All those things didn't bother her in the beginning. I'd rather go with her than with a mate. Do you think I'm being unreasonable?

It isn't unreasonable to expect your partner to 'stretch' for you, to sometimes do things they don't get a real kick out of just because you want to do them, *as long as you return the favour.* When we do something together, our pleasure comes from sharing the experience, from being with our partner, not necessarily from the experience or activity itself.

Be your own sex therapist

When was the last time you went out on a date with your partner, just the two of you?

When did you last spend a whole day alone with your mate?

When did you last do something that your partner enjoys but you don't particularly like, but you went willingly for his or her sake?

When did your partner last do the same for you?

Do you mostly do the same things and go to the same places when you go out together?

When was the last time you arranged a surprise for your partner? Or vice versa?

When was the last time you did something spontaneous together? A walk? A movie? Dinner out? A cuddle on the couch with the TV turned off?

Over the next two weeks, arrange to join your partner in an activity or interest that holds particular appeal for him or her but doesn't really interest you. Ask them to return the favour. Make this stretching for each other a habit rather than an exception.

Having fun — the child within

Inside each of us there is a little kid longing to get out. This 'child' part of you is the source of your spontaneity and creativity, your imagination and humour, your desire for affection and intimacy. Your 'inner child' is enthusiastic and energetic and knows how to have fun. Your inner child enjoys romance as well as sensual and sexual pleasures.

One of the reasons that courtship is so much fun is that we let our inner children have free rein during limerence. They run along the beach together, laugh out loud, tease gently, make jokes, look at the stars. They love to kiss and cuddle and are just as keen for fun in the bedroom as fun outside. Pillow fights, tickling, nicknames, chasings and surprises are all the work (or play) of our inner children.

As courtship wanes and the partnership begins in earnest, the adult part of the relationship can take over. As the years pass, our inner children can be left behind, forgotten. This is a great loss because your inner child is a never-ending source of fun, excitement and passion and can bring so much of value to your love life. To sustain a satisfying sex life, it is vital to nurture and stimulate your inner children. Shut down the relationship between your inner children and you are shutting out sexual fulfilment.

Surprises

Children love giving and receiving surprises. Let your inner child be your guide and surprise your partner from time to time with something that really means a lot to them. Surprise fuels passion, while habit smothers it. You can be the most considerate partner who ever breathed, but if you bring home flowers every Friday, or arrange dinner out every second Saturday night at the same place, the routine soon robs the experience of excitement.

Recently my husband gave me a wonderful surprise. Writing a book is a lonely task, and he popped home in the middle of the day with sandwiches and took me for a brief picnic on the fore-shores of beautiful Sydney Harbour. It was a wonderful surprise and shows how much he thinks about me and cares for me. My little girl inside had a wonderful time.

Be your own sex therapist

Write down 10 things you used to enjoy during courtship. How many of them do you still do?

What do you do to have fun together these days? Do your 'inner children' have a relationship? Did they ever? How has this part of the relationship changed over the years?

Make a list of five surprises your partner would enjoy. (Try to avoid anything that is extravagant or expensive. The best gifts are your time and your consideration.) Over the next five weeks, choose one each week and carry it out. It would be wonderful if your partner could do the same. Don't forget to thank each other.

After five weeks repeat the exercise with another five surprises. Ask your inner child for inspiration. Keep repeating the exercise.

Coupling activities

To create more recreational intimacy in your relationship, you need to discover coupling activities that you can enjoy together. A good starting point might be the activities you used to enjoy during courtship, but you need to be more adventurous than that. Remember how quickly humans get used to any particular stimulus — we need variety, variety, variety.

Be your own sex therapist

Following is a list of activities that you and your partner might or might not enjoy. Mark beside each activity how much you would enjoy sharing it with your partner. Have your partner do the same and compare lists. Add some favourites of your own. Make a separate list of activities that you both rated highly at 3 or 4 and put it up on your fridge so it doesn't escape your notice. Try to work your way through your list of favourite shared activities one by one. Keep adding to the list.

0 = no interest
1 = little interest
2 = some interest

3 = much interest
4 = highest interest

- A trip to the country
- Rock climbing or abseiling
- Boating (motor, sail, canoe)
- Having lunch with mutual friends
- Taking a nap
- Doing craft work — pottery, leather, beads, weaving
- Sitting in the sun
- Having friends over
- Enjoying beautiful scenery
- Sitting quietly
- Walking in the rain together
- Reading books together
- Taking a nap together
- Doing odd jobs around the house
- Relaxing together

- Window shopping
- Playing ball games — catch, frisbee
- Shopping
- Talking about politics
- Visiting departed loved ones at the cemetery or memorial gardens
- Playing with pets
- Going to the movies
- Getting dressed up and going out to somewhere special
- Reading the Bible, sacred or spiritual works
- Restoring furniture
- Playing sport, e.g. golf, tennis, skiing, ping pong
- Eating good food together
- Going to a party or social gathering

- Being with friends
- Playing games — chess, Scrabble, cards, crosswords, puzzles, etc.
- Riding bikes or motorcycles
- Going to a gym or sauna
- Being together at a family event
- Swimming
- Doing the housework
- Walking on the beach
- Entering competitions
- Going to the theatre
- Volunteer work
- Church and religious activities
- Watching TV
- Taking a bath or shower together
- Giving gifts
- Putting together a collection — art, shells, stamps
- Cooking together
- Listening to jazz
- Learning to do something new
- Doing heavy outdoor work — chopping wood, heavy gardening, farm work
- Jogging
- Bird watching
- Sleeping in
- Making a fire and sitting in front of it
- Talking about anything and everything
- Doing things with your children
- Staying up late
- Looking at the stars
- Going to a rock concert or musical event
- Redecorating the house
- Camping
- Going for a drive
- Learning a foreign language
- Going to a zoo, fair or amusement park
- Going away for the weekend
- Going out to breakfast, lunch or dinner
- Listening to music
- Reading comics, newspapers, magazines together
- Telling stories
- Going on holidays
- Art work — painting, drawing, sculpture
- Going to sports events — horse races, football, cricket
- Going to a pub or hotel for a drink
- Going to a lecture, talk or seminar
- Singing together
- Going to the park
- Bushwalking and exploring
- Playing music together
- Gardening
- Dancing
- Talking about philosophy or religion

- Repairing things
- Giving and receiving massages
- Outdoor events — picnics, barbecues
- Walking the dog
- Talking about your children and grandchildren
- Going to a museum or exhibition

- Fishing
- Watching a late night movie
- Being with parents
- Talking about old times
- Watching a video
- Getting up early in the morning together
- Praying together
- Meditating or doing yoga.

Be adventurous

It is very important to keep adding new activities to your repertoire and to have a go at things outside your comfort zone. If you are a home body, why not try something active and outdoorsy? If you are sporty, why not go for something intellectual such as attending a public speaking course together?

Being adventurous and getting out of your comfort zone together actually heightens your sense of attraction to each other. A famous experiment in Vancouver, Canada, asked male volunteers to meet female researchers and rate their attractiveness. This appraisal was repeated after the men had traversed the Capilano suspension bridge, which sways at an alarming 90 metres above a rocky gorge. Not only did the men rate the same researchers as being significantly more attractive after crossing the bridge, but some men even asked for their telephone numbers! Getting the adrenaline flowing and increasing emotional arousal heightens feelings of attraction. So perhaps you should take that whitewater rafting trip together after all!

> Pleasure is very seldom found where it is sought;
> our brightest blazes of gladness are commonly kindled by unexpected sparks.
> SAMUEL JOHNSON

One of my maxims is that the amount of sex you have is directly proportional to the amount of time you spend enjoying yourselves together. Put simply, if you don't have much fun, you won't have much sex.

AFFECTION

There is a direct link between sexual desire and affection. Oxytocin, the 'cuddle chemical', makes humans more sexually responsive to each other. Regular loving touch and non-demand affection (affection that doesn't necessarily lead to sex) — kissing, hugging, holding and touching — enhances sex drive by increasing levels of oxytocin in the bloodstream.

Different individuals have differing needs for touch. This can lead to conflict and un-happiness.

> It was not my lips you kissed but my soul.
> JUDY GARLAND

> **Patty:** When I was married the first time I longed for affection from my husband. At night I would lie in bed beside him and my body would ache. The only touch he enjoyed was during sex. After a while my sex drive, which was quite high in the beginning, just shrivelled up. I felt like something inside me had died.

Learning to enjoy touch

The pleasures of touch are learnt, starting from birth. If you are touched frequently and lovingly and have opportunities to touch others appropriately, you will learn to enjoy touch and stay connected with your needs for touch. If you experience neglect, unpleasant touch or abuse, you can easily learn to avoid or dislike intimate touching and shut down your need to touch and be touched.

Tiny babies first learn about *nurturing* touch as we pick them up, comfort them and feed them. The next lesson is *playful* touch. We blow raspberries on babies' tummies and tickle them gently. We play pat-a-cake and round-and-round the garden with older children. While they are learning about nurturing and playful touch, children are also learning about *sensual* touch. The pleasures of lying in the sun or in front of a heater, rolling in the grass, smelling flowers, looking at lovely picture books, and being held and loved are all sensual lessons. Finally, lessons about *sexual* touch are also being mastered. Exploration of the genitals often

starts during the first year, and lessons about sexual touching continue throughout life. Inappropriate touch of any sort will colour
an individual's enjoyment of intimate contact.

> **Martha:** When I was about 12, a friend of my grand-
> mother's, Uncle Bernard, molested me. He pulled me onto
> his lap and started to rub my breasts. It took place right in
> front of my grandmother and nothing was said. I knew it
> was wrong and my Granny didn't even seem to notice.
> Later he gave me a present and I took it, but I felt guilty
> about accepting it. Now I can't stand having my breasts
> touched by my fiancé.

Affection avoiders

There are many reasons why people shy away from physical contact and affection. When a couple with desire discrepancy is
caught in the pursuer/distancer cycle the distancer may long for
closeness but be afraid that if they allow affection it will be seen as
a readiness for sex. Affection avoiders may be people who never
learnt to enjoy close physical contact within their families. Men
especially have not been socialised to stay in tune with their need
for touching. They may be people like Martha who have been
traumatised through touch. Or, like Troy, they may be selective
about the sort of contact they enjoy.

> **Troy:** Clarissa is a very 'snuggly' person who wants to
> cuddle and kiss a lot of the time. The only physical contact I
> like is rough and tumble play. I like to grab her and squeeze
> her, wrestle her, tickle her, play tag and muck around gener-
> ally. She doesn't really enjoy my rougher antics and prefers
> cuddles, so I'm trying to oblige. However, she is also begin-
> ning to enjoy mucking around a bit more, as long as I'm not
> too enthusiastic.

The only way to communicate to your partner what sort of touch
you like is to talk about how you like to be approached, touched
and held. Once again, there is no place for mind-reading. When

making a suggestion to your partner about what you like, always start with a positive.

> **Virginia:** 'I really like the way you hold me. Your arms feel so strong. When you kiss me, only put a little bit of tongue in my mouth. I'll show you what I mean ...'
>
> **Sergei:** 'I love the way your body feels against mine. I love it when you touch me. When you rub my penis, could you do it gently like this? Give me your hand and I'll show you ...'

Or if there is something you don't like and you want your partner to stop or change that behaviour, use the 'instead of' technique. Once again, start with a positive:

> **Ed:** I want you to enjoy sex with me as much as I do with you, but it seems to hurt you. Instead of me pushing my penis in, perhaps you could guide it. It might not hurt that way.
>
> **Roberta:** I really like making love with you. Instead of lying with all your weight on me, could you take some weight on your elbows during intercourse?

Gentle affirming feedback like this is much easier to hear than 'If I've told you once I've told you a thousand times, don't touch me there! Are you deaf?'

Affection and desire discrepancy

When couples have been struggling with DD for a long time, they often lose touch with each other, literally. To overcome DD, affectionate touching needs to be reinstated slowly and safely, in a way that detaches it from sex.

Often in the early stages of the DD treatment program I put a ban on intercourse for a while (don't faint — most couples are having very infrequent sex anyway) and encourage the couple to start to touch and cuddle again. Separating affection from the pressure of sex reduces the fear of the situation going beyond either partner's control. In many cases the reintroduction of non-demand affection has triggered sexual desire in a lower drive partner for the first time in many years.

> **Suzy:** Howard was stunned when the therapist put a ban on sex. He was there to get *more* sex — instead, he ended up with none at all! We were instructed to start to hug and kiss again, and to hold each other in bed at night. No sex, of course! It was very strange at first, like starting all over again, but much more uncomfortable. With time, our touching became more pleasurable. One night I was lying in Howard's arms and I felt desire. I think it was the knowledge that I could relax with Howard again and put all the sex stuff aside for a moment that made the difference. It's getting better all the time, and although Howard is impatient, we both recognise that we need to take things slowly.

Simply by holding each other for five minutes every day, your relationship and closeness will begin to improve. We will be looking at re-establishing touch in damaged and distant relationships in the final section of the book.

ROMANCE

Most people's idea of romance includes the ever-popular chocolates, flowers, gifts, balloons, soft toys, love songs and candlelit dinners for two. Our culture recognises these 'love tokens' as romantic symbols. (In other cultures a billy goat or a sack of grain might well be considered equally seductive.) When we are courting, we employ these romantic tokens and gestures to signify that we are interested in a partner.

However, such tokens are fairly impersonal — you could give flowers or chocolates to a workmate, a teacher, even an enemy if you wished. When you have been living together for some years, these tokens and gestures of early courtship can become meaningless. They are nice, but they are not necessarily chosen out of a deep knowledge of our loved one's personal preferences.

Lois: Most men think that long-stemmed red roses are the ultimate romantic gift — not for me. I have told my husband how much I love the paler hued roses — apricot, white or yellow — but he seems to be stuck in a mind-set that says, 'Red roses are romantic.' Each time he brings me red roses, it makes me quite irritable, which is no doubt the opposite of what he intended.

The Language of love

Romance means finding out what says 'I love you' to your partner and doing it. We each have specific ideas about what romance is. I call this our *language of love*. We have a natural tendency to show love the way we want love to be shown to us. Take a typical couple. She thinks that gifts, cards and little surprises are meaningful. His language of love is affection and time spent just lazing around together. She gives him cards and gifts (because that's what she likes), and he's always kissing her and hanging around (for the same reason). Both partners are trying to express their love, but the message just doesn't get across because they are using the wrong language. It's like expressing your love in Greek when your partner only speaks Italian.

We must learn what *our partner* considers an expression of love; by doing that, we say 'I love you' and inject romance in our relationship.

Bonnie: My husband is the most romantic man I've ever met. He's romantic in the traditional way with flowers and cards, but he shows his love for me in many other ways. For example, the other day I mentioned that I was running out of time to get the children's school shoes. While I was at work he took both the boys to the shops and bought them their school shoes — without being asked. Now that meant so much to me.

Be your own sex therapist

You need to let your partner know what says 'I love you' for you and find out what is romantic for him or her. Following is a list of traditionally romantic gestures. Rate which ones have more meaning for you. Ask your partner to do the same and compare lists.

0 = no interest
1 = little interest
2 = some interest

3 = much interest
4 = highest interest

I feel loved and cared about when you ...

- Give me chocolates
- Shower or bath with me
- Give me flowers
- Walk with me
- Give me a surprise gift
- Give me a kiss
- Call me from work for a chat
- Make me a cup of tea or coffee
- Tell me about your day
- Ask me about my day
- Massage my back
- Say 'I love you'
- Hold my hand
- Send me a card
- Call me pet names
- Whisper to me
- Initiate lovemaking

- Prepare a meal for me
- Buy champagne or wine
- Pay me compliments
- Praise me in front of others
- Open the car door for me
- Arrange a night out
- Arrange a weekend away
- Hug me
- Make my birthday special
- Remember our anniversary
- Make our anniversary special
- Celebrate Valentine's Day
- Write me a poem
- Gaze into my eyes
- Give me a scalp or foot massage.

Add to this list any activity that you used to enjoy during courtship, plus any activity that makes you feel loved from the coupling list given previously to increase recreational intimacy.

Surprise, surprise

Ongoing romance requires *variety and novelty*. The same old tech-niques will soon lose their effect. Romance has an element of *playfulness and surprise*. Let your inner children out for a run and they will come up with fresh ideas. *Romance doesn't have to involve money*. In fact, the best gifts are the ones where we give of ourselves.

For example, my husband was in dire need of an area to do some work at home. When he was at work one day I cleared a space for him, set up a table, a lamp, family photos, phone, filing cabinet, chair, bookshelf, pens and paper. When he came home, his 'office' was set up and he was thrilled.

> Too much of a good thing can be wonderful.
> MAE WEST

Birthdays, anniversaries and special occasions

Special occasions like birthdays, anniversaries, Valentine's Day, Christmas, Mother's Day, Father's Day, religious days and the like are often a sore point for couples. Each partner has an idea about how these days should be celebrated. This programming usually comes from how their families celebrated special days as they grew up. Too often we expect our partner to guess what our pref-erences are, and when they trip up, we feel entitled to display our disappointment and anger.

Greg: In my family we always made a big fuss of birthdays. There were phone calls in the morning, cards in the post, presents and always a special family dinner at night with the person's favourite food. We always had a cake with candles and sang 'Happy Birthday' even for the adults.
Carmel: Greg was so upset the first time his birthday came around with me. I thought I did well turning up at Greg's work that evening with a card. He had been stewing all day waiting for my call or some other special surprise. Mind you, these days we make a huge fuss of his birthday, but I still like mine to be fairly low key and he respects that.

Be your own sex therapist

List all the special days in the year and describe how you would like to celebrate them. Have your partner do the same. Swap lists and discuss.

Keep in mind that romance is not just a two or three-day a year affair. It must be a daily effort. This means waking up every morning and asking yourself, 'What can I do for my beloved today?'

Encouraging an unromantic mate

There is much that can be done to encourage an unromantic mate.

- Make sure your partner knows what you want. Although you may believe romance should be spontaneous, he or she can't know what you want unless you spell it out.
- Focus on what you are getting rather than what you are missing. Make a big fuss over any little flicker of romance — cup of tea, a kiss. Positive reinforcement like this tends to increase wanted behaviour.
- Don't nag or criticise your partner's lack of romance or they may withhold even more.
- Sometimes in order to get, you must give. Find out what says 'I love you' to your partner and get in the habit of doing it.
- Learn more about creating lifelong romance by reading Dr Love's easy-to-follow and practical book *Hot Monogamy* (see Resources).

LONG-TERM PASSION

Maintaining passion takes hard work. You need to heal your relationship and build strong lines of communication, intimacy and trust. Areas of conflict and disagreement need to be resolved as they present. Couples need to feed their relationship with time spent together in coupling activities, romance, affection and fun.

> You must not force sex to do the work of love or love to do the work of sex.
> MARY MCCARTHY

Loss of desire is your early warning system that there is something amiss in your relationship. When you neglect your relationship and ignore your partner's needs, passion will die.

There is no quick fix for desire discrepancy. It takes time and it takes work. If you and your partner aren't prepared to do what it takes to heal your relationship and maintain love, you can expect to kiss sexual desire goodbye sometime in the near future, if it hasn't already flown out the window.

Hopefully these last five chapters will have guided you to areas of your relationship that need your joint time and attention. The greatest benefit will come to you when you deal with those areas that seem too hard, too painful or just too time consuming to deal with. If you can't manage it on your own, seek professional counselling. Out of this healing will come your chance for good loving and, ultimately, great sex.

Key Points ❦

Couples with high levels of recreational intimacy, who have fun and enjoy activities together, have higher levels of interest in sex.

Affection that doesn't necessarily lead to sex will enhance sexual desire through hormonal pathways. If you want more sex, share more hugs, kisses and cuddles with your partner — every day.

Achieving Sexual Compatibility

16

Getting Your
Sex Life Back on Track

I n this final part of the book we will look specifically at how
couples can work together to overcome the challenge of
desire discrepancy. This section outlines a wide range of
strategies which have helped many couples to achieve sexual compatibility, regardless of their individual levels of sexual desire.

Sexual compatibility does not rely on a perfectly matched set of
sex drives. Expecting your sexual desire to peak and dip in concert
with your partner's is a ridiculous notion. Sexual compatibility is
defined as sharing a similar understanding of sex drive, similar
expectations of sex drive, similar attitudes to what constitutes a
satisfactory sex life and, most importantly, a positive attitude
towards each other.

If you have been caught up in the DD dilemma for some time,
your attitude towards each other is probably less than rosy. The
pursuer/distancer cycle polarises partners, alienating them from
one another and disrupting their mutual goodwill. This is not a
sound basis on which to build a satisfactory sex life. The previous
section looked at healing your love relationship and creating more
intimacy, trust, romance and passion in your lives. Now we will
look at neutralising the P/D cycle and getting your sexual relationship back on track.

NEUTRALISING THE PURSUER/DISTANCER CYCLE

The P/D cycle doesn't solve desire discrepancy. In fact, it usually makes the situation worse. Before there can be any improvement in your sexual relationship, this vicious cycle must be interrupted.

Partner empathy — walk a mile in my shoes

The first step towards rejoining each other in a hassle-free sexual relationship is called *partner empathy*. When you have empathy, you see things from your mate's point of view. You walk a mile in their shoes. Empathy emerges when you accept that *both* of you are in pain, you are *both* struggling and *both* are missing out. Empathy means that you have compassion for your partner's pain and they have compassion for yours. It puts you on the same team, no longer fighting against each other, but working together to solve the problem.

> **James:** Up until now I felt I was the one who was hard done by, while Felicia was getting it all her way. We were only having sex every couple of months and I thought that suited her just fine. It wasn't until I understood how miserable and guilty she was feeling that I could feel any sympathy for her. I realise now that she has been just as unhappy as I have and just as helpless.
>
> **Felicia:** James has been a complete bastard about the sex stuff. I couldn't see past my anger to realise that he was feeling totally shut out and unloved. I see we have both been stuck on a merry-go-round and we couldn't get off. I feel a lot warmer towards him now that I know what the P/D cycle has been doing to both of us.

Personal responsibility — no more blaming

This step involves acknowledging how *your* behaviour has fed into the P/D cycle and affected:

- your partner

- your partner's sex drive
- your partner's behaviour and feelings, and vice versa.

This step means taking responsibility for *your* actions and the consequences of those actions. It means *no more blaming*. Your partner did not create this unhappiness all on their own. This is a very positive step. If you have been responsible for making things worse, you can also be responsible for making things better.

> Ned: For years I thought Vera was the problem. I needed sex and she wouldn't give it to me. I now see that it must have been very hard for her all these years, with me sulking and nagging and carrying on all the time. I saw how I had made her unhappy with my demands for sex and my lack of understanding. It's not surprising that she turned off sex completely after a while.

Partner acceptance — no more judging

This step requires you to stop judging your partner's level of sexual interest to be abnormal. By now you must realise that a wide range of sex drives is normal, from very low to very high. Your partner may be different from you, but that doesn't make him or her strange or peculiar. You must learn to accept the level of sex drive that your partner currently experiences, completely and without censure.

The distancer should no longer be labelled frigid, controlling or withholding. Nor should they be seen as abnormal or lacking. Keep in mind that we live in an age where a high sex drive is prized and low lust levels are labelled inadequate. We must work very hard to refute society's ignorant and unrealistic expectations of sex drive.

The pursuer, too, deserves an image revamp. Pursuers with their high level of interest in sex are often seen as base and disgusting.

> Vera: For years I secretly thought Ned had a big problem. He was always leering at me and groping me. When he didn't get sex he was like a bear with a sore head. In the beginning I thought his interest was a little coarse, but I

put it down to being a man. But as things got worse I started to see him as degraded and dirty. I thought he was no better than an animal and eventually I told him so. Now I can see how hurt and rejected he was, and how cut off from me he felt.

Once you stop judging and blaming, you are in a position to see your partner's intimate needs in a softer light. If your partner enjoys cuddling and kissing but is not very interested in sex, these sensual needs are valid and important. Or if your partner likes full-on sex and plenty of it, these needs too are valid, not shameful or disgraceful.

Putting your partner's needs into perspective — bonding behaviours

Sex in a relationship is much more than penis-in-vagina intercourse. It is a continuum of bonding behaviours, each step an integral part of the others.

Communication ➔ Intimacy ➔ Sensuality ➔ Sexuality

The first step is *communication*. As we communicate and self-disclose, emotional *intimacy* develops. This leads to physical intimacy, which delights the five senses — sight, sound, taste, touch and smell, expressed as affection and *sensuality*. The final step is *sexuality*, a broad range of sexual behaviours. This range of bonding behaviours is known as the *CISS continuum*.

For lower drive partners, or distancers, the *Communication ➔ Intimacy ➔ Sensuality* components of the CISS continuum are most important. It is through these nonsexual components that distancers most strongly *express* and *experience* their love and bond with their partners.

Ally: When Mark and I are sitting on the couch talking about the day, sharing our thoughts, our feelings, our anxieties, our plans for the future, I feel really close to him. I'm always ready to chat with him, to listen to him and give him a hug or a cuddle. This is the most powerful way for me to express my love for him.

I not only *express* my love for him in this way, but I

also *experience* it. When we are communicating and intimate, sitting close together, I get in touch with loving feelings for him that are too strong to describe. These feelings really help me to tune into positive thoughts about him and about our relationship. I feel like I would do anything for him. Without the communication, intimacy and affection, for me there would be no relationship. I wish we could have more times like this together.

Ally shows her love for Mark by talking to him and listening to him, through sensual affection and close intimate contact. When she is engaged with him in this way, her love for him is deeply affirmed — she really *feels* her love for him. If Ally was getting enough of this sort of interaction, she would feel bonded to Mark, satisfied and fulfilled, with or without sex.

When Mark and Ally came for counselling, Ally asked: 'Why can't Mark just be satisfied with the *Communication* ➔ *Intimacy* ➔ *Sensuality* part? Why does he always have to have sex?' Mark, like many men, is the higher drive partner, the sexual pursuer. It was difficult for Ally to see Mark's needs in a positive, empathic light until we looked at the CISS continuum and compared their experiences. While Ally found fulfilment in the *Communication* ➔ *Intimacy* ➔ *Sensuality* components, for Mark the bond with Ally was mainly affirmed through *Sensuality* ➔ *Sexuality*.

Mark: When I am holding Ally close, when we are making love, I love her with all my heart. I feel like we are one and she means everything in the world to me. I know she thinks I'm sexually demanding, but all I want to do is show her how much I love her.

For Mark, sensuality and sexuality are his most meaningful expressions of love. Their love bond is affirmed most strongly for Mark when they are physically and sexually close. It is at that time that Mark really connects with his loving feelings for Ally.

Ally had always considered the emotional part of the relationship to be more meaningful and significant than the sexual side. She judged Mark's sexual needs as 'inferior' to her need for a more spiritual connection. She regarded lovemaking as a second-rate bonding behaviour compared with emotional intimacy. In order to increase Ally's empathy for Mark, I asked her how it would feel if Mark refused to talk to her.

Placing the shoe on the other foot

I painted a scenario: What if every time you wanted to talk to Mark, to sit with him or to cuddle him, he said he had a headache or wasn't in the mood? What if Mark saw your need for talking as unnecessary and a waste of time? How would you feel if Mark said 'No' when you approached him for conversation? How would it affect your relationship?'

> **Ally:** I realised that if Mark refused to talk to me like I refused to have sex with him, I would be brokenhearted. I would feel abandoned, rejected, shut out. I would rapidly lose any loving feelings for him. It would make me resentful and bitter, and I would want to end the relationship. For the first time I was able to see Mark's sexual needs as valid, not as selfish cravings that could be ignored. I had been judging Mark's sexual needs as inferior to mine. I expected him to be like me, to connect like I did. I saw his bonding needs as non-essential while I viewed mine as vital. I didn't realise how my judgmental attitudes were hurting him and damaging our relationship.

Mark, too, was able to more fully validate Ally's needs for emotional connection.

> **Mark:** Ally is always patting the couch, wanting to sit and have a chat. Sometimes I just can't be bothered. But I know what it feels like when someone says 'No' when you're needy — it's happened to me often enough. Ally is always wanting more time with me. Now I know why she needs so much attention and affection. She needs emotional intimacy to feel loving feelings and express her love for me, just the same as I need to love her through sex.

Mark was much happier to give Ally more of what she needed when he realised what it meant to her. He knew exactly what it felt like to feel shut out and rejected. What Mark would find is that by giving more time and energy to Ally out of the bedroom, he would reap the benefits inside the bedroom. If Ally's emotional and sensual needs were being effectively met by Mark, she would be much more willing to make the effort to meet his sexual needs, desire or none.

Once she understood the situation from Mark's point of view, Ally was keen to find mutually agreeable ways to meet Mark's sexual needs, especially when she realised what it would mean to their relationship. If Mark could be bonded with her, more in touch with his loving feelings and sharing them with her, he would be more likely to make an effort to give her the time and attention she needed.

Mark and Ally had been stuck in the negative P/D cycle for four years. Now they are learning about a new cycle, a positive feedback loop that nurtures the relationship, creating mutual goodwill and bringing partners closer together. This new cycle is founded on respect and acceptance of each other's bonding behaviours and *creates a willingness to meet each other's needs*, sexual or otherwise. Such willingness is the basis for sexual compatibility, regardless of levels of sex drive.

Be your own sex therapist

Communication → Intimacy → Sensuality → Sexuality
Which of these bonding behaviours allows you to experience and express your love for your partner most strongly? What about your partner?
In the past, have either of you denigrated and rejected each other's bonding behaviours? How has this affected your relationship?

Reversing the pursuer/distancer cycle

John: I know I'm a pain in the neck sometimes about sex, but if Marie would just 'put out' occasionally there'd be no need for all the fuss.

Many pursuers claim that if only distancers would provide more sex, the cycle of chasing would automatically stop. This approach throws the ball (and the blame) right back into the distancer's court. Not unexpectedly, John's aggressive pursuing behaviour has reduced Marie's sex drive to nil. There's no way she'll be 'putting out' until he changes his attitude and his behaviour.

For distancers to come back into the sexual relationship, pursuers *must* back off. They must stop all pursuing behaviours. This is not easy because, although ineffective, from the pursuer's point of view, they are at least doing something about the situation. Ceasing pursuit feels like giving in or giving up.

So how does a pursuer back off? Pursuers are driven to 'do' something about the problem, but they 'do' in all the wrong places. Instead of focusing on forcing distancers to provide sex, pursuers need to look very carefully at the best ways to rehabilitate the nonsexual side of the relationship. Instead of pursuing, take the focus off trying to get more sex and put energy into building good feelings like love, intimacy, trust and security, the natural sources of sex desire. Put more time and energy into your partner's preferred bonding behaviours.

Both partners must agree that there will be no more fighting or bad behaviour about sex from either side. All criticism, sarcasm, blaming and bickering must stop. Find ways to decrease conflict, rather than throwing fuel onto the fire.

As pursuers withdraw and take off the pressure, distancers must also make the effort to re-enter the relationship, to rejoin their partners both emotionally and sexually. This can only occur if the relationship is in reasonable shape. If your relationship is not satisfactory, use Chapters 11 to 15 to pinpoint areas that need work. Another prerequisite for re-entering the sexual relationship is having a wide range of sexual options and full entitlement I to say 'Yes' or 'No' to sexual activity as you see fit. We will be looking at these tasks shortly in the sexual hierarchy. Distancers must recognise that their partner's sexual needs are valid bonding behaviours and cannot be wished away.

Be your own sex therapist

The first step in neutralising the P/D cycle is to notice your pursuing and distancing behaviours. The best way to become more aware of these behaviours is to work together and give each other constructive non-critical feedback.

Distancers: Each time your partner does something that makes you feel pressured and uncomfortable, say in a light and calm manner, 'I'm feeling like I want to move away from you right now. Do you think that you might be pursuing?' Or 'When you do such and such I get that distancing feeling.' This constructive feedback, which acknowledges both your own feelings and your partner's behaviours, will help you both to become more aware of how the P/D cycle works in your relationship.

Keep focusing on your own feelings and try to detect any distancing behaviours. You might like to discuss these with your partner on an ongoing basis: 'Today, I noticed that when you were in the bathroom I decided not to have a shower. I realised that it was an old distancing behaviour I used to do all the time.'

Pursuers: When you feel the urge to pursue your partner, when those familiar angry or abandoned feelings resurface, acknowledge them. 'Right now I'm getting those pursuing feelings. Do you think you might be distancing?' Or 'When you do such and such, I feel like you're avoiding me or shutting me out.'

Talk to your partner about your pursuing behaviours and what triggers them. 'When you said you were going to stay up and watch a movie without me last night, I suddenly got this rush of anger. It tapped into all those times I would try to get you to come to bed and have sex with me but you avoided me. It was hard for me to be nice and kiss you goodnight, without adding a sarcastic comment.'

The most effective way to disarm the P/D cycle is to get it out in the open, to take control of it rather than having it control you.

Neutralising the P/D cycle is a major step in overcoming DD. While couples revolve on this vicious merry-go-round they will remain in pain and the desire problems will persist. The P/D cycle will lose its power once you bring it out into the open, acknowledge it and work together to neutralise its destructive impact.

RE-ENTERING THE SEXUAL RELATIONSHIP — CHANGING YOUR ATTITUDES TO 'SEX'

To overcome desire discrepancy, you and your partner will have to rethink some of your attitudes about sex. We each have a fantasy blueprint of our 'perfect sexual relationship'. It includes our idea of perfect frequency of sexual activity, perfect type of sexual activity and the response of our perfect sexual partner. For many couples it's this rigid formula for a satisfying sex life that prevents them from solving their DD dilemma.

Be your own sex therapist

Can you estimate your current sexual frequency?

Has your sexual frequency decreased in recent times?

When answering the last two questions, did you immediately assume that these questions referred to occasions on which you have had physical relations with your partner that included sexual intercourse?

Do you ever have physical relations without engaging in intercourse?

Do you regard such non-intercourse sexual encounters as being valid and satisfying sexual experiences?

For many people sex = intercourse, nothing more, nothing less. It's as if sexual activity is a freeway with no exits. Once you embark on it you must travel right to the end, engaging in intercourse before you stop. Lovemaking must not only end in intercourse, but it must also involve desire, arousal, erections, and orgasms for both partners. Such rigid views of sexual activity make DD impossible to resolve.

Taking the focus off intercourse

Most people think intercourse is the be-all and end-all of sex. Penis-in-vagina penetration is considered to be the only real grown-up form of sex. Rachel's story illustrates how entrenched this attitude is.

> **Rachel:** When I was in high school 25 years ago, the girls had a code to describe how far they had gone with their boyfriends on the weekend.
> - Two was a kiss.
> - Four was outside up top.
> - Six was inside up top.
> - Eight was outside down below.
> - Ten was inside down below.
> - Twelve was intercourse — going all the way, getting to home base, scoring a home run.
>
> Our attitude was that if you hadn't had 12, you hadn't had sex. I wonder what we thought all that heavy petting and groping in the car was if it wasn't sex. Funnily enough, I was talking to my girlfriends recently and we all agreed that 2, 4, 6, 8 and 10 gave us the highest sexual arousal and the greatest excitement we have ever experienced. Intercourse is nice, but you can't beat a steamy session in lover's lane to really get the chemistry going. It's almost as if when you can have intercourse, you stop all that exciting foreplay.

Rachel has a point: we regard 2, 4, 6, 8, and 10 as 'foreplay' — something you do *before* something else. That something else is, of course, intercourse.

SEXpectations

Much sexual unhappiness stems from this mistaken belief that anything less than penetrative sex is second class and inferior. By forcing all the burden of our sexual satisfaction onto this one act, we have created a powerful way to make ourselves very unhappy.

Consider for a moment all the conditions necessary for satisfactory intercourse, according to current expectations. The man has to have a firm and lasting erection, and the woman has to be aroused (otherwise intercourse will be uncomfortable). He must not ejaculate before he inserts his penis, no matter how long they spend in 'foreplay'. During penetration he must last long enough to 'satisfy' his partner. According to most men I have questioned, the magic figure is 10 to 15 minutes. She must have an orgasm through intercourse, preferably simultaneously with him. Intercourse must give them both total sexual ecstasy and satisfaction.

Curiously we don't have such rigid expectations of any other form of sexual activity. How long should masturbation last? What is the right amount of time to spend massaging your partner? Should toe sucking be maintained until all toes are sucked or can you stop after one or two? How long should oral sex continue? (A wag at one of my lectures yelled out: 'As long as possible!')

Where is it written in stone that intercourse *must* last 15 or 50 minutes? This notion of everlasting intercourse doesn't take into account factors like frequency of male orgasm. A bloke who hasn't seen a woman's delicate parts for three weeks is going to climax a lot more quickly than a fellow who is getting sex three or four times a week.

Nor does this focus on intercourse in any way acknowledge the fact that only about 30% of women can have an orgasm through intercourse alone. For most women, intercourse just does not give enough clitoral stimulation to bring them to climax. Nearly 90% of women can achieve orgasm through clitoral stimulation, before, during or after intercourse, manually, orally or using a vibrator.

An orgasm is a reflex, just like a sneeze. Trying to have an orgasm at the same time as your partner is like trying to sneeze simultaneously — and isn't that a ridiculous idea! Sex in a relationship is an expression of love and affection, not a test of agility and timing.

Last but not least, the average length of intercourse from penetration to ejaculation is between one and six minutes. This figure surprises most people, although it usually reflects their own personal experience. Most are relieved to find that, despite their fears to the contrary, they are quite normal. Time wise, intercourse is a relatively minor part of physical intimacy between two people. Lovemaking, as compared to intercourse, can last for hours if a couple wishes.

To burden sexual intercourse, which is a means of procreation throughout the animal kingdom, with all our sexual satisfaction as well as our needs for physical and emotional bonding is unrealistic. Humans need much more than penetrative sex to celebrate and cement their relationships. It is also a little too optimistic to expect that intercourse alone can keep the fires of sexual interest and passion burning. Humans need variety, in sex perhaps more than in anything else.

Intercourse and CISS

People say to me, 'So where does intercourse fit into your continuum of bonding behaviours?' My answer is simple. Intercourse is a tiny part of our sexual functioning, no greater than the dot on the 'i' in 'sexuality'.

Communication ➔ Intimacy ➔ Sensuality ➔ Sexuality

Intercourse is *not* the full stop at the end, the climax, the pinnacle of sexual behaviour. Nor is it a goal to be achieved at any cost. It is one of many forms of sexual expression. *Sex does not = intercourse.*

A new sexual reality

Imagine a different world where intercourse takes its rightful place as an important part of sexual functioning, but only a part. In this new reality, activities that don't involve penetration are considered no better and no worse than intercourse. In fact, it is quite possible for couples to have a perfectly satisfying sex life without intercourse.

I met June and Harry, a couple in their early fifties, when I was in general practice. I couldn't help noticing what a happy and affectionate couple they were, always laughing and joking, being cheeky and flirtatious with each other. I was surprised when one day June booked to see me for sexual counselling.

June had been brought up in a strictly religious home with no sex education. She and Harry had married, both virgins, in their late teens. From the beginning, sex was an important part of their relationship. They made love nearly every day, even after more than 30 years of marriage.

June's eyes filled up with tears as she said, 'I'm going to tell you a secret that I've had for over 30 years. Harry and I have never been able to have intercourse. When we tried on our honeymoon, it hurt me so much. As soon as we got back, I went to see my local doctor. I told him with great embarrassment that we couldn't have intercourse. He crossed his arms, looked down at me and said, "June, you go home and tell your husband to do his duty as a man."'

June was shattered and she could never again summon up the courage to speak to someone about their problem until she got to know and trust me.

June was suffering from a fairly common problem known as vaginismus. Women with vaginismus are unable to have penetrative sex because spasms in the muscles of the pelvic floor around the vagina close it down, causing pain and preventing intercourse. Most cases of vaginismus can be treated and cured, especially if intervention is started early.

This couple's story has both a positive and a negative side. The negative side was that June longed for a family. She and Harry watched as their friends married and had children.

'The worst times,' June said, 'were when people would ask when we were going to start a family. Later, people accused us of being selfish for not wanting children. All the time my heart was breaking.'

The reason June had come for counselling was that her periods had suddenly stopped due to menopause and she was facing a great wall of suppressed grief about missing out on being a mother and grandmother. June didn't want sexual counselling to help her achieve intercourse — she and Harry had a great sex life. She needed grief counselling to help her with her losses and regrets.

The positive side to this story is that June and Harry had a terrific sex life. They both enjoyed a hearty level of sexual interest. He had orgasms, she had orgasms. Sex was a lot of fun for them and helped to bond them very closely together. Sex was a very important part of their marriage — but they had never had intercourse.

There are many people who, for whatever reason — sexual difficulties, illness, arthritis, back pain, pelvic surgery — cannot have intercourse but who can still have an active sex life. Instead of having 'intercourse', like June and Harry they can enjoy the pleasures of 'outercourse'.

THE JOYS OF OUTERCOURSE

Outercourse is any sexual activity other than penetrative sex. It is 2, 4, 6, 8 and 10. It is what we normally regard as foreplay, plus anything else that is sexy and arousing. Despite our current focus on intercourse as the 'best' form of sexual expression, outercourse is just as capable of giving sexual pleasure and sexual satisfaction as intercourse, perhaps even more. A very astute client of mine summed up this new style of sexual thinking.

> **Syd:** What you're saying, Rosie, is that, in the race for sexual satisfaction, intercourse and outercourse are a dead heat.

Exactly. The beauty of this way of thinking is that suddenly couples have a whole new range of sexual options to play with to overcome DD. Lower drive partners often don't feel like intercourse. They often don't feel like getting aroused. They don't have the energy or the inclination. Outercourse only requires as much energy and participation as you are willing to put into it.

What is outercourse?

Outercourse is any erotic activity that doesn't involve sexual penetration. Anything you may have regarded in the past as foreplay can be classed as outercourse. Outercourse is total body sex as opposed to genital–genital sex. It involves self-stimulation as well as partner stimulation. Outercourse includes sexual activities such as:
- *Manual stimulation:* This activity involves pleasuring of your partner's genitals, to orgasm if desired, with or without lubricant.
- *Oral sex.* Man to woman (cunnilingus), woman to man (fellatio).

- *Frottage.* This lovely French word means rubbing your genitals against your partner, with or without the goal of achieving orgasm. You are engaged in frottage when you rub your genitals against your partner's thigh, stomach, pubic area or buttocks. For men, frottage includes rubbing the penis on or between a partner's breasts, as well as interfemoral frottage (rubbing the penis between a partner's thighs). Frottage can be performed dry, but is even more arousing with a lubricant.

> When faced with two evils
> I choose the one I haven't
> tried before.
> MAE WEST

I was trying to explain 'frottage' to a middle-aged miner who had come down from the bush to seek my help. Despite my explanations, he could not quite get the idea of what this fancy new word 'frottage' meant. Suddenly he exclaimed, 'I know what you mean now, Dr Rosie. That frottage thing is just the same as a dry root! Why didn't you say so? I remember all about that from when I was a teenager.'

Not quite my preferred terminology, but he certainly got the message.

- *Mutual masturbation.* This means manually stimulating your partner's genitals while they are stimulating yours — lubricant and a vibrator may be used.
- *Parallel masturbation.* Where each partner self-stimulates simultaneously.
- *Self-masturbation by one partner in the presence of the other.* This can be enjoyed with or without assistance from the partner. Partner assistance might mean something as simple as holding or affectionately stroking the partner who is self-pleasuring, or taking a more active role by providing erotic fondling or mutual touching.

People of all ages can enjoy the benefits of outercourse. Some women like to avoid intercourse during menstruation. People with recurrent genital herpes should avoid genital contact during attacks. Pregnancy, especially in the later stages, can make intercourse difficult. Elderly people often opt for outercourse when intercourse becomes difficult or impossible.

Teenagers, too, should be taught the benefits of outercourse. Not only does outercourse include a range of safer sexual activities, but it is the best way for young people to experiment with sex, rather than feeling a pressure to rush into intercourse with all its emotional and physical hazards. For all these situations and many more where intercourse is not an option, loving outercourse is a perfect alternative.

LOVEMAKING WITHOUT AROUSAL

Lovemaking does not need to involve intercourse. Nor is sexual arousal a prerequisite.

> **Martin:** I work on Julie for ages sometimes, just trying to get her turned on, but nothing happens. It makes sex a real chore for me. I know it's my responsibility to get her aroused, but sometimes it's impossible.
>
> **Julie:** When my desire is low, Martin works on me like I'm some sort of project to be completed by a deadline. What makes sex yucky for me is his insistence that I get all hot and steamy when I'm just not in the right frame of mind.

Martin's attitude is that he must turn Julie on. Julie feels compelled to respond, even if she's not in the mood. They believe that, to enjoy sex, they must both be highly aroused.

Without a doubt, intercourse requires arousal for both men and women. Men must gain and maintain an erection and women need to be lubricated and ready for penetration. However, high levels of arousal are not necessary for outercourse. It's nice to be sexually aroused, but it is also pleasing to feel close and relaxed with your partner, to share a pleasurable experience that doesn't demand anything of you. The best way to ensure that a partner doesn't get turned on is to demand arousal from them.

THE DRIVE TO ORGASM

Don't start anything you can't finish. This pithy piece of folk wisdom has absolutely no place in the bedroom. For many people, to 'finish' sex means at least one and preferably both partners have an orgasm. When this sort of thinking is in play, no wonder distancers don't want to get sexually involved. All they want is a kiss and a cuddle, and suddenly they find themselves on a roller-coaster ride to intercourse and orgasm with no way to get off. Perhaps the idea of making love sounds good: being held, snuggling close to your partner while they have an orgasm by some means or other. But if the pressure is on you to strive for orgasm, you are more likely to avoid intimacy with your partner.

Lovemaking should not be a highway with no exit except via the 'orgasm toll booth' at the end. Lovemaking should be more like a highway with plenty of 'off ramps' on either side. To overcome DD, the lower drive partner will often need to start something he or she can't 'finish'. But why should you have to follow through to arousal, orgasm and intercourse if you don't want to? Isn't that a form of sexual coercion, being forced to do something you don't feel like doing?

Off ramping

Unless a person can say 'No' to sex, they can never truly say 'Yes'. If an individual feels coerced, manipulated or pressured into sex, or performs acts out of guilt or obligation, this is sexual exploitation and abuse. Strong words, but true. Although sexual activity may be permitted by the distancer, it is often undertaken unwillingly. It is this experience of non-consensual sex, repeated over time, that reduces sexual desire in distancers. The lower drive partner *must* feel free and entitled to stop at any point along the continuum of sexual relations, even during intercourse if they choose. This is the true meaning of *sexual consent*.

You are not responsible for each other's sexual fulfilment. Unless your partner is willing to participate in genital stimulation of some sort, that fulfilment lies strictly in your own hands (so to speak). Either partner must feel free to say 'No' to sex or to 'off ramp' from sex at any point they choose.

LOVEMAKING WITHOUT SEXUAL DESIRE

The idea of lovemaking without desire is a heretical one. Of course you must feel sexual desire to engage in physical relations!

Not necessarily. The only sexual advantage to feeling horny is that it makes getting turned on so much easier.

Stop for a moment and consider — do you ever have sexual relations for any other reason apart from desire? Do you make love sometimes because you need comfort or attention? Because you long to feel desired or connected? Because you just want to be touched or kissed?

Sexual desire is *only one* of a large range of sexual motivators. It is not, as most people think, the most important motivator, the only valid and authentic reason to pursue sexual activity. There are many other genuine, meaningful reasons for people to engage in sex.

> **Tony:** I had been broken up from my girlfriend for a few months when suddenly I got a phone call from her. She was in tears and told me that her only sister had been killed in a hit and run accident. She begged me to come over. When I got there, she couldn't wait to get me into bed. At the time I thought it was really strange, her being horny at a time like that. But later I realised that she wasn't feeling lust — she needed comfort from me, not to feel alone and abandoned. After we made love, she lay in my arms and cried and cried.

REASONS FOR ENGAGING IN SEX

Sexual desire is defined as the motivation and inclination to be sexual. There are many valid motivators to be sexual, other than sexual desire. Here is a list of common reasons for engaging in sexual relations.

- Sexual desire
- Expression of love and affection
- Fun
- Pleasure — to give and receive
- Passion
- Sensuality
- Communication

- Intimacy
- Procreation
- Sexual release
- Tension release
- Affirmation of desirability
- Security — confirmation of relationship
- Affirmation of gender
- Nurturing
- Comfort
- Reward
- To get to sleep (I call this the Mogadon motivation for sex)
- To please one's partner
- Skin hunger (the need for skin-on-skin contact)

This list of reasons for engaging in sex has very important applications in overcoming DD. Partners should work to maximise desire through maintaining a healthy relationship and the introduction of enhancers, but some lower desire partners never experience the sex urge, or only infrequently. Of course, low desire makes sexual arousal more difficult, although never impossible.

Using the Reasons for Engaging in Sex list, *the lower drive partner need not put off sexual activity until he or she experiences a high level of sexual desire*. Many other good reasons to engage in sexual intimacy can be found apart from desire. Sexual activity can still be mutually satisfying as long as both partners are willing to negotiate the type of sexual activity and the participation of both partners, as set out in Chapter 17. The lower drive partner can freely choose whether they want to engage in intercourse have an orgasm or get aroused on each occasion.

Your level of desire is not as important as your *willingness* to be sexual with your partner. The DD program is designed to increase both your desire for sex *and* your willingness to be sexual. After all, you can have plenty of desire, but sex is no likely to happen if your willingness is low.

When you are faced with the needs of a partner who is more sexually interested than you are, you simply cannot wait to feel surges of sexual desire before you engage in sex. As we have learnt, for many men and women, a high level of sexual interest may rarely if ever occur. Instead, out of mutual love and goodwill, couples can join together and enjoy lovemaking regardless of their individual levels of sex drive. This willingness to be sexual is the basis for consensual, respectful lovemaking, with or without sexual desire, arousal, orgasm or intercourse.

By changing your attitudes about what constitutes satisfactory sexual relations, you create many more sexual options. The more options that are available, the easier it is for you and your partner to say 'Yes' to sex.

MORE ABOUT MASTURBATION

For some people the idea of masturbation, either on their own or in the presence of a partner, is totally unacceptable for religious or moral reasons.

> Don't knock masturbation.
> It's sex with someone I love.
> WOODY ALLEN

If you have firm moral or religious beliefs that dictate that masturbation is wrong, your views should be respected. You will need to explore other types of outercourse with which you feel more comfortable.

However, you might like to stop for a moment and reconsider the issue if your negative feelings about masturbation come from repressive sexual programming in your childhood and teen years or from rigid expectations about what sex in a relationship *should* be like.

Ginny: When my dad discovered me playing with myself, he gave me such a hiding. I knew what I had done was dirty and wrong and I never touched myself again.

Rick: As a teenager I knew all guys did it, but I thought it was something you only did until you got a girlfriend. I felt abnormal because even when I was having regular sex with my girlfriend, I was still masturbating just as much as ever.

Dianne: I was always trying to give it up. I had this chart on the wall when I was about 11 where I would mark off the days when I had been good — when I didn't bite my nails and when I didn't do you-know-what. There were plenty of days I resisted biting my nails, but very few when I didn't touch myself in bed at night.

Charlie: I used to have to go to confession and tell the priest that I was masturbating. I hated it so much I stopped going to confession, but then my family wondered why I wasn't taking communion at church each Sunday. The clash between my religious upbringing and my sexual urges made my teen years a misery.

Dan: I caught my wife masturbating one day and it really changed our relationship. I felt she was unsatisfied with me. After that I was always trying to catch her at it when she went to bed early. Or I'd drop home during the day in case she was doing it. I really took it personally.

Bridget: One night I was asleep when Matt started to pull himself off. I was dreaming that I was in the middle of an earthquake when I eventually woke up. I made him get out of bed right then and there, and he had to sleep on the couch for a week. How dare he insult me by doing a thing like that!

A learning experience

Masturbation is not only normal, it is also a powerful way for individuals to learn about their own sexuality so that they can transmit this information to a partner. Babies reach for their genitals and pleasure themselves as soon as they have the hand coordination to do so. Children will self-pleasure absently when watching TV or lying in bed. It is a natural step from this unconscious self-stimulation to active self-pleasuring and the achievement of orgasm. Many young men and women experience their first orgasms through self-pleasuring.

There is an old joke that claims that 99% of men masturbate and 1% of men lie. While masturbation is more common in men than in women (because of social conditioning), most women who are orgasmic first learn to climax through self-stimulation.

There are now many people who accept masturbation as a normal, natural form of sexual expression — as long as they are not in a relationship. In a relationship, any form of self-stimulation is still taboo for many people. Masturbation away from a partner is often viewed as a sign of sexual dissatisfaction, a type of infidelity or a sick compulsion to be resisted at any cost. Masturbation in front of the partner is widely regarded as completely inappropriate and improper.

> **Gloria:** When I first imagined Doug masturbating in front of me, or vice versa, I felt sick. I was having sex therapy for problems with orgasm and the therapist said that now that I had learnt to masturbate and have orgasms on my own, I needed to share that experience with Doug. She said that because he felt more comfortable with sex, he should display his masturbation to me first and then it would be my turn.
>
> It turned out to be a really intimate experience for us both. We did it with the lights low, when we had plenty of time and privacy. I had never seen a man do that to himself. I found it quite sexy, even the first time. It was less difficult for me to show him than I had anticipated. It certainly helped him to learn how to pleasure me.
>
> These days we both touch ourselves whenever we feel like it, sometimes instead of sex or during sex. I always thought that once you were with a partner you should never have to stimulate yourself. Often it's the only way I can have an orgasm.

The most powerful way to teach your partner what you like is to self-pleasure in front of them. For years, sex therapists have been recommending this strategy to couples who wish to create more satisfying sex lives. Such 'display masturbation', as it is known, certainly helps to rapidly move a couple towards greater intimacy and shared eroticism. It builds trust and closeness and teaches good sexual technique. No two people masturbate in an identical fashion. Telling your partner what you like is a good idea, but showing them is an even better one.

Taking more responsibility for your own sexual satisfaction

> **Mikal:** Masturbation! Once you are married there should never be any need for that sort of thing. What's a wife for?

Like many people, Mikal believes that once you are in a relationship your partner becomes responsible for looking after all your sexual needs. This is a sure-fire way to create sexual unhappiness. What happens when you want sex and your partner doesn't? If you don't take responsibility for your own sexual satisfaction, you either force your partner to do something they don't wish to do or you miss out. It sounds like a lose–lose situation to me.

Self-pleasuring does have a role to play in relationships. The higher drive partner can self-pleasure to take pressure off the lower drive partner and reduce sexual tension. It is often a matter of acknowledging what is already happening. Most pursuers engage in masturbation, often in secret, feeling resentful and upset that they have to 'stoop' to self-stimulation. Embracing self-stimulation within the relationship reduces these bad feelings, increases a couple's sexual options and provides more sexual flexibility to deal with DD. Masturbation is simply another dish on a varied sexual menu. When you are hungry you don't always need to eat a five-course meal — sometimes a pizza or a sandwich will do.

To make a place for masturbation in your relationship, you need to alter your attitudes. Typical sexual attitudes are listed below; each is followed by a new, more helpful approach.

- *Masturbation is just for kids.*
  Masturbation is a lifelong source of pleasure and sexual satisfaction for all men and women.
- *Once I get into a relationship, I will never need to masturbate again.*
  Even though I have a partner, I can still take care of my own sexual needs if necessary.
- *My partner is responsible for meeting all my sexual needs in whatever way I wish.*
  If my partner is unwilling to join me in lovemaking as I choose, I can negotiate for sexual options or look after myself and still feel good about my relationship and my partner.

Overcoming practical objections to masturbation

Most objections to masturbation can be overcome with a little innovation.

Jane was quite happy to give Roland genital stimulation, but she hated getting semen on her skin. A simple solution was for him to finish off, or to wear a condom. They tried both styles and found them equally acceptable.

Hugh had a very high sex drive and was very happy for Laura to stimulate him manually. However, he found her technique clumsy and sometimes uncomfortable. Showing her how he masturbated helped to improve her technique, and using plenty of lubricant on his penis helped to prevent discomfort.

Bernie wanted to bring Denise to orgasm manually, but she needed at least 10 minutes of prolonged, regular, rhythmical stimulation. Bernie found he could not keep up the stimulation, as his arm and hand became very tired. They tried a vibrator instead. Sometimes Bernie held it, sometimes Denise, depending on what felt best for her.

If you are struggling with DD, you need to consider expanding your sexual repertoire to include a variety of masturbatory activities. This may mean stretching, and getting out of your comfort zone, but it will help you, your partner and your relationship. It's certainly worth discussing with your partner.

> Masturbation; the primary sexual activity of mankind.
> In the nineteenth century it was a disease; in the twentieth, it's a cure.
>
> THOMAS SZASZ
> PSYCHIATRIST

Be your own sex therapist

What messages were you given about masturbation when you were young?

Did you masturbate as a child or teenager? How did you feel about it?

Do you ever masturbate now? If the answer is 'Yes', is your partner aware of this practice? How would he or she react if they knew?

Do you know or suspect that your partner masturbates? What would your reaction be if you knew for sure that your partner was masturbating?

Can you see any benefit to your relationship from including some or all of the different styles of self-pleasuring in your shared sexual repertoire?

Which of the following sorts of masturbation would you be prepared to permit?

• Masturbation away from your partner (you or your partner).

• Masturbation in your partner's presence (you or your partner).

• Helping your partner to reach orgasm as he or she masturbates.

• One partner masturbates the other to orgasm.

It would be very helpful if you could discuss these questions and answers with your partner.

Key Points ♥

Partner empathy and a cessation of judging and blaming begin the process of interrupting the P/D cycle. Respect for and acceptance of each partner's bonding behaviours is the next step.

Pursuers and distancers must identify and desist from pursuing and avoiding behaviours. The pursuer can put effort into rebuilding and maintaining the nonsexual side of the relationship, while the distancer can take steps to gradually re-enter the sexual relationship again.

There is much more to lovemaking than intercourse, orgasm, erections and lubrication. Outercourse options are key strategies in overcoming DD.

Lower drive partners need not wait until they experience sexual urge to enjoy sex. Desire is only one sexual motivator. There are many other good reasons for sex, and sexual activity can be mutually negotiated to suit the lower drive partner.

17

Making it Easier
To Say 'Yes' To Sex

TOO FEW CHOICES

Jason: Tiffany, how about some sex tonight?
Tiffany: No, I'm not in the mood.

The problem for most couples with desire discrepancy is that their sexual options are very limited. When Jason asks Tiffany for sex, she only thinks of having sexual intercourse with him. The end result is a 'No' — but let's look at what's going on inside Tiffany's head while she considers Jason's request.

Tiffany (thinks): I'm really tired. When I didn't feel like it last time, it was dry and uncomfortable. And Jason gets so upset when I don't get right into it with him. I don't have the energy for all that. I'd better say 'No'. Oh dear, that means no cuddles for me either.

For intercourse to be comfortable, Tiffany has to get turned on. She knows it's much harder to get turned on when her desire is on the low side. Jason expects her to be as interested in intercourse as he is, to enthusiastically participate in everything he likes.

Otherwise he thinks it's a sign that she doesn't desire him. If Tiffany can't get turned on, she'll have to pretend in order to keep him happy. Maybe even fake an orgasm again. The whole thing is too much of an effort, so Tiffany declines his offer of intimacy even though she would really like to be close.

Tiffany and Jason have only two sexual options. Intercourse where they both participate fully and equally — or nothing. This limited sexual repertoire makes it much more likely that they will experience a low sexual frequency.

Hilary and Fred have a similar problem. Hilary is very keen on sex, while Fred's sexual interest could best be described as luke-warm. This couple also has a limited sexual repertoire, so that when Hilary wants sex, Fred feels under pressure to supply intercourse. For Fred this means getting turned on, gaining and keeping an erection, and providing athletic thrusting. It's all a bit much for Fred.

> **Fred:** It's easy for women. All they have to do is lie there, spread their legs and give us a mark out of 10. Men *have* to perform and we can't get away with pretending. Women can fake an orgasm, but no man can fake an erection!

Tiffany and Fred feel stuck. As much as they would like to fulfil their own and their partners' intimate needs, the thought of 'performing' intercourse is just too demanding. It's easier to say 'No' or to avoid sexual situations altogether. If Jason and Tiffany had more sexual options they would probably have more frequent sex. What if Jason and Tiffany's conversation went something like this:

> **Jason:** Tiff, I feel like sex tonight. How about you?
> **Tiffany:** Not really, Jason. I'm too tired for intercourse.
> **Jason:** Fair enough, but I really feel like some sort of sex with you. If you don't feel like intercourse, how about if I give myself a hand job while you cuddle me? Would that be OK?
> **Tiffany:** Sure — let's go to bed early.

Fred and Hilary also need a broader sexual repertoire.

Hilary: Fred, I'm in the mood for a bit of loving. How about you?

Fred: I really like making love with you, but I'm just not up to intercourse tonight. Why don't you give me a bit of a back rub and then I'll make you come, or we can use the vibrator?

Hilary: OK, that's fine; but can we set aside some time on the weekend for a bit of a long session? Would that be all right with you?

Fred: Sure, sounds like a good idea.

Can you imagine having a conversation like this with *your* partner?

These two couples had to learn new ways of communicating about sex to overcome their DD dilemma. They had to expand their sexual activities beyond intercourse so that, instead of frequently saying 'No' to sex, distancers Fred and Tiffany have a range of outercourse activities to choose from, depending on their mood and energy levels.

A BROADER SEXUAL REPERTOIRE

Intercourse can be a very pleasurable activity but if it's all you've got on your sexual menu, you could soon lose your appetite. Gay and lesbian couples encounter fewer problems with learning how to overcome DD because they usually enjoy a wider sexual repertoire and are more experimental than heterosexual couples.

A sexual repertoire may include a range of sensual and sexual activities:

	Current Activities	Forgotten Activities	New Activities	Not Interested
Having a bath or shower together				
Light kissing on lips				
Deep passionate kisses				
Kisses on parts of the body other than lips				

	Current Activities	Forgotten Activities	New Activities	Not Interested
Holding hands				
Hugging fully clothed				
Hugging naked				
Looking at each other's bodies				
Massaging each other				
Sucking your lover's toes and fingers				
Nibbling your lover's ear lobes				
Sharing a fantasy				
Acting out a fantasy with your partner				
Using lubricant				
Whispering sweet nothings in your partner's ear				
Having missionary position intercourse				
Having intercourse in other positions				
Oral sex — fellatio, cunnilingus				
Sensual thrills — ice, feathers, food, music, candles, incense, silk, leather, satin				
Anal sex				
G spot stimulation				
Anal stimulation				
Lying in each other's arms				

	Current Activities	Forgotten Activities	New Activities	Not Interested
Genital stimulation of self				
Genital stimulation — giving				
Genital stimulation — receiving				
Masturbating self to orgasm				
Masturbation of you by your partner to orgasm				
Masturbating your partner to orgasm				
Making love in the car				
Making love outdoors				
Wearing blindfolds				
Making love in bed				
Licking your partner's body				
Being licked				
Making love anywhere apart from bed				
Gazing into your partner's eyes				
Shaving pubic hair				
Dirty dancing				
Quickies				
Lights on				
Lights off				
Making love half dressed				
Using sex toys — vibrators, dildos				

	Current Activities	Forgotten Activities	New Activities	Not Interested
Long slow sessions				
Using mirrors				
Dressing up				
Talking sexy				
Watching a sexy movie				
Making love in unusual places				
Wearing sexy clothes				
Undressing your partner				
Your partner undressing you				
Doing a striptease				
Soft bondage, e.g. using scarves				
Reading erotic books and magazines				
Brushing your partner's hair, or vice versa				
Phone sex				
Swimming naked				
Any other activities you enjoy				

Creating your shared sexual repertoire

Scan through the list above and ask yourself which of these activities are comfortable for you and which ones fall outside your comfort zone. You will find that some activities are totally OK — they go into your *OK basket*. Some activities will definitely not be OK. They go into your *Not OK basket*. You may be undecided about some activities, or your attitude may change depending on your circumstances. The contents of your and your partner's individual repertoire baskets will help to determine the sexual repertoire in your relationship.

When two individuals get together, they develop a shared sexual repertoire. Let's look at Bruce and Kate, who have been dating seriously for about eight months, but are still very much in the courtship phase.

Out of the whole range of possible sexual activities (for argument's sake, let's say there are 60 as in the list above), Bruce has developed a clear idea about what sexual activities he's comfortable with and enjoys — he allots these 20 activities to his OK basket. The 40 activities that he doesn't enjoy or that make him feel uncomfortable are put in his Not OK basket.

> **Bruce:** I think I'm pretty broad-minded about sex. Most sexual stuff is OK, but I don't like dirty talk or pornography. That's smutty. I'd never have anal sex, and I think there's no need for things like striptease or lingerie in a committed relationship. Most of the other things on the list are OK except for oral sex, where he does it to her. I'll do it occasionally, but it's not my favourite thing.

Meanwhile Kate has done the same thing, deciding from the total possible list what is, for her, OK and Not OK. Being a bit more adventurous than Bruce, she has 45 activities in her OK basket and only 15 in her Not OK basket.

> **Kate:** I'm more open to sexual stuff than Bruce is. I've had more sexual experience and tried more things than he has. He's a bit narrow-minded for my liking, and it does cause a problem. He doesn't seem to like giving oral sex, although he loves to receive it. The easiest way for me to orgasm is through oral sex from a man. He never asks whether I've had an orgasm, so I haven't told him this yet. I guess I'm worried about how he will react.

When Bruce and Kate get together, their shared sexual repertoire is based on what is *mutually* OK, what they have in common in their OK baskets. In this case it turns out that Bruce and Kate

mutually enjoy only 10 different activities out of a possible 60.

You can see how a couple's shared sexual repertoire is diminished by a filtering process that excludes activities from both partners' Not OK baskets. The shared repertoire includes only those activities from each person's OK basket that are mutually agreeable. As a result, couples who have been together for some time often have very limited sexual repertoires. DD usually reduces the sexual repertoire even further. After a few years of DD, a bit of desultory foreplay and unenthusiastic intercourse may be all a couple have left to offer each other.

Limerence expands the sexual repertoire temporarily

The news for Kate isn't good. She and Bruce are still limerent. When a couple first gets together they are more likely to step outside their comfort zones and do things their partner likes, even if those activities have actually been slotted in their Not OK basket. Once limerence wears off, both individuals' sexual repertoires shrink back to normal. Their shared sexual repertoire is then based on what they can find to do that is mutually acceptable.

Be your own sex therapist

When you first began a sexual relationship with your current partner, who had more activities in their OK basket, you or your partner?

How has your repertoire changed since then? And your partner's?

Do you think that DD has had an effect on the range of sexual activities you currently share?

Are there any activities that have disappeared from your sexual repertoire that you miss?

Exclusion of preferred sexual activities causes conflict, unhappiness and sexual boredom. Ray and Rena have been together for 15 years.

Ray: Every time with Rena it's the same old thing. I can touch her breasts, but not down below. She presses against me, but never touches my genitals. We kiss a bit, rub a bit, then she rolls on her back and that's the sign for me to put it in. I can't tell you what I'd give for a blow job or even just sex in a different position. She says these things are dirty, although when we were first sleeping together she was keen to try them out.

Rena: What turns me on is to kiss and cuddle on the couch downstairs before we come to bed. I used to love petting before we were married. It helps to get me in the mood. That was why I was so willing to please Ray back in those early days. I gave him oral sex and more variety because he put me into the right frame of mind for it.

Ray thinks that petting and affection is kid's stuff and has cast them aside into *his* Not OK basket. Rena has thrown sexual variety, including different positions and oral sex, into *her* Not OK basket. As a result, Rena and Ray are left with the same old routine every time. If Rena doesn't feel like intercourse, there's not much else on offer.

Expanding your sexual repertoire

Couples need to have a wide range of sexual activities at their fingertips so as to meet their needs on any given occasion. I'm not talking about anything wildly kinky. Perhaps there are activities you enjoyed early in your relationship that have disappeared from your sexual repertoire. Perhaps there are things you have always wanted to try but were too shy. Here's your chance to improve the variety and flexibility of your sex life.

Be your own sex therapist

Each partner should complete this exercise separately then compare answers. Make two photocopies of the repertoire list on pages 253–56, one for yourself and one for your partner.
In the first column, 'Current Activities', tick all the sexual activities in which you currently engage. If you would like to do more of any activity, put an arrow pointing up beside it. If you would like to do it less frequently, put an arrow pointing down beside the activity.

In the second column, 'Forgotten Activities', tick any activities you used to enjoy but no longer share. Underline any activities that you would like to reintroduce into your relationship.

In the third column, 'New Activities', tick any activities you would be interested in trying. In the fourth column, tick any activities that don't interest you at all.

Beside the activities that you consider to be pleasurable (those you would like to do more often, those you would like to include from the past, or those you are interested in trying out), rate each item from 0 to 5, according to how interested you would be in doing it. Five means very interested, and zero means not very interested at all. Compare lists with your partner.

To increase your repertoire, start with activities that you both rate highly on your want-to-try list. You might like to experiment with these activities, adding a new one each fortnight or so. Try to increase desired activities and decrease activities that are less enjoyable through mutual agreement. When you have explored the highly rated items, move onto items that one partner rates highly but the other doesn't.

Here is a sample of the repertoire table with regard to the first 10 activities.

	Current Activities	Forgotten Activities	New Activities	Not Interested
Having a bath or shower together		✔ 4/5 ↑		
Light kissing on lips	✔ 5/5 ▲			
Deep passionate kisses	✔ 4/5			
Kisses on parts of the body other than lips			✔ 5/5 ↑	
Holding hands	✔ 4/5			
Hugging fully clothed	✔ 3/5 ▲			
Hugging naked	✔ 3/5			
Looking at each other's bodies	✔ 2/5			
Massaging each other			✔ 4/5 ▲	
Sucking your lover's toes and fingers				✔

The benefits of stretching yourself

The first part of the repertoire expansion exercise is easy — experimenting with what you both enjoy. But what about activities that one partner enjoys but the other isn't keen on? Why should you try something you don't like? Shouldn't your partner just put up and shut up? Not necessarily — there is much to be gained from venturing outside your comfort zone to please your partner, *as long as the effort is made on both sides.*

When one partner stretches to please the other, it creates a great

> One half of the world cannot understand the pleasures of the other.
>
> JANE AUSTEN

deal of goodwill in the relationship. Meeting your partner's needs, inside or outside the bedroom, is a way of showing how much you care for and value them. When you are mutually meeting each other's needs, the relationship will flourish and grow, and so will your sexual desire.

HELPING YOUR PARTNER TO EXPERIMENT MORE

Increasing your shared sexual repertoire is a two-way street requiring the cooperation of both partners. You cannot expect your partner to give you what you want if you aren't willing to give them what they want.

If you want your partner to experiment more:

- *Don't demand — discuss.* Use your repertoire lists to calmly discuss activities that you would like to try. It's much better to negotiate new sexual activities when you aren't sexually involved. If you pressure your partner, say for oral sex during lovemaking, you will more than likely turn him or her off and cruel your chances of any negotiation further down the track.

- *Examine your relationship.* Your partner will be more willing to experiment if there is a high level of goodwill and trust in the relationship. Make sure you are meeting your partner's needs generally.

If you remember from Chapter 14, negotiation uses strategies such as *tit for tat* and *part of what you want and part of what I want.* This worked for Charlotte and Gino.

> **Gino:** I really wanted Charlotte to be a bit more adventurous in bed. She reminded me how important communication and intimacy are to her. She promised that if I gave her more affection, time and attention outside the bedroom she would be willing to be more flexible inside the bedroom. We agreed to try harder to meet each other's needs. This small adjustment has really improved our relationship in every way.

- *Build trust.* One specific area of the relationship must be strong to allow for sexual stretching — trust in each other. To lose yourself in sex you must feel safe. If you want your partner to experiment, they must feel they won't be criticised, ridiculed, shamed, or expected to perform or respond in any particular way. Your attitude must be, 'We'll give it a try and see how we go.'

- *Help your partner to understand you.* Your partner may have no idea why you want a particular activity. They may think you are being fickle or demanding. It may help if you explain to them why you are drawn to a certain activity. For example, a woman may be unable to reach orgasm without a vibrator, or a stressed or ageing man may find that he just can't get aroused without direct genital stimulation. Knowing why you want something can help to motivate your partner to experiment.

> I shall light a candle of understanding in thine heart, which will not be put out.
>
> BOOK OF ESDRAS
> THE APOCRYPHA

Noelene: Des thought I was a bit weird wanting to spend so much time kissing and hugging before we move into sexual activity. I explained to him that I need that time to relax. If I'm not relaxed I can't get turned on, and then it's not so good for both of us. Now he keeps asking me if he has cuddled me enough!

Tony: I know I don't *need* to make love doggie-style with Marie, but nothing else gives me that great feeling. Marie told me she felt that sex in that position was for animals and I respect that. We talked it through. She agreed to try sex from behind lying down side by side, and when that was pleasurable for her she was willing to go a bit further. Now she is OK about having sex doggie-style, but I know she doesn't get a lot out of it so I don't ask for it often. I really appreciate what she does for me and I tell her so.

- *Create arousal.* The more aroused a person is, the more adventurous they will be. Try to enhance your partner's sexual arousal by making sure their conditions for good sex are met (see page 285). For both men and women, high levels of arousal transfer more activities into the OK basket.

- *Praise your partner.* You catch more flies with honey. Make sure you praise and acknowledge any effort on your partner's part. Certainly Tony's appreciation of what Marie does for him keeps her coming back for more. She may not get much out of doggie-style sex, but she sure does love the praise and recognition Tony gives her.

    Marie: I do it for him, but I also do it for me. He's so loving to me afterwards and I feel really great that he's happy with me. I'm glad we worked it out.

- *Accept a 'No' graciously.* If your partner says 'No' to a particular activity, hear them out graciously. Don't sulk or get angry. Help them to explore their feelings. Discuss ways of getting something close to what you want, even if it's not the full kit and caboodle. Ask them what you can do to increase their willingness to experiment.

    Dave: I love to look at Kim's body, but she is really shy. She's OK now with a dim bedside light on, but she's still not keen on making love during the day. That's OK — at least she's been trying to please me.

- *Focus on what you* are *getting rather than what you* aren't *getting.* Dave is focusing on what Kim is giving rather than on what he is missing out on. This helps him to maintain a positive attitude to her and their sex life together.
- *Find out what your partner will do.* Start with something that's not too confronting. If you want to look at erotica with your partner, it's a mistake to bring home hard-core porn — start with some sexy movies from your local video store and get your partner comfortable with this first. Or if you want to use a vibrator, use it occasionally and for a short time only at first until your partner gets more used to it.
- *Keeping perspective — knowing the difference between needs, wants and desires.* The truth is that nobody ever died from failure to get complete sexual satisfaction from a partner. It is very important to realise that many of the things we want from sex

are preferences rather than needs. A food analogy can be used to describe needs, wants and desires:

We *need* food — otherwise we will die.

We *want* good food enough food — that is a preference.

We *desire* (well *I* do, anyway) chocolate, smoked salmon and anything with melted cheese on it! Desires are what we fancy.

Many of our sensual, sexual and emotional needs are appetites or cravings — very important, but not necessarily life threatening in their absence. Certainly our quality of life improves if we have our sexual wants and desires fulfilled, but we can survive without them, and so can our relationships. Keep a realistic perspective on your sexual 'needs'. Don't make your partner's life miserable for not accommodating you totally. After all, do *you* always accommodate your partner in everything?

GOING OUTSIDE YOUR COMFORT ZONE

What if the shoe is on the other foot and your partner wants something from you that is outside your comfort zone — something that you might consider 'perverted' or 'sick'? Often the pursuer is more keen to experiment than the distancer. That makes sense. If you have more desire for sex, you are likely to have more desire to experiment with sex. What can you do to overcome the differences between what's in your OK basket and what's in your partner's OK basket?

- *Reflect on your sexual programming.* Examine your reluctance to participate in activities outside your comfort zone. Our sexual likes and dislikes are often not conscious choices but knee-jerk reflex reactions to what other people have said or done. Usually your sexual programming as a child, teenager and adult will dictate what activities you do and don't like.

  Camilla: When I was a teenager, a boy tried to French kiss me and I was horrified. I kept my lips firmly pressed together and pushed him away. Once I realised passionate kissing like this was quite a normal activity, I experimented with it and really got to enjoy it. These days, kissing deeply turns me on more than anything else.

Remember that your partner isn't trying to be difficult by liking a particular activity. They, too, have been sexually programmed, just differently from you. Neither of you is right or wrong.

- *Try it — you may (or may not) like it.* If you have no dramatic objections to your partner's requests, why not give them a try? You won't know until you try whether it's something you'll want to do again. An important point: if you experiment begrudgingly or resentfully, I can guarantee you won't like anything you try. Keep an open mind. Even if the activity does nothing for you, you might get pleasure simply from pleasing your partner.

- *Don't be too serious about experimentation.* You may feel shy about trying something new because you don't quite know how to go about it or you like to be an expert at any sexual activities you participate in. If so, make it a bit of a laugh the first time. The worst thing you can do is to try something new and be deadly serious about it.

> **Greg:** When Amber first tied me up, we had a huge laugh. She got some silk scarves and tied me to the bed. Then we just looked at each other and burst out laughing. We didn't know what to do next. So she sat across my hips and started stroking my chest. Nothing happened, we just kept laughing like hyenas. So we tried turning out the light. That was the trigger. Suddenly I was strapped down in the dark and she was in charge, and we both found it very sexy.

Have fun with sex — after all, sex is funny business!

- *Take baby steps.* Doing something unfamiliar is always scary. To make it easier, approach the activity in small steps rather than plunging in first time. Let's say you are a female who is OK touching her partner's genitals but not OK with oral sex. However, you are willing to give it a try. You may prefer it if your partner has a good wash before making love. Initially you might like to lie with your head on his thigh while you stimulate his penis manually. Slowly over weeks you can bring your face closer to his genitals, pleasuring him with your hand, gradually coming closer until your mouth is very close to his penis. Then you might like to kiss or lick his genitals lightly, perhaps when he is not aroused at first, and later, when he is erect. Once you feel comfortable with this, you can masturbate him while putting just the head of his penis into your mouth for a short time. This may be all you are able to achieve, but manual stimulation plus limited oral stimulation is the next best thing to more involved oral sex, especially if you use a lubricant. This technique worked for Grace.

Grace: I couldn't stand the thought of giving Mal oral stimulation at first. But slowly I got used to stimulating him manually and putting the tip in my mouth. I can't swallow or anything like that, but we have reached a happy compromise. Mal is thrilled with how hard I have tried to please him, and he lets me know all the time what a hot woman I am now.

Grace could not 'deep throat' Mal, but he accepted and appreciated the effort she made.

- *What am I afraid of?* Although you may feel scared, ask yourself whether you are really in any danger. Often it's the unknown, the taboo, the new, the different that is scary, rather than the activity itself. Some people avoid certain activities, not because they turn them off but because they are scared the activity might turn them on and they judge this to be immoral or kinky. There is often a very fine line between what turns us on and what turns us off. Within a loving relationship, *any* sexual activity is acceptable as long as both partners consent and the sexual activity does not hurt either partner or anyone else.
- *The next best thing.* If the activity is something your mate really wishes to try but it's firmly in your Not OK basket, try to be imaginative and come up with the 'next best thing'. You have the absolute right to say 'No' to anything that makes you uncomfortable, but sometimes close enough is good enough.

Evelyn: Rod is always on at me about anal sex. It seems to be a bit of a thing with men. There's no way I could go for that, but we did a bit of experimenting. We came up with a great alternative where we are both comfortable. I lie on my tummy and, using lots of lubricant on my lower back, he gets on top and rubs his penis against me. His penis is nowhere near my personal parts, just between my buttocks, so I feel safe but the feeling for him is wonderful and he can have great orgasms this way.

What you cannot supply, your partner can make up for with fantasy.

Fiona: I really wanted Greg to give me oral stimulation, but he just didn't feel comfortable. We worked out that as long as he put his face close to my genitals, and stimulated me manually or using the vibrator, my imagination could do the rest. For a long time it was a big issue for us, but now we are both content.

- *No obligation.* Of course, if any activity really offends you or brings up bad feelings for you, there is no obligation to do it, or even try it. Instead, look at other activities you might be willing to try. If your fear is very great and you want to deal with it, you might like to consider seeking sexual counselling.

Rhiannon: Rupert can touch me anywhere on my body except down below. When I was a child I was sexually abused by a neighbour who used to put his fingers inside me. When Rupert tries, or I think about him trying, I get panicky. It's like that area is numb or part of someone else.

Survivors of sexual abuse will often suffer bad feelings or flashbacks during certain sexual activities and this can usually be remedied through counselling.

DESIRE DISCREPANCY AND YOUR SEXUAL REPERTOIRE

Over time, desire discrepancy has a predictable effect on sexual activity. DD reduces:

- sexual frequency (how often you do it)
- sexual repertoire (what you do)
- distancer participation (how involved the lower drive partner is)
- variety of styles of lovemaking (the way you make love).

You might be surprised at the number of couples with DD who rarely have physical relations with each other. When couples come for counselling, it is certainly not uncommon for them to be having sex six times a year or less. When you think about it, that's once every eight weeks; after eight weeks, enough time and tension have accrued to necessitate mercy sex on the part of the distancer in an attempt to defuse the situation. When sex *does* occur, it is often unsatisfying and awkward and does little to help the situation.

Many couples with DD have sex much less frequently than that, or not at all. They may be able to count on their fingers the number of times they have had sex during their entire married life. Some couples have not had any sexual relations for years. If you fall into this category, it is important that you realise you aren't alone or even unusual. This is how chronic DD affects couples in the long term.

> **Doreen:** You know how people jokingly say they are 'C of E' by religion, meaning they go to church at Christmas and Easter. Well, we have 'B and A' sex. We have sex on my birthday and our anniversary. Other people worry about having sex twice a week. We're lucky if we have it twice a year.

DD doesn't just *decrease sexual frequency* and *reduce the sexual repertoire*. It also *reduces partner participation*. Typically the lower drive partner participates as little as possible.

> **Rory:** I'm lucky if Jo lets me touch her now. I wait months until she gives me the nod, and when it happens she just lies there. I'm dying to make love, but all we do is copulate.

DD also *restricts sexual style*. Where once you might have enjoyed quickies, extended sex sessions, sex for fun, comforting sex, lazy sex, tired sex, adventurous and exciting sex on weekends, and good old home-baked sex on a week day night, couples with long-term DD are often left with a brief, infrequent, tense sexual interaction where neither gets much pleasure.

Adding sexual variety

To overcome DD, couples need to add more variety to their style of lovemaking as well as increase their sexual repertoire. Even couples without DD can settle into a routine of lovemaking where they spend the same amount of time and energy doing the same sorts of things. Couples will benefit from having several different styles of lovemaking to suit different occasions.

- Sometimes a **quickie** is good — before guests arrive, or first thing on a weekday morning before work. This quick, uninvolved sex can also be good for when you are both highly aroused and don't need too much of a lead-up, or when one partner is more keen for sex than the other. Quickies are good for adding spontaneity. Men generally find a quickie very exciting.
- **Bread and butter sex** — this is good old domestic sex for week nights. The aim is for you both to have a cuddle, some skin contact and perhaps an orgasm. Fifteen to 30 minutes is all that's required for this style of lovemaking.
- More leisurely sex. We are looking here at a **sex session**. This is an event that requires some planning. Despite popular opinion, good sex does not have to be spontaneous. Some of the best sex you can have is the result of careful allocation of time and energy. Make the time available and see what happens spontaneously. This style of lovemaking occurs early in relationships (remember those weekends in bed) but fades away. The aim of a sex session is deep sensual and sexual pleasure for both. What quickies are for most men, long sessions are for many women.
- **Adventurous sex**. The aim is to have fun and enjoy the excitement of trying something different and out of the ordinary together — dressing up, fantasy, sex toys, erotica, different

positions. We need to reserve certain activities for special times. If we enjoy adventurous activities all the time, we develop tolerance and they soon lose their appeal.

- There is also the concept of **'he'** sex and **'she'** sex. The two genders often enjoy different sorts of sex. Julie likes long slow sex sessions, while Jim loves a hot and steamy quickie. Julie likes affectionate sex, while Jim likes raunchy sex. Julie likes romance and candlelight, while Jim likes to watch porno movies. It's important to meet the needs of both partners. Each must get their fair share of 'he' and 'she' sex.

Overcoming DD means much more than having more frequent sex. Each damaged area of sexual interaction must be healed.

THE SEXUAL HIERARCHY

Discussions about broadening one's sexual repertoire lay the groundwork for introducing a key strategy for overcoming DD. Called the *sexual hierarchy*, this strategy is simply a way of saying 'Yes' more often to loving sexual interaction (not necessarily intercourse). The beauty of the sexual hierarchy is that it is very flexible and allows for negotiation of both the *type* of sexual activity to be shared, plus the *degree of partner participation*. There are two parts to the hierarchy — the participation hierarchy and the activity hierarchy.

The participation hierarchy — percentage sex

Degree of participation in sexual activity is a very important factor in overcoming DD. The more desire and arousal you experience, the keener you will be to participate in mutual sexual pleasuring. When both partners have a high level of desire and arousal, they have no problem engaging enthusiastically in sexual activity. Let's call this level of participation 50%/50% because both partners are equally involved. Both are aroused, both are active, both are enthusiastic.

However, when one partner has a lower level of desire than the other, it is imperative that differing degrees of participation can be negotiated for the lower drive partner, permitting less arousal and less sexual performance. We explored this notion when we were looking at desire behaviours in Chapter 5 — initiatory people find it easy to get turned on, as do receptive people. However, for available, neutral and disinterested people, getting sexually aroused can be a bit of a struggle.

> **Sarah:** We've been using the sexual hierarchy for ages and it has really helped us to overcome the differences in our levels of desire. Simon and I were driving home after a party the other night and he looked at me in that certain way. I said to him, 'Baby, I love how you lust after me, but I'm really worn out tonight and it's late. Sex is fine by me, but how about if I do 10% of the work and you do the rest?'
>
> Simon knows that when I do 10% of the work I just lie there like a log. We might have intercourse or frottage, or I cuddle him while he masturbates, but I don't really get involved. These days he's fine with that as an option from time to time.
>
> It's curious — in the old days I often used to just lie there, but I was always tense and wishing it was over. We both felt lousy and sex wasn't ever enjoyable for either of us. The difference is that with 10%/90% sex, although Simon knows he's going to do most of the work, I lie there relaxed and comfortable, happy just to share the moment with him. There's no pressure, no stress, and we both feel good.
>
> The other night after the party, Simon hadn't finished negotiating. He said with a winning smile, 'How about I do 60% and you do 40%?' He was asking for a bit more involvement on my part. So we split the difference and agreed on a 20%/80% split. I would do a bit more than just lie there, but not too much. He was happy and I was happy, and we had a really nice lovemaking experience.
>
> What we often find is that although I agree to, say, 20% participation, I actually feel so relaxed and close to him that I start to get turned on. Before long I'm up there doing 40% or 50% of the work and we're having a grand old time.

For me what's important about the hierarchy is that I don't have to get turned on and I don't have to do anything I don't want to do, while Simon never has to miss out on some sort of sexual relief and closeness. It's definitely a win–win solution.

NEGOTIATING SEXUAL PARTICIPATION

50/50 sex — mutual, participatory lovemaking	↑	Increasing participation of the less interested partner
60/40 sex		
70/30 sex		
80/20 sex		
90/10 sex		

This section of the sexual hierarchy allows couples to negotiate *sexual participation*. It allows lower drive partners to determine their level of involvement based on their willingness to participate or their level of arousal. As Sarah remarks, at times the behaviour may not be much different from lying there and thinking of England, but the feelings of both partners are completely different.

Bringing the sexual agenda out in the open

The reason negotiation of participation is so helpful is that it brings both parties' sexual agendas out in the open. Instead of the pursuer manipulating to get sex and the distancer trying to avoid sex, they are both open about their wants and desires. Talking about where you are at sexually increases intimacy and erotic bonding and allows both partners to feel they share control of the sexual relationship. It also means that a partner with a lower interest in sex and one with a higher interest in sex can both get their needs met.

NEGOTIATING SEXUAL ACTIVITY

The second part of the sexual hierarchy negotiates the *type of sexual activity*. Not only does a couple need to negotiate *how much* they are prepared to participate, they also need to decide *what they are going to do*. Negotiation of mutual sexual activity is based on what type of activity suits the less interested partner's level of desire, arousal and energy. The options include:

- No partner participation
- Minimal partner participation
- Low partner participation
- Outercourse options
- Intercourse.

Regardless of what the lower drive partner chooses, the higher drive partner always has the option to be sexual through self-stimulation.

No partner participation

There are two options in this category. The lowest option is *no sex at all*, for either party. You can't have much lower participation than that! When a distancer doesn't care for any mutual sexual activity, the pursuer may decide not to be sexual after all.

Or they may choose another sexual option from the hierarchy. One rung up the hierarchy, still under the heading of 'No partner participation', we find *masturbation away from the lower drive partner*. Let's say the distancer doesn't care for sex, but the pursuer is in the mood for sexual release. The couple can negotiate that the pursuer goes into another room and masturbates. This is usually new behaviour for most couples.

> **Judy:** It took me a long time to get used to the idea that it was OK for Rick to go off and masturbate. I felt like I wasn't doing my 'duty' as a wife and that he was missing out. Counselling helped me to see that he was entitled to sexual release if he wanted it, by himself, and if he needed a hug and a cuddle I could be there for him without feeling sexually threatened. It took Rick a while to get used to the idea as well. He had been masturbating in secret for some time, but we both pretended it didn't happen. I haven't been able to embrace the idea of him masturbating in bed with me yet, but we're working on it. It'd be nice if he didn't have to go into another room.

Minimal partner participation

For most couples, even more confronting is the idea of *one partner masturbating beside the other, usually in bed*. This option comes under the heading of 'Minimal partner participation' because it requires just a little more involvement from the lower drive partner, but nothing actually physical.

> **Joe:** For years I would masturbate every day under the shower or in the bathroom with the door locked. I felt resentful and angry about doing it. Tina only wanted sex once every few weeks and I used to go nuts. It was very hard for us to openly accept that masturbation was a legitimate answer to our desire problems, even though we had actually been using it for years. It's made such a difference to our relationship that I know I can lie in bed beside my wife, pleasure myself without troubling her and then fall asleep in her arms. Her sex drive isn't much higher, but we certainly have a better sex life than we used to.
>
> **Lorraine:** I usually touch myself while we have intercourse because I need the stimulation to be just right. Still, I had never openly masturbated in front of Tony when I felt like sex and he didn't, although it happened quite often. It was tough to relax at first beside him, but with his encouragement it's become much easier. It's taken the pressure off him and brought us closer together.

Low partner participation

The next rung up on the activity hierarchy is low partner participation. Once again this involves a masturbatory solution, but one with more contact with the partner. The first option, *masturbation with partner assistance and no fondling*, means that while the higher drive partner masturbates, the lower drive partner can hold, caress, kiss, stroke or erotically stimulate the masturbating partner. Partner assistance means *helping* your partner to get turned on and achieve orgasm if that is what is desired.

Karen: I am a nurse working shifts at night and Robbie works normal hours. Our sex life was really limited by lack of time and energy. He needs a lot of sex and I just wasn't up to it. We tried the 'no' and 'minimal partner participation' options, but he felt very disconnected from me unless we had some physical contact. Next we tried low partner participation and this works well when I'm too tired for full-on sex. Sometimes I'll hold him, kiss his ears and neck, fondle his testicles or squeeze his buttocks while he gives himself a hand job. I might whisper a sexy story in his ear about what I'd like to do to him. If I'm really tired we negotiate that I will simply put my hand on his chest while he masturbates. Even if I fall asleep, he still really appreciates the loving gesture.

The next option up is *masturbation with partner fondling and assistance*. This option involves a little more participation by the lower drive partner. While the higher drive partner is masturbating, the lower drive partner is assisting as described above. However, at this level there is also mutual touching between partners, not necessarily sexual if the lower drive partner doesn't wish it, but more physical contact.

Jodie: We like this option — I need more sex than Gil does, so I now masturbate regularly in bed with him cuddling and caressing me. With this option I get to touch him, too — I love to hold his penis while I masturbate, even if it's not hard. I love to run my hands over his body and push my breasts up against him while I bring myself off. It's so much better than when he used to try and get it up to have intercourse and then feel bad when he couldn't. This way works really well and sometimes he gets so horny helping me that we end up having full-on sex together.

Outercourse options

The next rung up the hierarchy includes many of the outercourse activities described in the previous chapter. This level involves much more partner participation and arousal and possibly orgasm for both if desired.

The list includes *partner masturbation*, where one person stimulates the other.

> **Marita:** We found an easy solution to Joel's need for regular sex with me. When I'm not in the mood but he wants to be close, we cuddle and kiss a bit until he's turned on, then I pop a bit of lubricant into my palm and he thrusts into it. It only takes him a few seconds to come and he says it's the closest thing you can get to the warm, wet feeling of intercourse.

With *parallel masturbation*, two people who don't really feel like intercourse or mutual pleasuring can bring themselves to orgasm side by side, either taking turns or together.

Mutual masturbation means genital stimulation of each other, either simultaneously or in turn.

Frottage, using a vibrator together and oral sex are all ways of achieving high arousal and orgasm if desired.

Intercourse

Top of the list of participation options is *intercourse*. Keep in mind that you can negotiate the degree of participation in outercourse and intercourse using percentage sex.

HIERARCHY OF SEXUAL ACTIVITIES

Intercourse

Outercourse
- Oral sex
- Frottage (genital rubbing)
- Vibrator
- Mutual masturbation (stimulating each other)
- Parallel masturbation (self-stimulation)
- Partner masturbation (stimulating your partner)

Low partner participation
- Masturbation with partner fondling and assistance
- Masturbation with partner assistance and no fondling

Minimal participation sex
- Masturbation in presence of partner

No partner participation
- Masturbation away from partner

No sex

Increasing participation of the less interested partner

Saying 'Yes' to sex

The goal of the sexual hierarchy is to increase sexual frequency by making it easier for distancers to say 'Yes' to sex. Even when the Distancer chooses to say 'No' to sex, the pursuer can still decide to enjoy sexual release through masturbation. The choice to have 'no sex' is no longer made by the distancer on the pursuer's behalf. Instead, the pursuer makes the decision whether to have sexual release through masturbation or not. Decisions about sexual frequency become mutual, instead of being controlled by the distancer.

> **Gary:** I used to feel like Fay was doling out sex whenever she saw fit, with no regard for me. I felt helpless and without any power in the relationship. After all, I couldn't

make her give me sex. Using the hierarchy, I can now have sex whenever I want and she can join in if she feels like it. I feel more in control and less resentful of her now.

Personalising your sexual hierarchy

Listed above is the basic activity hierarchy. It includes sexual activities ranked in order of increasing participation of the lower drive partner. However, each couple will need to draw up a personalised activity hierarchy for their own use.

> **Sue:** I feel like sex about once every couple of weeks. Ron likes it every day or so. We use most of the activities on the hierarchy, except parallel masturbation and Ron giving me oral sex. I've never really been keen on that. The vibrator makes it really easy for me to come and Ron will occasionally have a go with it, too.
>
> Not having to have intercourse every time was a big relief for me. When my desire is low, my arousal is slow and I just don't get anything out of penetration. I was really feeling used. But I don't mind participating in any of the other options, even if I'm not turned on. Ron loves frottage between my thighs and on my pubic area and can come really quickly. For me there is a big difference between that and intercourse — I don't know why. I'm very happy to accommodate him whenever he wants sex as long as we only have intercourse when I'm in the mood.
>
> **Ron:** What I love about the hierarchy is the variety. In the past we did the foreplay bit, then intercourse. A lot of the time Sue wasn't all that keen, but we didn't know what else to do. I used to think she had a problem with enjoying sex, but now we both have plenty of fun in bed. I don't mind how I have an orgasm, just as long as I can have one when I want to.

Be your own sex therapist

Before you can use the basic sexual hierarchy, you have to personalise it. The lists of activities above are just guidelines. You need to go through the sexual hierarchy with your partner and carefully consider each activity. Ask yourself these questions:

Is this a pleasurable activity for me?

Is this a pleasurable activity for my partner?

If not, can I and/or my partner stretch to include this activity in our sexual repertoire? Would I or my partner be willing to try?

What other activities can we add to our sexual hierarchy?

You might like to add activities that are especially pleasing for one or both of you from the sexual repertoire list.

Key Points ❦

DD not only reduces sexual frequency but it also shrinks a couple's sexual repertoire, restricts their sexual styles, and reduces the lower drive partner's participation in sex.

A broad sexual repertoire provides more choices for couples with DD, as well as adding more variety. It can only be achieved when both partners experiment with activities that fall outside their comfort zones. Partners are much more likely to experiment if the general relationship is happy and supportive.

The sexual hierarchy allows couples to negotiate both choice of sexual activity and degree of participation.

Putting the Sexual Hierarchy To Work

The sexual hierarchy provides a broad range of sexual options for couples, but there are further skills for partners to learn before they can put the hierarchy to its most effective use.

- The higher drive partner will need to learn how to initiate sexual contact appropriately.
- The lower drive partner needs to focus on reasons for engaging in sex other than desire and learn how to say 'No' in an empathic and constructive way when sexual contact is not desired.
- Both partners need strategies for meeting nonsexual needs within the relationship.

Let's start by looking at initiation techniques.

SEXUAL INITIATION

Sexual initiation refers to the methods used by men and women to indicate a readiness, a willingness or a desire to be sexual with a partner. Initiation techniques can range from a wandering hand in the middle of the night to a romantic weekend away for two. Initiation can be verbal — 'I'm in the mood for love ...' and non-verbal — the famous tap on the shoulder.

When a couple has been under pressure from desire discrepancy, initiation really suffers. Initially pursuers often increase their initiation rate in an attempt to get more sex. They treat sex like a lottery where the more tickets you buy, the more chances you have to win. Initiation eventually comes to be viewed by the distancer as an annoying behaviour to be sidestepped or ignored if at all possible.

The pursuer gets more and more frantic trying to find initiation techniques that work. Eventually pursuers may give up initiating sex at all. In this advanced phase of DD, sex only happens when the distancer initiates (or rather 'allows') sex. To overcome DD, you and your partner need to discuss what sort of initiation techniques work best for the two of you.

Initiating sex

Most often men are the sexual initiators and they have a difficult job. Women are not always easy to approach for sex and can be fickle.

> **Sally:** I like sex with Craig but he has to initiate it in just the right way or I'll be put off. He finds it hard to judge my moods. Sometimes he comes on too slow, sometimes too fast. He might put me off with one wrong word or by not touching me just right. It's hard because we often end up not having sex even when I am in the mood because he doesn't approach me the way I like.

Men need help from their partners to learn how to make more effective sexual approaches. Some women find verbal initiation ('How about sex?') offensive. They may not like the words used (naughty, quickie, screw, etc.), or they just automatically say 'No' because they don't like the context of the request, even if they feel like sex. A poor context might mean asking a woman for sex while she is peeling the vegetables, feeling very stressed or trying to study. Another common blunder is the way men initiate sex nonverbally — by grabbing a woman's breasts, fondling her buttocks or, worst of all, going straight for her genitals.

Men adopt these strategies because they work — for men. They are just giving out what they like to get. If you ask most men 'for a screw' or sensuously fondle their genitals, many will jump at the chance to have sex. This is because men, thanks to the desire enhancing effects of testosterone, have a higher baseline of sexual tension. They don't need their sexual tension to be built up — it's automatically there. Many men are constantly looking for ways to reduce or release sexual tension. On a graph, a man's sexual tension would look like this:

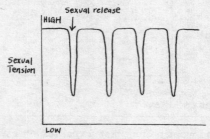

Women, on the other hand, have a low background level of sexual tension. In order to be sexually receptive, many women will need to have their level of sexual tension built up before they feel any need for sexual release.

This is where the CISS continuum can be really helpful. A woman's sexual tension can be built up through *communication* — by asking her about her day, listening to her anxieties and worries, telling her about some aspect of your own day. This will edge her into emotional *intimacy*. Working to increase those lovely feelings of closeness will move her towards *sensuality*.

Once the sensual stage is firmly established, that's the time to initiate *sex*, either verbally or nonverbally, according to her preferences. The CISS continuum builds up sexual tension in women so you are much more likely to get a positive answer at that time. If you initiate sex without putting any work into communication, intimacy or sensuality, you can look forward to hearing 'No' on a regular basis.

The graph on the next page reminds us how important relationship factors are in generating female willingness. If you fight, criticise or ignore each other all day, no sexual tension will build up for a woman. Women experience 23 and a half-hour foreplay — everything that happens to a woman impacts on her capacity for desire and arousal. If you want more frequent, passionate sex with your female partner, you need to put in the groundwork before you initiate. On a graph, a woman's sexual tension would look like this:

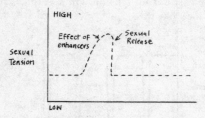

Conditions for good sex

Many men and women think that sexual response and pleasure are reflexes that automatically leap into action once the right buttons are pushed. In fact, sexual response is most likely to occur when the 'conditions' for sex are right. These conditions are factors that increase sexual interest and responsivity. The best way to describe conditions for good sex is to use the analogy of driving a car.

When I drive my car, if I want to have a good driving experience, I meet certain conditions. I do this automatically without thinking about it most of the time. For example, I sit in the front seat with my hands on the wheel (not in the back seat or the boot). I open my eyes, and I drive on the road (not through a muddy paddock or down a cliff). When it's raining I use the wipers, and when it's dark I switch on the headlights. I put my feet on the pedals, using the brake to stop and the accelerator to go ahead. I use my blinkers, put petrol and oil in the car, and organise a regular service. If I neglected to do any one of these things I wouldn't expect to have a good driving experience. These are my conditions for good driving.

We all have conditions for good sex. These conditions are

especially important to women of all ages, lower drive partners of either sex, and to men as they get older.

Be your own sex therapist

Both partners should complete this exercise.

To discover your conditions for good sex, get a piece of paper and a pen and set aside half an hour or so. Think back to your best ever sexual experience or experiences. If you have never had a good sexual experience, imagine how it would be.

Now write down all the factors that made the experience(s) so good. They could be emotional factors (being in love or happy and relaxed), physical factors (feeling fit, well and sober), relationship factors (feeling safe or in love with your partner), situational factors such as privacy or timing.

Next think of your worst (or your imagined worst) sexual experiences. Write down all the factors that made those experiences so unsatisfactory.

What you have now is a list of positive and negative factors that are your basic *conditions for good sex*. Write them out carefully and discuss them with your partner.

If you wish to initiate sexual activity with your partner, it is in your best interests to make sure that his or her sexual conditions are met.

What is most exciting about these concepts is that they give the higher drive partner something constructive to do, rather than engaging in destructive pursuer behaviours which reduce their partner's sexual interest and drive them away.

The physical approach

Prue: I know when Graeme wants sex. He suddenly grows five extra hands and they are all over me at once. He chooses the worst possible times to grope me, and all it does is turn me off.

Men often make the mistake of approaching a woman for sex in a direct physical fashion not realising that there is a big difference between male and female sensuality. Men and women turn on in opposite ways. Men have 'central arousability', while women have 'peripheral arousability'. Men turn on from the centre out; to be more precise, from the genitals out. A man can be thinking of anything but sex, but if I go up to him and slip my hand down his pants, he'll probably smile. My touching of his genitals is a pleasurable experience. He might even ask my name or offer me dinner! Once his genitals are aroused, a man's arms and legs, feet and hands, lips and neck and other erogenous zones become more sensitive to erotic stimulation.

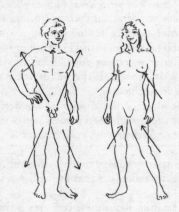

MALE AND FEMALE AROUSABILITY

A man can enjoy direct erotic stimulation even when he is totally unaroused. Women are the exact opposite. Women turn on from the toes, the fingertips and the hairline in. They turn on from the outside in. If you stimulate a woman's erogenous zones (breasts, buttocks and genitals) when she is not turned on, your touch will feel irritating, ticklish, uncomfortable or even painful. Clitoral stimulation when a woman is unaroused can feel quite distressing and often makes the clitoris numb to further stimulation.

Graeme: It always confused me how Prue would push me away if I tried to make out with her in the kitchen or the bathroom. She would say that I was hurting her and it felt bad. Yet a little later on when we had had a chat and a cuddle she would often take my hand and put it on her breast or between her legs. I didn't know what was going on. One minute she was cold and the next hot. Now I understand that she had started to get turned on through our emotional connecting and was ready for more direct fondling and touching.

It's not until a woman has been prepared by CISS and stimulated peripherally by non-erogenous stimulation — holding hands, stroking of the arms, kissing of the fingers and neck, caressing of the feet, legs and thighs, plenty of gentle lip, ear, cheek and fore-head stimulation — that she becomes receptive to more direct stimulation of the breasts and genitals.

Women turn on from the outside in, while men turn on from the inside out. We usually give what we like to get. While men err by approaching a woman too directly in a physical and verbal way, women often don't give their men enough erotic stimulation when they want it.

Graeme: Prue's busy stroking my hair, kissing my fingers and massaging my legs and back, and all I can think of is: 'Honey, when are you going to get to where the action *really* is! Forget the hair and the feet. Try down there — between my legs!'

When it is the man who has the lower desire in the partnership, direct sexual overtures may be too confronting. Asking a man for sex directly will often lead to a 'No'. Further attempts to initiate feel like pressure to perform and close off all possibility of sexual connection. A gentler way to initiate sex with a man is to display availability for sex.

Geraldine: When I get into bed at night I always wear a nightie and knickers. If I leave my knickers on it's a sign that I'm not interested in sex, but if they are off it's quite another matter.

The signals could be what you wear, what you cook for dinner, how you kiss, what time you go to bed, anything that tells him it's safe for him to make a sexual move. If he doesn't take the hint, you can start to negotiate your sexual hierarchy and see what he might be up for.

Verbal initiation — words of love

There is 'he-language' and 'she-language' around sex. She is much more likely to talk in terms of making love, sleeping together, intimacy, seduction, passion. He is more likely to use terms like bang, naughty, root, quickie, screw, shag and the good old four letter f–. Men and women must learn the language their partner finds most acceptable and inviting if they want to entice him or her into sex.

> Graeme: I'm much more likely to get a 'Yes' from Prue if I suggest we have a kiss and a cuddle than if I tell her I want to get into her pants.
> Prue: Graeme loves to hear me talk raunchy. He likes it when I use gutter terms for anatomical parts and sex acts. When I indulge him, he gets really excited.

It's easy to find out what language your partner likes — he or she is probably using it to unsuccessfully get you in the mood for sex! Sexy talk or romantic phrases may not come naturally to you, but your partner will appreciate your efforts to tune into their erotic needs.

When pursuers learn to initiate skilfully, both verbally and non verbally, and make the effort to approach sensitively, their mates feel secure in the knowledge that the goal is not just anonymous sexual release, where just anyone would do, but lovemaking and emotional contact as well. It's important to feel that your partner doesn't just want sex — more than anything, you must feel that your partner wants you.

TUNING INTO YOUR NEEDS

When we ask for sex, are we just looking for sexual release through orgasm? Sometimes this may be all there is to it but more often than not, sexual activity between loving partners is much more complicated than that. Initiation of sex should be seen *as an expression of a range of needs* that are both sexual and nonsexual, rather than just as a demand for sexual activity. When both partners grasp this concept, it gives couples with DD even more options to overcome their desire differences.

What is my true need?

Let's say that you, the pursuer, initiate sex with your partner and your partner chooses the bottom rung of the hierarchy, offering 'No sex'. At this stage you can make the choice to go off and masturbate or do nothing. If sexual relief was all you were after, an orgasm by any means should satisfy. But you might need something more than just sexual relief.

Ask yourself: 'What is my true need here? Is my need sexual or nonsexual? Can it be satisfied through nonsexual activity with my partner?' If the masturbation option doesn't appeal to you or is insufficient to meet your needs, consider the list of other reasons for Engaging in Sex set out on page 243 in Chapter 16.

Pursuers need to become clearer about their motives for wanting sex. Men frequently use sex to meet nonsexual needs such as intimacy, closeness, affection, reassurance and comfort. Yet there are nonsexual ways to meet all these needs.

- *Love and affection* can be expressed verbally and through nonsexual touch.
- *Fun* can be enjoyed by letting your inner children have a romp together — try tickling or a pillow fight. Or go see a funny movie.
- *Pleasure* — there are many nonsexual ways to give and receive pleasure — a cup of tea in bed is one and a surprise gift is another.
- *Passion* — passion can be found in every area of life, not just through sex. You can be passionate about your partner, your children, your friends, your hobbies, your work, your spiritual beliefs, or meaningful causes.

- *Sensuality* — sensuality is available 24 hours a day, with or without another person. It's anything that appeals to the five senses — recorded or live music, massage, perfumed oils and incense, soft lighting, a beautiful view, eating and drinking, massage, basking in the sun ...
- *Communication* — a chat or a deep discussion can fill this need.
- *Intimacy* — these needs can be met through self-disclosure and sharing.
- *Procreation* — even making babies can be done without resorting to sex (but it's more fun the old-fashioned way).
- *Sexual release* — masturbation.
- *Tension release* — progressive muscular relaxation, meditation or vigorous exercise.
- *Affirmation of desirability* — acknowledgment, praise and compliments from your partner.
- *Security* — reassurance from your partner.
- *Affirmation of gender* — acknowledgment and appreciation from your partner.
- *Nurturing* — anything from a good loving cuddle to a special dinner.
- *Comfort* — nothing beats a hug for comfort, except perhaps a good cry.
- *Reward* — appreciation can be shown in many different ways.
- *To get to sleep* — try a warm bath, a glass of hot milk or a back rub.
- *To please one's partner* — ask your partner what you can do to delight them — there's more than one way to pluck a duck.
- *Skin hunger* — massage, foot rub, scalp massage.

So if even if your partner says 'No' to sex when you initiate, you can still negotiate to get your nonsexual needs met in one way or another.

Be your own sex therapist

Pursuers: Apart from sexual desire, what other five reasons for sex motivate you most strongly?

Increasing the distancer's motivation to be sexual

The Reasons for Engaging in Sex list can also be used by the distancer to find lots of good reasons to be sexually active, even in the absence of desire. After all, for many people in the neutral, available and disinterested zones, a strong urge to engage in sex comes along only rarely, and is often fleeting, gone before they can act on it.

Lower drive partners can avail themselves of a whole range of reasons to be sexual other than desire. They need to be looking at sex from the point of view of what they can *get* out of sex, not what they can give. You may not want sex, but you could well have other needs that can be met through partner contact. Your partner might be wanting an orgasm while you just want a cuddle — why can't you both get what you want?

Sex is essentially a selfish activity. This is not a bad notion. It acknowledges that at the peak of pleasure our focus is not necessarily on the wonder of our partner but more on our own physical and sexual ecstasy. Good lovers are selfish to the extent that they feel entitled to ask their partner for what they need. They feel good about receiving pleasure as well as giving it. They take responsibility for their own sexual satisfaction and don't expect their partners to create all the magic on their own.

Be your own sex therapist

Distancers: If your desire is on the low side, what can you get out of intimate contact with your partner that will fulfil and satisfy you? Make a list of five factors, other than sexual desire, which might motivate you to engage in physical relations.

Discuss with your partner.

When you know that you are getting something out of having a physical relationship with your partner, it is much easier to give in return.

The Soft 'No' Sandwich

If one partner initiates sex and the other says 'Yes', there's no problem. You simply negotiate the type of sexual activity and the degree of participation from choices on the sexual hierarchy, depending on the less interested partner's desire for involvement.

But what if you don't want to have sex this time? How do you normally decline sexual activity with your partner? Do you ignore nonverbal overtures? Do you roll over and pretend to be asleep? Do you push your partner's hand away? Do you say: 'I'm too tired.' 'I have a headache.' 'It's too late. I have to get up in the morning.' 'You only had it last night (last week, last month, last year).' 'Not again.' 'You must be kidding.' 'Over my dead body.'...?

Whenever you say 'No' to a sexually or emotionally needy person it feels like 'No' forever. Men especially are very vulnerable when sexually aroused, and saying 'No' harshly or without tact to a man can be very hurtful. In order to keep the lines of sexual negotiation open, distancers must learn to say 'No' in a way that keeps the closeness and good feelings alive in the relationship.

This can be achieved by using the *soft 'No' technique*. This strategy is adapted from a management technique which states that you should always couch a negative between two positives. I call it the soft 'No' sandwich because the 'No' is like the filling between two slices of delicious freshly baked bread. Sandwiched in the middle of two positives, a 'No' loses its sting.

The first layer of the sandwich involves reassurance of some sort. Then the soft 'No', followed by an offer of sexual or nonsexual options to meet the pursuer's needs.

Reassurance

the Soft 'No'

Options for higher drive partner — Sexual and nonsexual

Reassurance slice

Reassurance might sound like this:

- I really love what we're doing right now ...
- I love it that you desire me so much ...
- I love you and your gorgeous body ...
- You want me so much — it makes me feel great ...
- You're the best husband in the world ...
- Every man would want a lady like you ...
  and so on.

Soft 'No' filling

Follow up your reassurance with a soft 'No':

- I love it that you desire me so much, *but I don't really feel like intercourse tonight* ...
- Every man would want a lady like you. *I think it's too late to have full on sex now because we have to get up early in the morning* ...

Follow your 'Reassurance slice' and your 'No filling' with 'Options for the Higher Drive Partner slice' which will depend on the lower drive partner's willingness to be sexual. This format makes it much easier for the higher drive partner to accept a 'No' graciously.

Options for the higher drive partner

If the distancer is unsure about being sexual
If the distancer is ambivalent about physical relations, willingness may be generated by looking at the Reasons for Engaging in Sex list. The focus is on what the lower drive partner can get out of having intimate physical contact. Remember to be selfish — ask yourself, 'What's in it for me?'

> **Claudia:** Joe wants sex a couple of times a week, while I'm only horny just before and after my periods. But I can usually think of a good reason to cuddle up and have some fun and games with him most of the time. I love to kiss and hug him. I have a lot of sex just so I can enjoy that part of it. Another reason is comfort. I need his big warm

body close to mine to feel safe and secure. They're good enough reasons for me.

If the distancer isn't willing to be sexual

If the pursuer's sexual tension is high, masturbation is the obvious answer. If masturbation isn't fulfilling enough for the higher drive partner, he or she is looking for more than just sexual release from sex. This is a sign that nonsexual needs are present. The higher drive partner should ask themselves, 'What are my needs right now? Are they truly sexual needs? What can I share right now with my partner that would fulfil me but not involve sex?' Nonsexual needs can be met in a variety of ways as described above. A lower drive partner can say 'No' to sex but still meet his or her partner's nonsexual needs in other ways.

Another option is to decline sexual activity but both partners can commit to creating the best possible conditions for desire and sexual responsivity over the next few days. By putting more effort into nurturing and supporting the distancer, the pursuer can increase sexual willingness. This gives both partners something to work towards and look forward to.

> **Peta:** When Gerard wants sex mid-week and I'm not in the mood, he lies beside me and masturbates while I hold him. But we also make a plan to set aside time on the weekend to set the scene for a good sex session. He will help me with the shopping and chores. We'll pop out and have a bite to eat together at lunch, then we'll have a nap in the afternoon. After that there's a very good chance that I'll feel in the mood for some steamy sex.

Some couples opt for a combination of all of the above strategies, having a quickie or masturbation mid-week, meeting nonsexual needs nonsexually, and planning for quality sex on a day, night or weekend when they have more time and energy.

PUTTING THE SEXUAL HIERARCHY TO WORK

This chapter outlines a range of important strategies for couples with DD. It gives ideas on how to initiate sex with your partner and how to say 'No' gracefully. It provides options for the higher drive partner for meeting both sexual and nonsexual needs. Lower drive partners can tune into a range of different reasons for engaging in loving sex regardless of their level of sexual desire. Now it's time to bring all these strategies together and put the sexual hierarchy to work.

Step 1: Higher drive partner

Provide desire enhancers.

Observe your partner's conditions for sex.

Employ CISS components to increase willingness.

Approach your partner in a sensitive way — verbally or non-verbally.

Bring your sexual agenda out in the open — ask for what you want.

Accept your partner's answer gracefully, no matter what it is.

Be prepared to negotiate sexual or nonsexual activity.

Take responsibility for your own sexual fulfilment — masturbate if necessary.

Step 2: Lower drive partner

Develop a positive view of your partner's sexual needs.

View *sexual initiation* as an *expression of a range of needs*, not just a demand for sexual activity.

Use the soft 'No' sandwich.

If your desire is low look for other reasons to be sexual.

Be prepared to negotiate sexual or nonsexual activity.

Step 3: Meeting both partners' needs

If the less interested partner is willing to be sexual → negotiate the type of sexual activity and the level of participation, depending on the less interested partner's willingness to participate.

If the less interested partner is unsure → the less interested partner *can focus on reasons to be sexual other than desire.* Generate willingness through the Reasons for Engaging in Sex list. Ask yourself, 'What can I get out of this?'

If the less interested partner is unwilling to be sexual → decline sexual activity at this time, using the soft 'No' sandwich.

Negotiate sexual and nonsexual options:

- Masturbation for the higher drive partner

  and/or

- If nonsexual needs are present, ask 'What is the true need here?' 'Is sexual activity the only way to satisfy this need, or are there nonsexual ways to meet this need?' Negotiate nonsexual ways to meet the higher drive partner's needs

  and/or

- Commit to creating optimum conditions for desire and arousal in the near future.

The combined strategies of sexual initiation, the sexual hierarchy and the soft 'No' are set out in this simple flow chart:

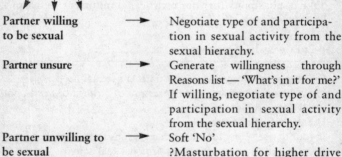

Initiation (verbal or nonverbal)

Partner willing to be sexual →	Negotiate type of and participation in sexual activity from the sexual hierarchy.
Partner unsure →	Generate willingness through Reasons list — 'What's in it for me?' If willing, negotiate type of and participation in sexual activity from the sexual hierarchy.
Partner unwilling to be sexual →	Soft 'No' ?Masturbation for higher drive partner +/- commit to optimising conditions for sex in near future +/- look for nonsexual ways to meet the higher drive partner's needs — 'What are my true needs?'

A win–win solution

The beauty of the sexual hierarchy is that it erases all the nasty, painful aspects brought into play by desire discrepancy and the P/D cycle. It provides hassle-free sex for both partners with no expectations, no pressures and no demands.

The success of the sexual hierarchy rests on a couple's ability to negotiate sexual and nonsexual options. When the sexual hierarchy is used correctly, both partners can get their needs met either immediately or in the near future while feeling good about each other and the relationship. It allows partners to make love *with* each other, rather than *to* each other. This is a win–win solution. Through this simple strategy it is possible for both partners, regardless of their levels of sexual desire, to achieve sexual compatibility and emotional and physical harmony with each other.

A SEXUAL VACATION

Although you might be keen to start using the sexual hierarchy immediately, under certain circumstances this is not a good idea. You may need a sexual vacation first. This is not, as you might think, a trip to a tropical island where you can indulge in every sexual whim you have ever dreamed of. In fact, it's quite the opposite. There will be many couples reading this book whose relationships have been so dreadfully damaged by DD and other relationship problems that they can barely speak to each other, let alone negotiate sexual activity. They may no longer be sharing the same bed or bedroom. They may not have had sex for years.

Perhaps you and your partner fall into this category. Before you can put the sexual hierarchy into action, before you can neutralise the P/D cycle, you need a complete rest from DD and its toxic influence in order to heal your relationship. *This means the total cessation of any sexual contact at all for a variable period of time.* In her book *The Sexual Healing Journey*, Wendy Maltz calls this a 'healing vacation from sex'.

The distancer is usually delighted by this opportunity to take a break from the hassles of sex. However, the pursuer often finds this idea much more difficult to swallow. Why might you benefit from a complete break from sex?

Couples whose love and sex life have been damaged by DD are often so disconnected and distrustful of each other that there is no basis left for loving, sexual negotiation. Often these couples rarely touch, let alone enjoy any form of sex. For couples like this, a vacation from sex is a must in order to rebuild their emotional, sensual and sexual relationship. One of the symptoms of this sexual breakdown is reduced or absent affectionate behaviour and infrequent sexual contact.

'Infrequent' sexual contact is a relative term. For a low desire couple, once a month might be just right. However, if your sexual frequency used to be three or four times a week and now it's once a month, every six weeks or less frequent, there is probably something going on that needs attention.

Only you can tell if you both need a complete break from sex for a while. I advise you to err on the conservative side — if you suspect you might benefit from such a break, take it. If you don't really need it, you will make such rapid progress with the program that you will be back having sex before you know it.

If you need a sexual healing vacation, agree to take a complete break from sexual relations. Begin with three months minimum. This may sound like forever to the pursuer who wants an instant fix, but many couples in this situation are often having sex less frequently than once every three months. *Both partners must make a firm and equal commitment to the sexual vacation, otherwise there is no point in even starting it.*

In essence, the sexual vacation allows couples to reconnect with each other in the same way they began their relationship — through coupling activities which build recreational intimacy and through non-demand affection which builds emotional and sexual closeness. This healing vacation allows the introduction of the sorts of activities couples enjoy during courtship. Often this sort of platonic closeness and intimate contact has been studiously avoided by the distancer for years in case it might be seen as an open door to sex. For the pursuer any opportunity to press for sex has often been too much to resist, so that closeness and physical intimacy become inextricably linked with pressure to go further and have sex. The only way to get out of this cycle and re-create physical closeness is to ban sexual activity so that the distancer can once again learn to enjoy intimate contact without feeling threatened.

Be your own sex therapist

Pursuers: Would a break from sex help your partner, your relationship and your sex life? It may seem like a sacrifice to pass up sexual activity for three to six months, but ask yourself how much sex you will actually be missing out on. Of course, during this time you can enjoy as much self-pleasuring as you wish. The benefit to you will be a much closer, more affectionate relationship with your partner and the knowledge that you are certainly doing your bit to exit from the P/D cycle. However, simply stopping sex is not enough. You must work diligently with your partner to improve your relationship during this time.

Distancers: This 'vacation' from sex is undertaken by both of you with the goal of re-creating emotional and sexual closeness. For this strategy to work, you cannot just retire from sexual activity and do nothing. You must work with your partner to improve emotional and sensual closeness in your relationship. This vacation is an active time giving you the chance to reconstruct your relationship.

HEALING YOUR RELATIONSHIP

Once you have both committed to take a healing break from sex, make plans to use the first four weeks to improve your relationship generally, using the suggestions given in Chapters 11 to 15. Having fun and enjoying activities together are especially important for re-creating passion, excitement and desire. Put the coupling activities exercise on pages 210–12 to good use and enjoy some quality time together. If you think you need relationship counselling, now is the time to start.

Reintroducing touch

As your relationship heals, you can begin to reintroduce loving touch. Remember how babies learn about touch — first they enjoy comforting, nurturing touch, then playful touch, sensual touch and finally sexual touch. Physical closeness must be reintroduced in this same gradual fashion.

To begin with, you might like to try *holding hands* on one of your outings. It might feel uncomfortable at first, but persist. See it as a homework task. You might also like to start giving each other greeting *kisses hello and goodbye* on a daily basis. Couples with DD often forfeit these gentle, bonding elements from their relationships.

After a couple of weeks of simple kisses and holding hands, you might like to try *lying beside each other*, very close, side by side fully clothed for at least half an hour two or three times a week. A good way to commence this activity is to take a book or newspaper and lie down together very close side by side. Even if it feels odd, do it. When you feel ready, leave the reading matter aside and just lie down together and talk. Avoid contentious issues. This is a peaceful, quiet time together.

Once this feels OK, *take turns in holding each other* loosely for 5 or 10 minutes. A lovely exercise described by Judith Maltz involves lying, fully clothed, with your head on your partner's chest listening to his or her heart beat. The next step up is mutual holding. Try to achieve 5 or 10 minutes of *mutual holding* each day, sitting or lying. Keep holding hands and greeting each other affectionately. You can now add *greeting hugs* to your repertoire.

You are making progress if your feelings of comfort with this physical closeness are increasing. If no progress is being made, look for unresolved issues or ongoing unpleasantness in your relationship. Make sure you deal with these problems or they will continue to poison your intimate relationship. Remember: good loving is the only basis for great sex. If your relationship is running smoothly and you are still not making adequate progress, don't avoid these connecting exercises — instead, do them more frequently. You will make faster progress if you practise these rebuilding exercises every day.

By now you will be kissing each other hello and goodbye lightly, holding hands whenever practical, lying together fully clothed, hugging affectionately and holding each other. None of this activity should *ever* lead to sexual or erotic stimulation at this stage, even if you both feel tempted. This would interfere with the whole process of rebuilding trust and sensual healing. You made a commitment to a vacation from sex — stick to it through to the end.

Reintroducing *playful touch* is a lot of fun. Think back to childhood games such as pat-a-cake (don't forget to sing the song), tips, cat's cradle, and writing silly messages on your partner's palm with your finger. Gentle pillow fights and arm wrestles are also a good way to get back in touch. Try games like intzy-wintzy spider and round-and-round-the-garden-goes-the-teddy-bear. Blow raspberries on your partner's tummy. Tickle their feet. Anything you can think of that is fun and involves gentle touch will do. Old-fashioned dancing is a lovely way to enjoy close physical contact. Engage in these fun activities twice a week. In the meantime, keep up those coupling activities and work on improving your relationship generally.

After a month or six weeks of gentle, affectionate touching, you can begin to be more sensual with each other. Using the factors listed in your Conditions exercise for good sex (page 285), make sure you are creating an optimum atmosphere for being close and loving together. *Sensual touch* could include giving and receiving a massage with or without lotion or oil, combing your partner's hair, rubbing their feet or massaging their shoulders, or scratching their back. Take turns, experiment with soft and firm touch, and give each other feedback about what feels good. Daily sensual contact is best, even for only a short time — say 5 or 10 minutes. Keep increasing affectionate contact with each other. It doesn't have to be serious. Be playful and have fun.

As you progress over a few weeks with this stage you can start *lying together partially clothed or without clothing and stroking each other* — don't touch each other's breasts, genitals or buttocks, and don't allow any sexual contact. You may get aroused, but this isn't the object of the exercise. You are trying to rebuild a trusting, intimate physical relationship, not striving for sexual relief. Be strong about this, as starting sex too soon can undo all your good work.

For the pursuer, especially, this can be a difficult time, but either of you should feel free to masturbate privately after the exercises if you feel sexually frustrated. At this stage you might like to *take a bath or shower together* a couple of times a week, just to get used to being naked together again. Sensual touching should take place at least three times a week for about 20 minutes to half an hour. Setting aside this time to be together is good discipline for couples who often make sex and intimate contact a low priority in their lives. If you are finding it hard to find the time — and you will — make sure you have your priorities right.

Once you feel comfortable lying together naked and you're feeling good about non-genital touching, you can start *gentle erotic stimulation* (genitals, breasts and buttocks). Make sure you enjoy plenty of sensual connection before you begin erotic touching. The aim here is not necessarily arousal and orgasm, but to give each other feedback about what feels good and what doesn't. You might like to tell your partner to touch harder or softer, faster or slower, here or there. Once again, 20 minutes to half an hour is enough, at least three times a week. You should continue to have regular recreational intimacy plus working together to reduce conflict and increase intimacy and trust throughout your healing vacation.

After three months of this gentle reintroduction to touching and sensuality you might be ready for the *sexual hierarchy*. Notice I didn't say ready for 'intercourse' — remember, penetrative sex is not the be-all and end-all. Rather, you are ready to begin negotiation about sexual participation and activity. If you need longer, take more time. The worst thing you can do is to hurry this process.

If you need a break from sex to heal your relationship, give yourselves this gift. Three to six months is a very small investment to make to get your sex life back on track.

ADVICE FOR THE HIGHER DRIVE PARTNER

Here are some tips for the higher drive partner to keep in mind.
- *Stop pursuing*. Reduce pursuing behaviours and take control of automatic responses to sexual situations. Stop reacting badly

and manipulating your partner for sex. Ask more directly for sex, rather than trying to coerce or persuade your partner to have sex. Redirect your energy out of the P/D cycle. Instead of putting energy into pursuing, try improving the relationship.

- *Accept minimal participation sex.* Get your head around the fact that great sex does not have to mean fully participatory intercourse with all the trimmings. Sex is a shared emotional and physical experience — nothing more, nothing less. Don't always demand a full five-course sexual meal when a sandwich will take away your hunger pangs just as well.

- *Be rational.* Keep a high level of awareness of what you are thinking and feeling. Cultivate the sort of thinking that reduces uncomfortable feelings and helps you to feel good about the situation. You may not be getting all the sex you want or sex how you want it, but this isn't the end of the world.

- *Ban on sex.* If your relationship has been damaged by DD, it can be in your best interests to suggest a healing vacation from sex. Sometimes you have to give before you can get.

- *Increase non-demand affection.* Don't only touch your partner when you are initiating sex. Keep up a high level of affectionate, loving contact and keep your wandering hands to yourself (literally). If you are a man, remember that while sex makes men feel loved, being loved makes women feel like sex. Make your partner feel like you want *her*, not just sex.

- *Desire can be created.* If your partner has a low level of desire for sex, willingness to be sexual can be built through your attention to your partner's enhancers and their conditions for good sex. Your behaviour and attitudes can go a long way to increasing sexual frequency with your partner. If desire is low, make sure your relationship is in tip-top shape and your partner's inhibitors are reduced to a minimum.

- *Broaden your sexual repertoire.* You may find it easier to expand your sexual repertoire than your partner does. If so, do all that you can to increase their willingness to experiment. This may mean behaviour exchange where, for example, you meet some needs for them outside the bedroom in exchange for a more adventurous attitude in the bedroom. Praise every step in the right direction.

- *Accept that your partner may need extra stimulation to get in the mood*. This might mean more time, more romance, more stimulation, or the use of erotica, sex toys, or whatever. Don't feel inadequate or that you are not 'enough'. When desire is low, arousal needs to be actively encouraged.

- *Make sex more enticing*. This means finding out what sort of sex your partner enjoys and providing it. You can't expect your partner to engage in sensual and sexual activities that aren't pleasurable.

- *Accept that you might always be the sexual initiator*. Many pursuers long to be approached for sex, but this may not be possible in your relationship. Don't take this personally. If you confuse being loved with being lusted over, you will make yourself miserable. It is possible to love a partner dearly and still have a low level of sexual desire.

- *Make sure that when you initiate sex, it is what you really want*. Many pursuers initiate sex out of habit, without stopping to think what they really want. Examine your needs, both sexual and non-sexual, and ask yourself how you can best meet them. Make sure you meet your nonsexual needs through non-sexual means. For instance, if you long for closeness, experience this emotionally rather than physically.

- *Make it easy*. If you really want partner sex from a disinterested partner, why not get yourself turned on and get them to join in just at the end?

- *Accept a 'No' graciously*. Don't sulk or fret. Using the sexual hierarchy, if you want sex you can always have it, regardless of whether your partner wants to participate or not. If a solo orgasm is not enough to fulfil you, negotiate with your partner to get your nonsexual needs met — refer to the Reasons list.

- *Don't take a 'No' personally*. Remember, a 'No' is not a personal rejection, simply a decision not to be involved sexually at that moment. Your partner must be able to say 'No' to sex to be able to truly say 'Yes'.

- *Accept 'off ramping' at any stage*. You wouldn't wish your partner to engage in sexual activity that isn't pleasing to them. This is sexual coercion. Allow your partner to participate up to the level of their interest and enjoyment — if they need to opt

out, allow them to 'off ramp' at any stage, even during intercourse. This permission to off ramp is very important in
cultivating a lower drive partner's willingness to commence
physical relations. If they know they can stop at any stage, they
will feel more in control and more likely to participate fully. If
this happens, take it in your stride. If your partner is unable to
continue with sexual stimulation, look after yourself.

• *Take responsibility for your own sexuality.* Don't burden your
partner with the responsibility of keeping you sexually satisfied
and fulfilled. You may need to masturbate to reduce sexual tension. Take care not to artificially heighten your own desire
using excess erotic stimulation.

ADVICE FOR THE LOWER DRIVE PARTNER

• *Practise the soft 'No' technique.* Be sensitive about how you
deal with your partner when they are sexually or emotionally
needy. They are extremely vulnerable at these times. Using the
soft 'No' technique, you are in effect agreeing to meet your
partner's needs in a way that feels comfortable for you, either
sexually or nonsexually.
• *Reasons for sex.* If you have a low level of desire, find other
reasons to engage in sex using the Reasons list. Ask yourself
what you can get out of sex, rather than focusing on what you
are giving. Be selfish!
• *Take more responsibility for your own arousal.* Use whatever
strategies you need to fuel your flames of passion. Initiate activities you find arousing. This may mean wearing nice clothes,
taking a long relaxing bath, using erotica, talking, kissing.
Occasionally make the effort to go to bed turned on and surprise your partner.

Alexis: Some nights I lie in bed beside Mike and read my
novel. Inside the book I hide my sexy magazine, one of
those ones you can get from the newsagent where people
tell their naughty stories. When I am all turned on and
ready to go, I just lay down my book so Mike can see
what I've been reading. That's all the signal he needs. He

loves it when I make the effort to get myself in the mood.

This sort of strategy shortcuts desire and leads you straight into arousal. Once the lower drive partner gets going, they often derive great pleasure from sexual relations. Being responsible for your own arousal can get you over the 'speed hump' between desire and the beginnings of feeling aroused.

- *Expand your sexual repertoire and participate in a range of sexual options.* Don't regard sex as only referring to inter-course. Your partner might be just as happy with a cuddle and some manual stimulation as they would be with intercourse. By using the sexual hierarchy, you can say 'Yes' to sex more often.

- *Add more variety to your sex life.* Many couples complain that their sex life is just plain boring. They do the same thing, in the same place, at the same time. You too would get bored if you ate chops, peas and mashed potatoes every night of the week and you would rapidly lose the edge off your appetite. Expand your sexual repertoire and vary your styles of lovemaking.

- *Keep your motor running.* In order to increase your level of sexual interest you need to think yourself into sex, rather than out of it. This means focusing on the positives in your relation-ship rather than the negatives. Remember back to good times with your partner to build your positive feelings towards them. It means paying attention to subtle sexual cues in your life. Rather than averting your eyes when you see nudity, a sexy body or a steamy love scene, use the opportunity to cultivate positive thoughts about sex. Take fantasy breaks during the day where you anticipate pleasurable sexual activity that night. Each time you have a cup of tea or coffee, treat yourself to a sexual daydream to prime your desire pump. It's just as easy to think yourself into sex as it is to think yourself out of it.

- *Make your conditions for good sex clear to your partner.* You have conditions for experiencing sexual desire and arousal. Make these clear to your partner. Meeting conditions is a team effort. For example, if you need relaxation to feel sexual, ask your partner to put the kids to bed for you while you have a lie down.

- *Enjoy your willingness to be sexual.* Even if you don't have much sex drive you can feel good about your willingness to participate in physical relations with your partner.

- *Make sex a higher priority in your life.* Lower desire partners often put sex low on their list of priorities. Create a balance in your life where there is time and energy for you, for your relationship generally and for your sex life in particular.

- *Reduce solo sexual activity.* If you are in the habit of masturbating, this will dissipate any sexual urge you might be generating. It's best to avoid solo sex in order to enhance levels of sexual interest with your partner.

- *Negotiate 'off ramping' at any stage with your partner.* Many lower drive partners are reluctant to engage in sexual activity because they fear losing control and getting into a situation from which they can't retreat. Negotiate with your partner that, at any time, you have the right to off ramp — you can stop or slow down at any stage of the sexual proceedings. You can either stop sexual activity altogether, or you can go back to a lower level of sexual participation. For example, if you find that stimulating your partner becomes unenjoyable, offer them the opportunity to stimulate themselves. Or if oral sex or intercourse isn't enjoyable, go back to manual stimulation. Be open with your partner about how you are feeling during sexual activity. Don't engage in sexual activity unless you want to. Giving your partner 'mercy sex' will reduce your willingness to be sexual and get you back into the P/D cycle more quickly than you can say 'Jack Robinson'.

Decrease inhibitors/increase enhancers
The introduction of enhancers has been dealt with in previous chapters. The reduction or elimination of inhibitors will be dealt with in the next chapter.

Key Points ♥

Learn from your partner what sort of initiation techniques works best for them. Women's sexual tension often needs to be built up and they prefer a less direct physical approach than men do.

Conditions for good sex maximise desire and arousal and enhance willingness to be sexual.

The soft 'No' sandwich and the sexual hierarchy allow both partners to say 'Yes' to sex more often.

You and your partner may need to take a break from sex to heal your relationship and re-create communication, intimacy and sensuality.

Reducing Inhibitors of Sexual Desire

Regardless of whether your desire problem is lifelong low sexual interest, temporary inhibited sexual desire or desire discrepancy with your partner, you will benefit from enhancing your levels of sexual desire by minimising sexual inhibitors and maximising sexual enhancers. For couples to experience an abundance of sexual desire, both male and female enhancers should be included. The introduction of male preferred enhancers was explored in Chapter 9, while strategies for including the typical female preferred enhancers introduced in Chapter 8 were covered in Part 3, 'Healing Your Relationship'.

All the enhancers in the world won't be effective unless desire inhibitors are reduced or eliminated altogether. Four categories of desire inhibitors were introduced in Chapter 6:

- Physical inhibitors
- Psychological inhibitors
- Relationship inhibitors
- Situational inhibitors.

Reducing Physical Inhibitors

Good physical health is one of the prerequisites for robust sexual passion. A person who is tired, unwell, or under the influence of drugs or alcohol is likely to notice a drop in sexual interest.

Fatigue

A tired person is not a sexy person. Fatigue may be caused by:

- lack of sleep
- having too much on one's plate
- lack of adequate rest
- too little recreation
- not enough relaxation
- all of the above.

When there is a competition between the need for sleep and the need for sex, the need for sleep will usually win. Short-term loss of sleep may have little effect on sex drive but when the sleep deficit goes on for months, sex rapidly falls to the bottom of the list of priorities.

Some people are tired because they do too much. Modern life gets faster and faster, busier and busier. With mobile phones and home faxes, it's getting more difficult to get away from work with all its worries and responsibilities. Individuals who have problems with their sex drive are often juggling too many balls at one time. They are overloaded, with neither the time nor the energy for regular sex.

Be your own sex therapist

If you think that you may be overcommitted, this juggling exercise might confirm your suspicions. Get a sheet of paper and at the bottom draw a stick figure, the juggler ... you. Now draw some juggling balls. Make them large enough so you can write on each one. Label each ball with an activity, responsibility or commitment that occupies your time. On the next page you will see my current circus act.

If you are tired and have low sex drive, then you must make some changes. Now prioritise those balls. Are there any you can put down, either permanently or temporarily? Remember, this circus act goes on 24 hours a day, 7 days a week, 52 weeks a year. Don't make a clown of yourself. The rules when it comes to juggling too many balls are:

Prioritise
Delegate
Prune.

I am stunned by the number of people who fail to recognise their need for rest, relaxation and recreation. They complain they are tired and lack interest in sex, yet they work 90 hours a week, haven't had a holiday in five years and fill

> Life is one long process
> of getting tired.
> SAMUEL BUTLER
> ENGLISH POET

every spare moment away from work with activity. The body is not a machine. Even a machine would break down under these circumstances.

Even if you don't work a seven-day week, you may not realise there is a difference between recreation and relaxation. I asked one client with low sex drive what she did to relax when she wasn't working. 'Well,' she replied, 'On Monday night I do pottery, on Tuesday I go to martial arts, on Wednesday I do Toastmasters, Thursday's my Women's Group and on Friday I go out with the people from work. I'm so tired on weekends I just collapse.' No wonder!

It took me some time to convince this woman that recreation is not relaxation. Both are active processes, but relaxation is an activity of stillness. I believe that relaxation should be an essential part of everyday life. Whether it's meditation, progressive muscular relaxation, hypnosis, chanting a mantra or any other form of stilling activity, true relaxation holds the key to greater emotional and physical wellbeing.

A balance between work, play and relaxation is essential to a regular sex life. When *you* are exhausted, so is your libido.

Physical discomfort, pain or nausea

Expecting to be at your sexual peak when you are feeling off colour is unrealistic. If you have a cold, your back is aching or you have a splitting headache, sex is probably the last thing on your mind. Loss of interest in sex while you are unwell is usually temporary and your libido generally bounces back to normal when *you* do.

However, chronic illness or pain can really take its toll on desire. People with, for example, chronic back pain, arthritis, cancer or heart pain from angina often report a lowered interest in sex. Pain reduces sexual desire and inhibits sexual arousal. Even if you have desire, it's much more difficult to get turned on when you are in pain. Here is some general advice about sex for chronic pain sufferers:

- As the advertisement for painkillers on television says, 'If pain persists, see your doctor.' There may be more than your sex life at stake.

- Time your lovemaking and your pain medication. Usually it takes half to one hour for medication to work, so take your tablets some time before you plan to make love. Make sure your medication is effective in providing adequate pain relief.
- If pain and stiffness are a problem, have a warm bath before making love. A heating pad can also help. Keep the temperature of the room warm and comfortable.
- Time your lovemaking to the hour of the day when your pain is at its lowest.
- Support painful limbs or body parts with pillows.
- Alter lovemaking techniques to avoid increasing pain. Intercourse is often the most painful activity of them all. Outercourse is especially helpful for couples where one partner has pain. The pain-free partner might need to do most of the sexual pleasuring.

Some women suffer from dyspareunia, or pain during penetrative sex. This may be due to low arousal, menopause, or vaginal or pelvic problems. Intercourse should *never* be painful, so make sure you have a thorough check-up. For chronic dyspareunia, outercourse is an obvious choice.

Some men and women suffer from angina during lovemaking. They also worry that they might actually have a heart attack during sex. As long as you are fit enough to climb two flights of stairs, you are fit enough for sex. Take your anti-angina medication before you embark on the sexual preliminaries. This allows the headache that some people experience as a side effect of the medication to settle and prevents angina occurring during sex. Keep the room comfortably warm, and work up gradually to any sexual callisthenics. If you suffer chest discomfort, stop activity immediately. By the way, research suggests you are 10 times more likely to have a heart attack if you are in bed with someone who is not your spouse — from the heart point of view, infidelity is *not* a safer sex activity!

Poor general health

If only we spent as much time looking after our bodies as we do looking after our cars. High fat diets, lack of exercise, smoking and excessive alcohol intake can cause serious health problems. If you want to feel better both in and out of the bedroom, then get fit, give up smoking, cut down alcohol intake and eat well. However, too much exercise can blunt sexual desire. Exercise addicts often report little or no interest in sex. A moderate exercise routine appears to stimulate sexual appetite.

With regards to drinking, I recommend the 'four by two' rule. No more than four drinks per day for a man and no more than two drinks a day for a woman.

By the way, fellas, here is another good reason to give up smoking. Did you know that smoking not only helps to clog up the arteries to your heart and brain, but also narrows the tiny arteries that bring blood to your penis to create your erections? Many men who smoke heavily become impotent. Instead of the usual warnings about cancer and heart attacks, cigarette packets should carry the message, 'The More You Smoke, the Less You Poke'!

When you feel at your best, your sexual desire is maximised. Eat well, exercise regularly and control your weight — what's good for you is also good for your sex drive.

Chronic illness

There are many medical and surgical conditions that interfere with the sexual urge. Any condition that causes symptoms like pain, breathlessness, fatigue, nausea or lethargy will diminish sexual interest. Surgery that affects body image through scarring, amputation or prostheses will have the same effect. Sometimes it's not the illness that causes the problem but the medication prescribed to treat it. The effects may be short or long term.

Loss of a breast due to cancer has sexual implications for both partners. Cancer of the prostate and its different treatments often result in loss of erection and loss of sexual desire. Chemotherapy and radiotherapy for the treatment of cancer reduce sex drive dramatically, as well as affecting sexual function through erectile difficulties and vaginal dryness. Chronic kidney failure is well known for negatively affecting sexual desire. The surgical creation of stomas and the subsequent need to wear a bag can seriously interfere with a couple's sexual functioning. Transplant patients also suffer from sexual difficulties, including loss of sexual desire.

A list of medical and surgical conditions affecting desire can be found in Chapter 2. If you are unwell and have a lowered interest in sex, see your doctor for more specific advice.

Excess alcohol

Many people believe that alcohol is an aphrodisiac. However, any enhancement of sexual interest is more likely to be due to the relaxation and pleasant social circumstances usually associated with drinking than to the effects of the alcohol itself. Too much alcohol kills off passion.

> Candy
> is dandy
> But Liquor
> is quicker.
> OGDEN NASH
> AMERICAN HUMORIST

Alcohol and women

Studies suggest that while most drinking women expect alcohol to enhance their sexual response, in physical terms it does exactly the opposite. Research has shown that as the level of alcohol in the blood increases towards intoxication, vaginal responses decrease. Orgasm takes longer to achieve and is less intense. However, many women report that they desire and enjoy sex more when they are drinking. This is probably due to a decrease of anxiety rather than an increase of desire or arousal.

Alcohol and men

Alcohol is widely known for its negative effect on male sexual function. Alcoholics suffer from reduced levels of testosterone due to damage to the testes, as well as alcohol-induced brain and nerve damage. As a result, erectile problems and low desire are common. Alcohol dependency also has a significantly negative effect on relationships, and this in turn can reduce sexual desire.

> It provokes the desire but takes away the performance.
> WILLIAM SHAKESPEARE

Drugs of abuse

Opiates

Opiates and their derivatives such as heroin, morphine and

codeine reduce testosterone levels, inhibit sexual desire and arousal, and delay ejaculation and/or orgasm. For many addicts, opiate addiction takes the place of sexual activity. Sexual apathy is common in opiate addicts.

Marijuana (THC)
A small amount of marijuana heightens sexual interest and responsivity, stimulates erotic thoughts, and increases sensual and erotic feelings. Altered sense of time and touch and increased feelings of emotional closeness contribute to sexual enhancement with marijuana. However, these effects produce a false sense of intimacy, and with chronic use, THC can impede true intimacy between partners. Higher doses interfere with sexual activity and reduce sexual motivation. As THC is stored in the body tissues, its effects can accumulate over time with regular use. Chronic use affects fertility by reducing sperm counts and sperm motility and increasing abnormal sperm. Women may suffer from menstrual disturbances, and THC use during pregnancy can affect the developing baby.

Hallucinogens: LSD, ecstasy, angel dust and amphetamines
These drugs have both enhancing and inhibiting effects on sexual functioning. Often it is the personal or social situation that encourages sexual freedom rather than the effects of the drugs themselves. These drugs may facilitate sexual pleasure, but they may also result in the agony of a bad trip. As with THC, an illusion of intimacy can be created but true intimacy is inhibited.

Cocaine
Cocaine does increase desire, but it simultaneously inhibits orgasm in both sexes. This is often more distressing for women who have more difficulty reaching orgasm. Like alcohol, cocaine may impair judgment and lead to indiscriminate sexual behaviour. This is not a reflection of enhanced desire but of impaired thinking. With chronic cocaine use a man may become impotent even though desire may remain.

Prescribed medications

Prescribed medications can impair sexual interest. The most common inquiry is about the contraceptive Pill in women. The Pill contains two hormones in different combinations. Oestrogen stimulates desire and increases responsivity in women, while progesterone decreases desire. A change of contraceptive Pill can help some women to experience more sexual interest.

Finding the right Pill can be like finding a comfortable pair of shoes — you might have to try on several pairs before you get the right fit. However, if your relationship is in tatters, you're exhausted from looking after the children and worried about money, changing your Pill isn't going to help your sex drive. You must also attend to all the other factors as well.

Some drugs from the following categories are known to have a negative effect on sexual desire:
- Some diuretics
- Some blood pressure medications
- Beta blockers
- Calcium channel blockers
- Benzodiazepines
- Tricyclic antidepressants
- Monoamine oxidase inhibitors
- Newer antidepressants — SSRIs
- Lithium
- Anti-psychotics
- Appetite suppressants — desire up or down
- Stomach acid suppressants prescribed for ulcers.

If you think your medication might be affecting your sex drive, consult your doctor.

Hormonal changes

High prolactin and low testosterone will reduce sex drive. The effects of menopause, breastfeeding and pregnancy will be dealt with in detail in the next chapter.

REDUCING PSYCHOLOGICAL INHIBITORS

We all have our down days, when our thoughts are blue and we just can't crack a smile for anyone. These are the days when our interest in sex is likely to dwindle.

Lack of emotional wellbeing

Sex is not just a physical function — it is also an emotional experience. Feeling good stimulates sexual appetite. Feeling unhappy or stressed has the opposite effect. Most people have never been taught how to deal constructively with uncomfortable feelings. We are taught by our families to suppress feelings of sadness, fear or anger.

Unfortunately, when feelings are not dealt with they tend to grow, like a cancer. They intensify until they are overwhelming. For example, anxiety that is repressed becomes fear. If fear is pushed down and not dealt with, it can turn into panic. Resentment becomes anger and then rage. Sadness becomes depression and then despair. Once the feelings have grown and become distorted, they are not only harder to deal with effectively, but they are also harder to keep inside and can burst out inappropriately.

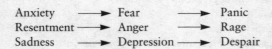

Anxiety   ⟶   Fear   ⟶   Panic
Resentment ⟶ Anger ⟶ Rage
Sadness   ⟶   Depression ⟶ Despair

If you are anxious or scared, then do something about it. Talk about your feelings. Write them down. Learn some coping skills. Face your fears and walk through them.

If you are resentful, then tell the appropriate person. Resentment in a relationship usually happens when our partner fails to meet our expectations. We have two choices — they can change their behaviour or we can change our expectations. Doing nothing will only make things worse.

If you are sad, then let the tears fall. Give yourself permission to feel and express your sadness, to talk about it and share it with others. If you have serious problems with feelings, counselling can teach you more constructive ways of dealing with them.

Depression

There are two types of depression — reactive and endogenous. Reactive depression is a sadness and grief in response to a painful life situation — loss of a job, a loved one, a pet, etc. Reactive depression may be severe but it is usually short-lived, resolving after a few months.

Endogenous depression is a chemical illness that responds to antidepressant medication and psychotherapy. Loss of interest in pleasurable activities is a hallmark sign of endogenous depression and this usually includes interest in sex. If you have lost interest in sex and you are feeling low, ask your doctor to assess you for depression. Depression can be a life-threatening illness, so diagnosis and proper treatment is essential.

Stress

Stress is any demand or pressure that induces physical or mental tension. It is the wear and tear of everyday life on a person. Stress is not in itself negative — without stress, life wouldn't exist. The only complete cure from stress is death!

Too much stress is bad for us. The best way to visualise the acute effects of stress is to think of your reaction when you get a fright. Your nervous system goes into the 'fight and flight' response: Your hair stands on end. Your pupils dilate. You break out in a sweat. Your heart rate, breathing and blood pressure head for the skies. Your skin goes pale and you may even faint. You might wet your pants or even worse.

This is the sympathetic nervous system in action, a primitive Cave Person survival response. It gets you ready to fight or run away from that sabre-toothed tiger or hairy mammoth. Muscular tension builds up in the shoulders and neck, making us ready to engage in hand-to-hand combat. Blood flows to the large muscles of the buttocks and thighs so that we can run away as fast as possible. Digestion and other non-vital activities of the body, including sex, are suspended. Mental alertness increases. The clotting ability of blood increases, preparing for possible injury.

Short-term anxiety like this can be life saving. But suppose, as happens all too often in the 1990s, the stress you are confronted with doesn't require action — for example, when you are in bumper-to-bumper traffic and late for an appointment. No movement, no escape and no action. Just stress. All stressed up and nowhere to go!

Our stress mobilisation system is non-specific; it responds to any demand situation — short or long term, whether it brings good news or bad news. In fact, good news is just as stressful as bad news — winning the lottery stresses the body in the same way that losing your job does, probably even more.

Be your own sex therapist

Do you suffer from any of these symptoms?
Headaches • swallowing difficultiess • heartburn • nausea • butterflies and stomach knots • cold sweats • neck aches • chronic fatigue • dizziness • chest pains • backaches • uinary frequency • muscle spasms • memory impairment • panic attacks • constipation • diarrhoea • insomnia • loss of sex drive.
These symptoms are common in people who are stressed.

Stress and sex don't mix. In fact, the sympathetic nervous system that mediates the 'fight and flight' response automatically shuts down the part of the nervous system that allows humans to become sexually aroused. For this reason it is difficult to be sexually aroused and uptight at the same time, especially for women. Stress management has many payoffs, including better health and a more enthusiastic sex life.

Stress management
Unfortunately, although many of us are experts at recognising our symptoms of stress, we do nothing about it. To manage stress you need to change the way you think about stress.

Remember that prevention is better than cure:
• Eat a balanced diet
• Take regular exercise — walking is great

- Make sure you get enough sleep
- Talk regularly to friends and family about how you're feeling
- Take regular time out to explore hobbies and interests
- Do something lighthearted — have fun
- Take annual holidays
- Set realistic short-term goals
- Say 'no' to excess demands
- Avoid drugs, especially the ones you prescribe for yourself — cigarettes and alcohol
- Relax or meditate daily
- Establish good friendships
- Spoil yourself
- Laugh
- Monitor stress levels regularly. Check your posture every time you look in the mirror. Check for jaw clenching and hunched shoulders — relax!

Here are some on-the-spot stress busters:

- Relaxation: Breathe in and out slowly and think 'relax'. Tense up muscle groups, hold tightly for a few seconds and then relax completely — repeat several times
- Tidy out a wallet, a drawer or a cupboard
- Do a crossword or jigsaw puzzle
- Go for a walk
- Do some sort of physical work
- Take a hot bath
- Relax to music with a rhythm slower than your heart beat.

Poor self-esteem

Self-esteem is our self-worth, how much we value ourselves. As I have said before, sex is essentially a selfish activity, as much about receiving pleasure as giving it. If you don't value yourself, you will find it difficult to believe that you deserve pleasure and all the other good things that sex can provide. If your self-esteem is poor, an excellent book to read is *Self Esteem* by Fanning and McKay (see Resources).

Poor sexual self- esteem — feelings of sexual inadequacy

No two people are alike in their sexual wants, needs and desires. Good sexual self-esteem means feeling good about your own individual sexuality. This is not an easy task, because of society's rigid attitudes to sex. We are sold the idea of a single 'normal' standard of sexual functioning that we are expected to match, regardless of our individual sexual preferences, attitudes and needs.

Fitting our sexuality into a single standard of sexual behaviour is like expecting everybody to fit into the same size T-shirt. This is a ridiculous notion but it is exactly what we do with our sexuality. We squeeze, mould and lop off parts of our sexuality to conform to some random standard of performance. Wouldn't it make more sense for each of us to slip into a sexual garment tailormade to fit us?

Poor sex education

If you suffered from an inadequate sex education as you grew up, you have plenty of company. Research has shown that only 10% of Australian children receive an adequate sex education. However, it's never too late to start. There are many books available about sex and relationships on the shelves of all large book shops in the health and psychology sections. A list of helpful books can be found in the Resources section at the back of this book.

Negative sexual attitudes

Most people are taught by their parents and other care givers that sex is bad, sexual feelings are wrong, and their bodies are dirty and shameful. Even parents who give adequate 'facts of life' lectures on human reproduction often fail to mention that sex is pleasurable, an expression of love and affection or, even more importantly, that sex can be fun!

These negative attitudes make it very difficult for people to enjoy their bodies and their sexuality. Sex for many people is a source of confusion, pain, disappointment and anxiety, and is bonded with guilt and shame. This is especially true of children who have been subjected to any form of sexual abuse.

Sexual abuse of children is more common than most people are prepared to believe. It has been estimated that 30% of women and perhaps 20% of men were abused as children. Abuse does not have to be penetration or molestation. Survivors of abuse can benefit from counselling and professional support. Wendy Maltz's book, *The Sexual Healing Journey*, gives advice to help overcome feelings of sexual shame.

Poor body image

One look at a glossy magazine or a glance at the TV and the message is clear: sex is only for the young and beautiful. If your body scores less than 10 out of 10, then forget about sex.

In order to truly want and enjoy sex, we must accept and enjoy our bodies. We must also look for the loveliness in our partners' bodies. Everyone has physical assets. Make the most of them. Obsession with thinness and eternal youthful beauty should be replaced by a focus on a healthy diet and regular exercise.

Instead of obsessing over how your body looks, give more attention to how it feels. Wear clothes that make you feel good, take care of your personal hygiene and maintain good grooming habits. You can help your lover to accept his or her body by acknowledging it on a regular basis. A simple phrase like 'What I enjoy about your body is ...' uttered every day or so can make all the difference.

> She is not fair to outward view
> As many maidens be;
> Her loveliness I never knew
> Until she smiled on me.
> Oh! then I saw her eye was bright,
> A well of love, a spring of light.
>
> HARTLEY COLERIDGE
> ENGLISH POET

Lack of pleasurable sexual thoughts and fantasies

Pleasurable sexual thoughts are crucial to fanning your flames of desire. If your thoughts are anti-sex, you will *feel* anti-sex. Many people are uncomfortable about their sexual thoughts and fantasies. They believe that if they think about something, it is a sign that they want to act on it. Fantasies are erotic thoughts, not suppressed wishes. Just because you think about something sexual, it doesn't mean you will up and do it. You can safely daydream about sexual acts that you would never in a million years carry out. Often the most exciting fantasies are the most taboo ones. Fantasies about sex with someone of the same gender, or erotic thoughts about a person, or people other than your partner are common sources of anxiety. These types of fantasies are perfectly normal.

Unless you entertain positive sexual thoughts and enthusiastically anticipate sex, you will drive yourself away from sexual activity. Engaging in positive fantasies about sex will increase your motivation to be sexual. Make a concerted effort to think pro sex. Fantasies don't have to be outrageous or kinky. Some of your most powerful fantasies may be memories of exciting times with your partner, or just the idea of being mutually close and loving.

During the day, try to regularly entertain positive thoughts about sex and your partner and this will help to prime your sexual pump. Use fantasies during lovemaking to increase your sexual arousal. Many women find that they cannot get aroused or achieve orgasm without the help of vivid sexual fantasies.

Find material to add to your 'fantasy library' from movies, books or erotica that turns you on. Nancy Friday's excellent books on sexual fantasy are an abundant source of erotic ideas for both men and women (see Resources).

REDUCING RELATIONSHIP INHIBITORS

Relationship inhibitors, except for sexual difficulties, were examined in detail in Section 3, 'Healing Your Relationship'.

Coping with sexual difficulties

Satisfying sexual functioning enhances desire and closeness, while sexual difficulties have the opposite effect. Couples may encounter a range of sexual difficulties.

Erectile difficulties

All men will have difficulty with erections at some time in their lives. Erectile difficulties, or impotence, may result from physical or psychological problems, or both. The older a man is, the more likely he is to have problems with erections. Physical problems contributing to erectile difficulties include hardening of the arteries, smoking, excessive alcohol intake, diabetes, extensive prostatic or pelvic surgery, multiple sclerosis, hormonal problems and prescribed medications. Psychological contributors include high levels of performance anxiety, guilt, shame, anger and resentment.

There are many different treatments available for erectile difficulties. *Counselling* involves education to reduce anxiety and make expectations more realistic. For men with psychologically-based impotence, there are programs to follow at home which can help them to gain and maintain stronger erections. Best results are achieved if your partner is also involved in the treatment program. To learn more about how to deal with erectile difficulties I recommend you read *Men and Sex* by Bernard Zilbergeld (see Resources).

Other options for men with erectile problems include:

- *Injection therapy*. A man can be taught how to inject a drug called prostaglandin into the side of his penis which rapidly creates a strong and lasting erection each time.
- *Vacuum devices*. A specially designed clear plastic cylinder with an air pump attached is placed over the penis. A vacuum is created, making the penis firm, and a constriction band is slipped onto the base of the penis to maintain the erection. The band can be left in place for up to half an hour. Orgasm and ejaculation occur as normal, although semen may not appear after ejaculation until after the band is removed.
- *Implants*. In this surgical treatment, semi-rigid rods or saline inflated cylinders are inserted into the shaft of the penis under general anaesthetic. An erection can then be created on demand. Orgasm and ejaculation occur as normal.

If you have problems with erections, see your doctor for advice and referral to an impotence specialist if necessary.

Premature ejaculation

Premature or rapid ejaculation is a very common experience, blown way out of proportion (excuse the pun) by myths about how long intercourse should last. Control of ejaculation depends on:

- the man's age (older men tend to last longer)
- his level of anxiety (the more anxious he is, the faster he comes)
- the time since he last ejaculated (infrequent orgasms make men more 'trigger happy')
- the partner's attitude to her man's sexual functioning — an unsupportive, critical partner will increase anxiety and reduce time to orgasm.

Rapid ejaculation is a very common experience with desire discrepancy because usually, by the time intercourse occurs, 'it's been a long time between drinks'.

> **Amber:** We would go for weeks without sex and when we did make love it would be over in a few moments. I realised after counselling that it was unrealistic for me to expect Jonathon to last a long time under the circumstances and that it was up to me to teach him other ways to bring me off. When he became more skilled at pleasing me without intercourse, it took the pressure off both of us.

It is quite natural for a man to ejaculate shortly after penetration, especially if he has already spent plenty of time arousing his partner. Rather than focusing on the duration of intercourse, we should pay more attention to ways of achieving sexual satisfaction for both partners that don't rely solely on penetrative sex.

It is fairly simple to gain greater control of ejaculation. A straightforward program, set out in *Men and Sex* (see Resources), can be followed at home. Once again, if a man is in a relationship it is very helpful if his partner can be involved. Other options include:

- putting more focus on lovemaking that doesn't involve intercourse
- having more frequent sexual contact and orgasms with a partner

- masturbating more often
- masturbating before sexual interactions with a partner
- learning muscular relaxation techniques.

I don't recommend the following treatments for rapid ejaculation:

- Injection therapy as used by men with erection problems, which sustains a prolonged erection regardless of ejaculation.
- Numbing sprays and ointments from sex shops or chemists. The idea of having a numb penis defeats the purpose of making love.

Delayed ejaculation

This is not a common problem, but it is a distressing one. Men with delayed (or retarded ejaculation) can gain and maintain strong erections, but they have problems achieving orgasm with a partner. There may or may not be a problem with orgasm during self-pleasuring. Men with this problem have difficulty getting and staying aroused, although they have no problems with erection. Treatment aimed at enhancing a man's arousal and decreasing his anxiety should be supervised by a sex therapist.

Low arousal in women

All women will experience problems with arousal at some time. This may present as difficulty having an orgasm, painful sex, or problems enjoying sexual touching and activity. Women may have problems getting turned on when they are self-pleasuring, as well as when they are with a partner, or they may find that they can get turned on by themselves but not with a partner.

Sexual enjoyment is a learned skill, acquired through repeated positive sensual and sexual experiences. To enjoy sex more, women need to learn to relax and take pleasure from sensual and sexual experiences, first on their own and then with their partners.

Women who have had negative sexual experiences, such as sexual abuse, assault, rape, harassment or molestation, may need to heal sexual trauma before they can learn to enjoy sex.

Orgasmic problems in women

Many women who seek help for orgasmic problems don't actually have a 'sexual' problem — more often than not they (and/or their partners) have rigid expectations about how a woman *should* have an orgasm. Women can often climax on their own but not with their partner; or they can achieve an orgasm with their partner but not through intercourse; or they can only have an orgasm using a vibrator. Unfortunately, most of these women and their partners cling to the idea that the only 'real' orgasm occurs through partner stimulation, preferably through penis-in-vagina intercourse.

Shere Hite, in her research in the 1970s, found that only 30% of women can achieve an orgasm through intercourse alone. Hite found that 40% of women need clitoral stimulation, either manual, oral or using a vibrator, before during or after intercourse, to reach climax. According to Hite's research, reaching climax through intercourse is the exception rather than the rule.

Women who can climax on their own but not with a partner usually have problems relaxing during partner sex and/or difficulties communicating with their partner about what they like. However, even with the best communication in the world, it's not always easy for men to make the right moves at the right time to regularly bring a woman to orgasm. Many a woman would be better off stimulating herself or using a vibrator during lovemaking, than striving to have an orgasm through intercourse or struggling to teach a partner to do what she can so readily do for herself.

Certainly there are some women who have difficulty achieving an orgasm at all. Often these women are young. What most young women don't realise is that arousal and orgasm, like desire, are learned experiences for women. It may take years for a woman to learn how to get turned on, stay turned on with a partner and consistently achieve a climax. Most women can learn to climax using a self-help program at home.

Painful intercourse
All women who suffer from pain during intercourse, known as dyspareunia, should visit their doctor for a check-up to exclude a physical cause. However, the commonest cause of painful intercourse is not physical. Rather it is psychological, due to inadequate sexual arousal. If a woman attempts penetration when she's not turned on, she will be dry, tight and uncomfortable and

may experience deep pain during sex. Once a physical cause has been excluded and/or treated, counselling for painful intercourse involves education and anxiety reduction, advice about sexual technique and positions, and the introduction of non-intercourse options for sexual satisfaction.

One cause of painful sex, vaginismus, prevents penetration of the penis due to involuntary spasm of the muscles of the pelvic floor around the vagina. Treatment of vaginismus is usually carried out with the guidance of a sex therapist.

For those who have sexual difficulties but don't have access to a sex therapist, Sandra Pertot's wonderful book, *A Commonsense Guide to Sex*, has self-help programs for the full range of sexual difficulties, both male and female.

REDUCING SITUATIONAL INHIBITORS

Many couples create an anti-sexual lifestyle and atmosphere that leaves little room for desire, romance and courtship. For them, the bedroom becomes little more than a 'bored room'. American sex therapists Masters and Johnson achieved magnificent results with their sex therapy programs which required couples to attend programs at the clinic together during the day and go to a motel at night to do sexual homework exercises. No work, no kids, no dogs. Even if the therapy program didn't work, the change in environment and the focus on each other would do most couples the world of good.

Take a look at your bedroom. Is there anything there that doesn't add to a relaxed and intimate atmosphere? Do photos of your kids and parents stare down at you while you cavort together? Is there a computer or anything related to work sitting near by? Perhaps some fitness equipment, a sewing machine or piles of papers and other unsexy junk. Move the TV out of the bedroom. I'll repeat that. Move the TV out of the bedroom.

What's the lighting like — by day and by night? Do you have effective privacy from curious neighbours' eyes? Fresh air and sunlight is a lovely sensual addition. Is your bed firm and quiet? — Nothing can damp down sexual activity more than a squeaky bed. If your mattress isn't supportive, you might be better off putting it on the floor. Little extras can make all the difference. A fan for summer, a heater for winter, a soft fluffy rug on the floor.

What are your sheets and pillows like? Are they rejects from years of family hand-me-downs, or do you make your bed special? Are your pillows fluffy and do you have enough of them? Do you change the bed linen regularly enough?

Can you put up some strategically placed mirrors? What about some relaxing and intimate artwork on your walls? Can you play music in your bedroom? What about candles or incense? Do you have a lockable drawer to keep your sexy toys, lubricant and other material away from prying eyes.

Ideally your bedroom should be your sanctuary where visitors (large, small or furry) are only allowed by invitation. You should be able to lock the door. Why not get a 'Do not disturb' sign if you have children old enough to read? After all, it is healthy for your kids to know that you have an enjoyable sex life.

Two other very important issues: You must have *contraception* and *safer sex* issues worked out. Fear of pregnancy or of catching or transmitting an STD are powerful passion killers. Taking equal responsibility for safer sex practices is a sign of mutual respect and caring.

Finally, what do you personally add to the intimate atmosphere of your bedroom? Do you come to bed prepared for lovemaking as you used to in the early years of your relationship, or do you collapse into bed in a dirty old T-shirt, roll over and steal all the blankets? If you want a hassle-free sex life you must put in effort every day to make your partner feel special. Looking after your own appearance and hygiene, plus your bedroom and bathroom manners, is a very powerful way of saying 'You are important to me.'

INHIBITORS OF MALE DESIRE

In Chapter 7 we looked specifically at factors that might decrease desire in men.
- Sexual boredom and habituation
- Lack of spontaneity
- Unresponsive partner — feeling undesired and undesirable
- Overwhelming sexual demands of partner

- Sexual problems — male and female
- Feelings of sexual inadequacy — poor sexual self-esteem
- Discomfort with sexual repertoire
- Fear of sexual rejection — repeated sexual knockbacks
- Birth control anxieties and interruptions
- Safer sex issues
- Fear of intimacy
- Lack of partner appreciation and acceptance — frequent criticism
- Unresolved relationship conflict and partner hostility.

Let's look at them briefly again here.

Sexual boredom and habituation

Men are more susceptible than women to sexual boredom. A varied sexual repertoire and a range of sexual styles can help to overcome this problem.

Lack of spontaneity

In long-term relationships, lack of spontaneity can be a problem especially if you have a young family. My suggestion is to make a date, set aside time to be together and see what happens spontaneously. You might decide to use the time to have sex, play Scrabble or have a sleep. The time may be planned, but anything that happens during it can be totally off the cuff.

Unresponsive partner — feeling undesired and undesirable

The best sex for men is when their partners really enjoy themselves. An unresponsive partner is a big turn-off for most men. This is known as the 'sexual corpse syndrome'. Men often go off sex after years of pursuing and trying to arouse an unresponsive woman. When he loses interest, she might start to chase and the pursuer/distancer cycle reverses.

Unfortunately, men are often doing all the wrong things — turning a woman off, rather than on. Women must realise that a man cannot intuitively know what his partner likes. More often than not, he will give her what *he* likes, and as we know, men and women have very different sexual needs.

Tell him what you like, and keep telling him. Men often need reminding because they go onto automatic pilot in bed. Sexual assertion is a crucial skill for both sexes in creating great sex.

Overwhelming sexual demands of partner

Sexual pressure on men results in sexual shutdown, just as it does in women. It may be somewhat worse for men because they are expected always to be ready for sex and to be the sexual pursuers. Being pursued affects men just as negatively as it affects women.

Sexual problems — male and female

Men with sexual problems often lose desire. They don't want to embark on anything they can't 'finish'. Of course, finishing for most men means prolonged, thrusting intercourse ending in orgasm. A change of attitude and plenty of outercourse options will take the pressure off men.

Feelings of sexual inadequacy — poor sexual self-esteem

The pressure is on men to be the biggest, the hardest, the longest, the best. Feeling inadequate as a lover will turn even the horniest man off sex. Women's attitudes to what constitutes a good lover often embrace a lot of unrealistic sexual expectations. Women need to cultivate a broader, more realistic view of what sex is and avoid making men jump through hoops like circus animals.

Discomfort with sexual repertoire

Men need encouragement and support to explore outside their comfort zones. No demanding, no judging, no criticising. If a woman can't get exactly what she wants (e.g. oral sex), she should gracefully settle for next best. You cannot *make* someone enjoy erotic activities.

Fear of sexual rejection — repeated sexual knockbacks

When men are sexually needy they are at their most sensitive. Unfortunately, many women turn men down with words and actions that make them feel ashamed or rejected. The soft 'No' technique overcomes this problem for both sexes.

Birth control anxieties and interruptions

Contraception is a shared decision. Like women, men fear unwanted pregnancies and need the assurance of effective contraception. Interruptions to insert a diaphragm or put on a condom can disrupt proceedings and cause loss of arousal. This should be seen as a natural response, not a disaster. Get together and decide what form of contraception is best for both of you.

Safer sex issues

The only thing a man should be giving a woman, and vice versa, is love. Concerns about unsafe sexual activities are passion killers. Once again, honesty, open discussion and negotiation are the answer.

> **Russ:** I was with a new date at lunch. We had set aside the afternoon to go to bed together for the first time. Lunch went on and on and she was getting more and more uncomfortable. Eventually she said to me, 'I have to tell you this. I've got an attack of herpes so we can't make love.'
>
> I replied, 'Don't worry about it, I used to get herpes years ago. We can just go for a walk if you like.' I tried to make light of it and added jokingly, 'As long as you don't have warts!' I was highly embarrassed when she replied, 'I've got those, too.'

Fear of intimacy

Fear of getting close is usually a result of negative past experiences with family members, friends or lovers. Intimacy requires a high level of trust. Building trust and intimacy are covered in Chapter 12.

Lack of partner appreciation and acceptance — frequent criticism

Men love to be appreciated. I say that it's a good idea to thank a man for breathing! I'm not being patronising but just trying to encourage women to praise and acknowledge men more. Often men's efforts go unnoticed because they aren't part of a woman's language of love. Perhaps a woman would prefer her man to gaze into her eyes than do her tax, but both activities should be seen as a contribution to the relationship. Criticism, too, will turn a man off. It's hard to desire a nasty, nagging, sarcastic woman. A resentful man is not a sexy man.

Unresolved relationship conflict and partner hostility

Some men can tolerate a high level of ongoing fighting, conflict and hostilities without losing interest in sex. However, there are many men who find such battles a total turn-off. The effect of conflict on desire is discussed in Chapter 14.

> O, she is the antidote to desire.
> WILLIAM CONGREVE

Be your own sex therapist

Look through the list of desire inhibitors in Chapter 6 and select any elements that may be negatively affecting your own or your partner's desire.

List these elements on a sheet of paper. Make some plans together to minimise or eradicate these inhibitors. Write down your plans step-by-step. Put the list somewhere where it will come to your notice on a regular basis.

Key Points -♥-

It is reassuring to know that we have some control over our own and our partner's level of sexual interest. By increasing enhancers and minimising inhibitors, every couple has a surefire way to maximise their sex drives and improve their relationship if they are prepared to make the effort.

Special Circumstances — Pregnancy and Breastfeeding, Menopause and Ageing

This final chapter looks at special circumstances that can impact dramatically on levels of sexual desire. Pregnancy and breastfeeding, menopause and ageing can all result in lowered levels of sexual interest and contribute to desire discrepancy.

PREGNANCY, BREASTFEEDING AND DESIRE

A common time for DD to appear is with the advent of the first pregnancy. If DD is already in operation, child bearing and breast-feeding can often make the situation worse.

From a medical point of view there is no reason why sexual relations, including intercourse, should not continue right up until the end of pregnancy, unless there is a history of repeated miscarriage or early labour. (Ask your doctor's advice if this is your situation.) However, *being able to have sex* and *wanting to have sex* are two different things.

Falling pregnant for the first time and starting a family are major relationship adjustments. A couple goes from being Romeo and Juliet to being Mum and Dad within the space of 10 months. Suddenly there is a (very sweet) permanent intrusion into the relationship that makes him or herself very obvious 24 hours a day. Frequently the first pregnancy occurs around the time limerence is finally fading. These factors all combine to alter the sexual dynamics in the relationship.

> **Sam:** I always blamed the birth of the kids for Sari's loss of interest in sex, but looking back now, the first one arrived just as our very hot and horny limerence was fading away. Within a few months Sari went from being a very sexy lady to a once-a-month girl, if that. I also realise that my poor handling of the situation really contributed to her lack of desire. I thought she was holding out on me. I really hassled her about sex for a few years and she just moved further and further away. I'm ashamed to admit it, but I also resented the boys because I blamed our problems on their arrival.
>
> Since we've been having counselling our sex life has been getting back on track, although now I don't expect it ever to be the same as it was when it was just the two of us.

Fantasy vs reality

Just as we are tricked into believing unrealistic myths about sex by the media, parenting magazines and baby product advertising can paint a fantasy picture of what having a baby is all about. Too many parents are ill-informed and unprepared for the changes wrought in their lives by the patter of tiny feet. Real parenting is very different from fantasy parenting.

> **Angela:** Before the baby was born I can remember telling all my friends and family that the baby would fit in. The baby would go where we went, do what we did — nothing was going to change in our lives or our relationship. And the baby did fit in ... right between the two of us!

The effects of parenthood on a relationship are variable. For some couples it's a time of great joy and fulfilment. For others the fantasy of the cosy threesome is just that — a fantasy! Unfortunately, most men and women don't have any understanding of the impact of a child on their relationship. Suddenly, instead of being a couple, you become a family. There are changes in roles, with Dad perhaps becoming the sole breadwinner while Mum spends time at home with the baby or vice versa. There can be conflicts and guilt about Mum resuming her career as the baby gets older. Few couples come to parenthood with a totally clean emotional, sexual and relationship slate. Existing relationship problems are magnified by these dramatic shifts and changes.

Research has shown that with the advent of the first child there is an increase in conflict in the relationship and a decrease of affection between partners. This persists until the last child leaves home, when the reverse occurs — less conflict and more affection. For the majority of couples, sex goes on the back burner in the early years of parenthood.

Fathers, especially, are caught unprepared for this enormous upheaval in their sex lives. They feel disappointed and upset, displaced and rejected. They cannot understand the changes their partners are experiencing nor why they no longer wish to have sex as frequently as they did in the past.

Couples particularly at risk for sexual problems during pregnancy and after the birth are those who have sexual problems prior to conception. If you think having a baby might help your relationship or your sex life, think again.

Another high-risk group is couples who have had fertility difficulties. These couples have often been investigated, poked, prodded and probed. Sex by the calendar is not much fun, and by the time many of these couples conceive, with or without assistance, their sex life has deteriorated.

Many first time parents assume that sexual frequency will be maintained during the pregnancy and once the baby is born. Or they expect sexual interest to take a quick dip when the baby is tiny and recover rapidly. My observation is that, for couples where DD develops during the child-bearing years, it can be up to five or more years before sexual relations get back to something like a normal frequency. If the pursuer/distancer cycle takes over as it usually does, desire problems can persist for years.

Desire during pregnancy

The effects of pregnancy on desire and sexual response are very variable.

> **Lisa:** When I was pregnant I felt like a hippopotamus rolling in the mud. Sex was the last thing on my mind. My best girlfriend, on the other hand, said she felt 'like a goddess, the abundant source of all good and growing things on the earth'. She had her first orgasms during pregnancy and couldn't keep her hands off her husband.

In pregnancy, desire often follows a down-up-down pattern. In the first three months, desire takes a nose dive for many women due to fatigue, nausea, sore breasts and other symptoms of early pregnancy. Fifty-four per cent of women experience lowered libido in early pregnancy. This makes arousal more difficult to achieve. Nausea is associated with high prolactin levels, a powerful anti-aphrodisiac hormone. Breasts are often very tender in the first three months. During sexual arousal they expand by a further 25%, so that normal lovemaking caresses can feel uncomfortable or even painful. Fatigue usually passes by the fourth month but returns in the last few weeks.

The middle three months are often a time of increased energy and wellbeing, and desire may return. By the middle trimester a woman's body is changing. Women are often ambivalent about body changes. Most can't wait for a belly to appear, then they can't wait for it to go away! Ninety per cent of women will develop stretch marks. Unfortunately, many women are upset by this. I see stretch marks and other bodily changes in pregnancy in a positive light, regarding them as our 'badges of motherhood'. A woman's feelings about her body will very much depend on her partner's response. A critical, unsupportive partner can easily make a woman feel bad about her body; he should not be surprised at the consequent lowering of her sexual interest.

Lowered sexual interest in the last three months is common. Apart from the growing bulge in front which can make intercourse more tricky, there is usually a great deal of focus on nesting and getting ready for the baby. By the end of pregnancy, one-third of couples are abstaining from intercourse. For those who want to continue lovemaking, there are always the pleasures of outercourse.

Desire can be affected during pregnancy by a variety of concerns.

- Some couples experience anxiety about intercourse bringing on miscarriage. If this has occurred before, couples will be advised to refrain from intercourse but they are not always told they can still enjoy outercourse. Under normal circumstances, lovemaking will not precipitate a miscarriage.

- Others worry about harming the baby. However, the baby is protected by the muscular uterus and the firmly closed cervix, and is buffeted by amniotic fluid. It is fully formed at 12 weeks and cannot be damaged by intercourse at any stage. These concerns are highlighted when the baby is very wanted, as is the case with fertility difficulties or after loss of a baby through miscarriage or cot death.

- In the later stages of pregnancy, some couples are put off by the thought that their nearly fully grown baby might be 'aware' of their lovemaking activities, especially intercourse. It's true that babies' movements do slow during lovemaking, but this is due to uterine and hormonal changes rather than an 'awareness' of parental pleasures.

Orgasm during pregnancy

Most women find it more difficult to achieve orgasm during pregnancy. By the end of pregnancy only one in four women are orgasmic. The pelvic floor and the entire uterus contracts with orgasm; in the last few months of pregnancy this can be quite a momentous experience for a woman. Some women also experience cramping during orgasm. Painless, irregular contractions of the uterus, called Braxton-Hicks contractions, begin early in pregnancy and are more noticeable in the last month or so before delivery. In the last trimester the uterus may be more irritable after orgasm with increased Braxton-Hicks contractions lasting for 20 minutes or so. This is not dangerous to mother or baby.

During pregnancy, women should be getting their pelvic floors into tip-top shape. A healthy pelvic floor helps to direct the baby during labour and minimises pelvic floor damage. Pelvic floor exercises promote healing after the delivery by increasing the blood supply, and they help to maintain vaginal snugness. If you want to know more about pelvic floor exercises you might like to listen to 'Dr Rosie King's Pelvic Floor Work Out Audio Tape' which teaches you all about how to keep your pelvic floor in great shape (see Resources).

Dad's desire

Men's sexual needs may remain unchanged during the waxing and waning of female desire during pregnancy. This is a perfect opportunity for couples to put the sexual hierarchy to good use. However, a man's sex drive may decrease during his partner's pregnancy or after the birth. Some men have trouble meshing the idea of their partner being both a lover and a mother. This is an extension of the Madonna/Whore conflict, where men can only see women as either mother figures or sexual beings but not both. Some women find that during pregnancy their man's sex drive is lower than their own for the first time.

While most men find childbirth to be a miraculous affirmation of human sexuality and reproduction, some men are negatively affected by the experience of birth in a way that interferes with their sexual functioning. They can experience loss of desire in the post-partum period and may experience erectile problems or rapid ejaculation. For this reason a man who has serious reservations about attending the delivery might want to think twice. His partner should not expect him to attend if his discomfort level appears to be very high.

'When can we start having sex again?'

Couples often have questions about when they can resume sexual activity. One obstetrician tells the story of the new father who was watching the birth of his first baby. After proudly holding his son for the first time, Dad turned to the doctor and asked when he and his wife could resume sexual relations. The doctor replied with a wink, 'Son, could you hold off until I deliver the placenta!'

So when *can* intimate relations resume? As soon as the baby is born! Of course, I'm talking about affection, sensuality and outercourse — kissing, hugging, touching, stroking, bathing, showering together, holding hands, massage, and mutual touching to the point of orgasm. Doctors advise that resumption of intercourse should be delayed until after the six-week check. Intercourse can be resumed before then if the lochia (post-delivery discharge) has ceased.

Breast worries

Another source of anxiety is the tussle over who owns the mother's body — the baby or Dad. Certainly, babies make a firm claim on the breasts during breastfeeding and some Dads are put out when they feel they're not getting their fair share. On the other hand, some men stop viewing the breasts as erogenous zones but associate them more with their milk bar function. Leakage of breast milk with sexual stimulation can strengthen this change in attitude. This can be disappointing for a woman who enjoys breast stimulation during sex.

While some couples have no trouble with who-gets-what, with everyone happily sharing everything, some new mothers can be very reluctant to share their breasts with anyone other than their baby. A breastfeeding mother can resent her partner's demands for breast contact.

> **Elaine:** I was so angry when Barry wanted to suck milk from my breasts after Sean was born. I thought it was such a yucky thing to even suggest and it really turned me off him for a while.

Sex drive after the birth

For a variety of reasons, most new Mums don't have much interest in sex, whether it be outercourse or intercourse. This lowering of sexual interest may persist for months and even years and is perfectly normal. Let's go back to Cave Man times again. If you think about it, the last thing a new Cave Mother needs is horny feelings when she has to protect her infant from danger. In addition, perhaps this drop in desire is nature's way of reducing the risk of conception in the months after a baby is born?

After the birth of a baby, many factors combine to decrease sexual desire in new mothers.

Fatigue

Being a new mother redefines the meaning of the word 'tired'. A combination of being on duty 24 hours a day, and night after night of broken sleep, will exhaust even the most energetic woman. A tired woman is not a sexy woman. She would much rather sleep than make love.

> **Peta:** There were times after my first child was born that I felt like cutting off my boobs and giving them to the baby, cutting off my lower half and giving it to my husband, and taking what was left of me to lie down in bed and sleep for two weeks.

Lack of time

> **Sally:** I can remember standing in my dressing gown as my husband went off to work in the morning and kissing him hello that night still in the same outfit. I just hadn't had time to get changed, let alone have a shower. I used to run a company with thousands of employees. I couldn't believe I had been brought to my knees by something wrapped in a fluffy bunny rug.

Looking after a baby consumes enormous amounts of time and energy. A baby's irregular schedule makes it impossible to plan your day. The resulting frustration and helplessness are powerful dampeners of desire. Sex becomes a very low priority, located below soaking the nappies and getting some sleep, not necessarily in that order.

Low skin hunger

As you will recall, skin-on-skin contact is a major motivator for sexual activity. When a mother has been feeding, burping, bathing, comforting and playing with a baby all the day, the last thing she needs is any more skin contact. Dad comes home from work looking forward to a big hug and all he gets is the baby thrust in his face and pleas for a break.

Breastfeeding

Breastfeeding relies on the hormone prolactin which markedly decreases both sexual desire and vaginal lubrication. Breasts may be tender and sensitive during lactation and they may also leak during sexual stimulation. These factors can decrease desire for sexual contact with a partner. Research has shown that when breastfeeding ceases there is an increase in sexual feelings, sexual activity and frequency of intercourse within four weeks of weaning. Some women notice marked sensual feelings when suckling their babies, and this is perfectly normal.

DHEA and DHEAS

These hormones, introduced in Chapter 2, are secreted by the adrenals and play a part in fuelling sexual desire. First pregnancies are followed by a permanent decrease in DHEA/DHEAS, which could well contribute to lowered desire after the birth of the first baby.

Problems with body image

> **Christie:** I thought my body would automatically spring back to normal six weeks after the baby was born. A year later my stomach still looks like play dough and my boobs are down to my waist, not to mention the stretch marks. I feel really daggy and miss looking desirable and sexy.

Many women have trouble coming to terms with their 'badges of motherhood'. A poor body image can significantly reduce interest in sex. Partners can really help here by affirming their partner's loveliness and desirability. Try 'What I really like about making love with you is ...' or 'What I love about your body is ...'

Postnatal depression

Loss of interest in sex may be a sign of postnatal depression (PND). I'm not referring to the two- or three-day blues, a period of weepiness after the delivery of a baby. PND is an illness that can range in severity from exhaustion, apathy and depressed mood to severe psychosis and a compulsion to hurt the baby. PND needs treatment with antidepressant medication or psychotherapy, or both.

> **Louise:** I wanted to sleep all day, took the phone off the hook and wouldn't go out. I was obsessed with feeding the baby enough and looking after him properly. I couldn't let him cry for even a second without getting panicky. I had no desire for sex. I thought all new mothers were like that.
>
> I had every reason to get postnatal depression. I was unhappily married to an alcoholic, I had a terrible pregnancy and a 21-hour labour with a huge tear, and the baby was born with a dislocated hip and was in plaster for months. It was nine months before I let anyone know how much I was suffering. I only saw a psychiatrist when I reported myself to the child abuse people because I was scared I might hurt my son.

If you are feeling very low or are worried about how you are coping, seek help from your doctor.

Painful sex

Another common passion killer after giving birth is discomfort during intercourse. High levels of the hormone prolactin during breastfeeding cause vaginal dryness. Women are naturally distractable in their arousal, easily turned off by anxiety and interruptions. When a woman has a baby or a young child this distractibility increases, so that all the baby needs to do is to make a mewing sound in the next room and that's the end of sex for Mum. I call this the 'invisible umbilical cord', a connection between mother and child that ensures that Mum is never so carried away by desire and arousal that she neglects her baby. Speaking as a mother this invisible umbilical cord never seems to disappear, even when your children leave home!

Women should use a water-based lubricant to overcome vaginal dryness and spend more time in pleasuring to enhance arousal.

Another cause of painful sex is vulval and vaginal trauma resulting from the delivery. An episiotomy or surgical repair can remain painful or tender for up to four months. Enjoy more outercourse or use intercourse positions that minimise pressure on the area, such as the woman-on-top position. If you are still experiencing discomfort after six months, you need to be re-evaluated by your gynaecologist. Your repair may need surgical revision. Pain is a powerful passion killer.

Fear of falling pregnant
The last thing most women want is to fall pregnant again very soon after the birth of a child. Effective contraception must be sorted out before sexual activity resumes.

Anxiety
New parents are often anxious about their unfamiliar roles. The anxieties may be general, such as 'Am I being a good enough mother/father?' or specific, such as 'Is our baby developing normally?' Anxiety decreases desire.

Low desire is normal

For all the reasons listed above, new mothers often experience very low levels of interest in sex. This widely experienced lack of interest after birth must be regarded as a normal phenomenon which often takes years to resolve.

As you can imagine, DD is very common in the months following the birth of a baby. Sadly the P/D cycle can kick in and banish all chances of a woman's sex drive returning in the future. For couples with young children, the DD program can be a real lifesaver for their sexual and emotional relationship.

Many doctors unfortunately give women who have lost sex drive, after the birth of a baby, shots of testosterone to 'kick start' their desire. The effect, if any, is only temporary and rarely gives any long-term benefit. There can be side effects during treatment, such as clitoral enlargement, facial hair and deepening of the voice.

Even if a woman does notice some beneficial effect from the injections, this can only ever be a short-term bandaid solution as more than three testosterone injections for women in a row are not recommended. Education about the nature of desire plus the teaching of relationship and sexual skills are better tools for dealing with lowered levels of desire than testosterone injections. When testosterone therapy fails to work in the long term, as it does when prescribed inappropriately, it only adds to feelings of sexual inadequacy and abnormality in both sexes. If your doctor suggests testosterone therapy, ask for a blood test first. If the level is normal, don't bother with the injection.

Resuming sexual activity

Try a little touching first. Don't rush straight into intercourse. Why not enjoy a bit of 2, 4, 6, 8 and 10, like in the good old days? A gentle massage is a great start. Use sexual negotiation, such as the soft 'No' technique and the sexual hierarchy.

Conditions for desire and arousal are even more important in the post-birth period. Maximise enhancers and minimise inhibitors. Always try to create good conditions for sex before you become sexually involved.

Remember that lowered desire means slowed arousal. Compensate by spending more time pleasuring and use anything that might increase arousal, such as fantasies or erotica. Increase your sexual repertoire by employing outercourse options.

Desire is likely to be low or absent. Look at the Reasons for Engaging in Sex list to find other motivations to be sexual.

When intercourse resumes, the woman needs to be in charge of the three Ps:

- *Pace* — how fast and how far you go.
- *Position* — on top can be helpful.
- *Penetration* — if you are not in the mood for intercourse, try outercourse.

Both partners need to accept that lowered sexual interest is a fact of life for new mums. Don't wait until you feel desire to resume sexual activities. After the birth of a baby you could be waiting months or years to feel flames of passion. Use the DD program to maximise desire and maintain regular intimate contact.

Keeping the magic alive

Make your relationship a high priority. Be Romeo and Juliet, not just Mum and Dad. The greatest gift you can give your child is a happy, secure parental relationship. Spend time together talking, not just about the baby. To maintain or improve recreational intimacy, pursue common interests together.

Don't crowd sex out of your life. If you are feeling overwhelmed, ask for help — from each other as well as from family and friends. You don't have to do it all on your own.

Plan for sex. Spontaneous sex is lovely, but once you have a family it tends to become a rare treat. Instead, set aside time to be relaxed and alone together and see what happens spontaneously.

Try to meet each other's needs, both nonsexual and sexual. You will need to compromise and negotiate.

All couples have sexual difficulties at some time. If you are having problems, seek help early. Attack the problem and not each other.

Pregnancy and parenthood are transition periods, times of great change. DD is a normal part of this hectic and demanding life experience. The challenge for parents is to create a happy and secure home life for their children and to keep their love and passion for each other burning brightly.

DESIRE AND MENOPAUSE

The effect of menopause on women's sex drive is variable. A recent Australian study reported that 62% of women said they didn't notice any difference in desire. However, 31% of women experienced a reduced level of interest in sex with the menopause. The same study showed that 7% of women said they were more sexually interested, although some attributed this to having a new partner in their lives.

A decrease in desire may be due to:

- lowered levels of oestrogen

- lowered testosterone levels (although some testosterone continues to be produced by the adrenal glands)
- changes in sexual function — vaginal dryness, painful orgasm and slowed arousal
- relationship boredom or conflict
- general life hassles.

Some women find that hormone replacement therapy with oestrogen alone, or a combination of oestrogen and progesterone, helps to reignite sexual desire. However, there are some menopausal women who need testosterone replacement therapy to maintain desire and improve their general sense of wellbeing.

After a blood test to check that hormone levels are indeed low, the first step is a trial of testosterone injections. If these injections have the desired effect, implants under the skin (like a tiny piece of spaghetti) that release testosterone over months can be administered under local anaesthetic. No effective testosterone tablets or patches are available for menopausal women.

If you have been through the menopause and think you might need some hormonal help for your sex drive, seek your doctor's advice. Although the average age of women undergoing the menopause is about 48 to 52, many younger women experience a drop in hormone levels in their late thirties and early forties, so a blood test to check testosterone levels can be a good idea if you have noticed a significant drop in sex drive, even if your periods are still regular.

DESIRE AND AGEING

Loss of interest in sex with age does not necessarily have any biological basis. Many older people give up sex because they think they should — they're past it, too long in the tooth, too decrepit for sex. They fall victim to widely held negative attitudes to sexuality and ageing.

We live in a society that worships at the altar of youth, growth and disposability. If something gets old, we throw it away and get a new one. We are careful not to

> I prefer old age to the alternative.
> MAURICE CHEVALIER
> FRENCH ACTOR

practise sexism, racial discrimination or religious bigotry — however, most people practise ageism, often against themselves.

Older people are stereotyped as 'useless, toothless, hairless and sexless'. Ageism is rife in our community because of ignorance and fear. A 'them and us' mentality develops in an attempt to deny our own ageing and mortality. *We* are young and sexual, therefore *they* are not.

Grey Power has attempted to redress many inequities against older people, but sexuality has been either forgotten or ignored. Older people who express their sexuality openly are judged and frowned upon. For example, imagine that you are walking through the park on a Sunday and you see a couple enjoying a picnic on a rug. They start to hug and kiss passionately. If they are in their early twenties you might be touched by this romantic scene. If they are in their eighties, you are likely to think 'They should know better at their age!'

What about a woman dressed for success? She's wearing a designer suit, high heels, volumes of glossy hair, and fingernails long enough to do brain surgery. If she's 25, she's a babe — if she's 65, she's mutton dressed up as lamb.

Let's go to a hospital ward. A young bloke who broke his leg on a motorbike is peeking down the pretty nurse's uniform. She catches him and thinks to herself, 'Boys will be boys.' Yet if he's a 70-year-old gentleman who broke his leg getting out of the bath and he does exactly the same thing, he's a geriatric sex maniac who must be sedated!

The media messages about sex and the elderly are very clear — there are none! In sexy movie scenes or erotic passages in books there's no mention of dry uncomfortable sex or flagging erections, let alone dentures, hiatus hernias and stiff hips. We deny the sexuality of older people, yet humans are sexual from the cradle to the grave.

Age plays tricks on us all. I am in my forties now, with a full load of responsibilities in every area. But I can tell you that there is a 16-year-old inside of me full of the joys of life and love, and as irresponsible as hell. I can only hope that my 16-year-old is still with me for all the decades to come. We all have a teenager inside of us — we can choose to ignore him or her, or we can celebrate their enthusiasm and energy and zest for all parts of life, including sex.

How often have you said to yourself, 'I'm too old for this or that'? As children we are always being told we are too young for one thing and too old for another — too old for a teddy and too young for a date. These are the roots of ageism. As adults we take up the baton and continue to discriminate against ourselves.

Want to leave your job and find another?

Tough luck, you're far too old.

Want to matriculate from high school or get a university degree?

At your age? You must be kidding!

Want to leave your soulless marriage and find happiness with another?

Sorry, you're over the hill.

Want to have good loving and great sex?

What a ridiculous thought at your age!

We do discriminate against ourselves when it comes to age. Most of us believe that sex is only for the young. It is these toxic attitudes that kill off sexual interest in people as they age, rather than overwhelming hormonal or physical changes. I have often seen elderly people too afraid to admit they are sexually interested and have sexual needs, for fear of society's censure.

When my good friend and colleague Dr Martyn Baker was a young resident in hospital, he admitted an elderly woman for a hysterectomy. Already sensitive to the sexual aspects of medicine he tactfully asked the woman, who was in her eighties, whether she was sexually active. She replied with a sweet giggle, 'No, young man, but thank you so much for asking!' She was flattered by his recognition of her as a woman and a sexual being, despite her advanced age.

Another medico with considerably less insight advised Mrs Jones, aged 90, that when he did her hysterectomy he would sew her vagina up. She replied, 'I don't think Mr Jones would like that at all.'

Figures from a survey in 1980 showed that 7 out of 10 healthy married couples over 60 were sexually active — this doesn't mean, of course, that they are necessarily having intercourse. Studies have shown that there is a decline in sexual activity for couples between the ages of 70 and 74, but this is due to illness and medical treatment, not lack of interest in sex.

Dr Alex Comfort, author of *The Joy of Sex*, says that people give up sex for the same reasons they give up riding bicycles:

- bad health
- thinking it's silly
- no bicycle.

Loss of a partner through death or divorce and the difficulty of meeting a new one are common reasons for both women and men to give up sex. There is a relative lack of men in the sixties age group, with a male:female ratio of 1:4 due to males' shorter life expectancy. Australian women can 'look forward' to an average of 10 years of widowhood. As women age, the partner pickings get slimmer each year.

If you want good loving and great sex in your life, don't let bigotry about age stand in your way. Learn what you can about how sexuality changes with age but don't see these changes as a sign that it's time to give up. You may not be able to have sex the same way that you did in your twenties, but you can still enjoy sensual closeness and sexual intimacy.

CHANGES IN SEXUALITY WITH AGE

Changes in men
- Erections less firm
- Slower to arouse
- Need more direct genital stimulation
- Lowered urge to orgasm and ejaculate
- Orgasms and ejaculation less intense
- Longer refractory period (need a longer time after ejaculation for erection to reoccur)
- Decreased tactile sensitivity.

Changes in women
- Slowed arousal
- Decreased lubrication during arousal
- Thinning of vaginal lining

- Shrinkage of vagina and vulva
- Decreased sensitivity of vagina
- Decreased clitoral swelling
- Decreased breast swelling and nipple engorgement
- Orgasm less frequent
- Decreased intensity of orgasm
- May get painful orgasm
- Loss of multiple orgasms
- Decreased tactile sensitivity.

Both sexes — Some decline in sexual interest, due to:
- negative attitudes to ageing and sex
- relationship problems or boredom
- poor health, illness and/or medications.
  Some of the changes in women can be reversed or diminished by hormone replacement therapy.

Solving specific problems

For many older couples, intercourse may no longer be comfortable or possible due to painful penetration, erectile difficulties or problems with mobility. However, there is always outercourse.

Slowed arousal
- Allow more time to get aroused.
- Increase sensual contact and affectionate behaviour.
- Enjoy plenty of general stimulation before erotic stimulation.
- Give and receive more direct genital stimulation.
- Use more fantasy — books, movies, memories.
- Perhaps use erotica and/or a vibrator.
- Use water-based lubricants to make intercourse more comfortable.

Painful intercourse
- Use water-based lubricants.
- Use oestrogen cream applied to the vagina or hormone replacement therapy.
- Practise outercourse.

Painful orgasms
- Use hormone replacement therapy.

Erectile Difficulties
- See section on erectile difficulties in Chapter 19 and refer to Resources.

Loss of libido
- Minimise inhibitors.
- Look to personal and relationship factors.
- Maximise enhancers.
- Treat depression.
- Find reasons other than desire to be sexual.
- Use hormone replacement therapy. Try testosterone replacement (injections or implants) if testosterone is deficient.

All alone?

What about older people who still wish to be sexually active but cannot find a suitable partner? This can be a very painful situation, especially if one is used to living in a loving relationship. Older people are often shy about admitting it, but many enjoy masturbation — one study found that 25% of 70-year-old women practise solo sex.

However, there are many nonsexual needs that can't be fulfilled through self-stimulation. Older people can make use of the Reasons list to work out what needs they are missing out on. They can then look for nonsexual ways to get these needs met. Skin hunger can be assuaged by regular massage, or contact with pets, friends or small children. Passion can be experienced through participation in sports, hobbies, volunteer work, religion or other interests. Friendships can provide intimacy. And so on. When there is no partner in your life, you need to work just that little bit harder to keep up your connections with other people of all ages.

Keeping sex going

Ageing signals a change of sexual life — not the end of it. The first task is to cultivate a positive approach to ageing and sex by challenging the many myths and misconceptions about these two topics. Growing old need not be ageing.

Learn the basic facts about what changes are normal with

ageing. Changes don't mean *no go*, they simply mean *go slow*. In later life, pleasuring and high arousal without orgasm can be enjoyable for both men and women.

Address relationship difficulties such as unresolved conflicts and poor communication. It's difficult to have great sex in the absence of good loving at any age.

Keep active. If you want to enjoy an active sex life into old age, keep sexually active as you grow older. Make sure you keep yourself physically fit as well as sexually fit.

Use it or lose it. Most older people know that if they sit in a chair for a week, then get up and try to do the tango, they will find it extremely difficult. It's the same with sex. If you don't use it, you'll lose it. The worst thing that can happen sexually in old age is a prolonged break from sex. If you are unable to be sexually active for a while, make sure you practise solo sex to keep those erotic wheels in motion. Once you stop, it can be very hard to get arousal, erections and orgasms going again.

Plenty of non-demand affection will feed into desire and enhance sensuality and arousal. Make sure you observe *your* conditions for good sex. In old age these are more important than ever.

Take the focus off intercourse and orgasm. Explore outercourse options. Vibrators can be very useful for providing increased stimulation for older men and women (see Resources).

Ageing provides a challenge for lovers, an opportunity to further explore their sexuality and generate sexual solutions.

Sexuality is an integral part of being a man or a woman, from childhood to the day you die. You have the right to decide that sex is no longer important to you and that you want to cease sexual activity. But don't be put off by ageism.

Sexuality does change with age but our need for contact and connection doesn't disappear. Older people may no longer be able to hang from the chandeliers as they once did, but they usually have the good sense not to want to.

> Grow old with me!
> The best is yet to be ...
> ROBERT BROWNING

Key Points ❀

Pregnancy and childbirth have a variable effect on sexual desire in both men and women. Desire discrepancy often surfaces at this time, and effective handling at these early stages can prevent long-term sexual problems.

Contrary to popular opinion the majority of women don't notice a huge change in sex drive with the menopause. Loss of interest in sex may be improved by hormone replacement therapy alone or in conjunction with testosterone replacement therapy. Dealing with long-term relationship problems and unresolved conflicts will also improve sexual interest.

Older people don't necessarily lose interest in sex. Often they are bowing to widespread prejudice that relegates the elderly into asexuality. Humans are sexual from the cradle to the grave.

Conclusion

This book teaches couples how to create a more satisfactory sex life. Yet sex is not the most important thing in life. A loving relationship is much more meaningful than any repertoire of bedroom gymnastics.

Sex often becomes overly important when it's causing problems between partners. The conflict and unhappiness these problems cause can diminish all the good aspects of a loving partnership by comparison.

I have a theory about life. Life is tough. It's full of lessons and challenges. Most days are difficult and have more than their fair share of hassles. It's easy to feel overwhelmed by day-to-day living. We can't get rid of all the hassles in our lives. Try as we may, we can't make all the trains run on time or turn grey skies to blue on command. We must accept that this is the nature of life.

However, there is something we can do to make life a little easier and a lot more enjoyable. We can treat ourselves to the good things in life. We need to find little things that lift our spirits and remind us that the sun does shine after rain and that there's always light at the end of whatever tunnel we find ourselves in at any particular moment. These 'goodies' can be anything — gardening, reading a good book, swimming in the sea, cuddling a child, listening to music, taking a walk. Without regular goodies, life can seem very grey indeed. Goodies don't have to cost anything, but they are worth a great deal. To my way of thinking, one goodie is worth 100 stressful moments. Our task is to find a few goodies to enjoy every day to balance up the tough times.

When sex is working well it can be a terrific goodie for loving couples. For a little while you can leave your cares behind and indulge each other and yourselves. You can forget about the real world and experience pleasure and fulfilment together. Just for a few moments, all can be well in your world.

I hope this book helps to make your loving sex a shared goodie that will enrich your relationship and smooth your passage through life, today and for all the days to come.

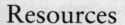

Resources

All resources are available throughout Australia via mail order from The Written Word, on freecall 1800 636 748, unless specified otherwise.

Sexual dependency and sexual aversion

Carnes, Patrick. *Don't Call it Love — Recovery from sexual addiction*, Piatkus, 1987.

Pertot, Dr Sandra. *A Commonsense Guide to Sex*, HarperCollins, 1994.

Sex education

For children
Mayle, Peter. *Where do I come from?*, Sun Books, 1973.
Mayle, Peter. *What's happening to me?*, Pan Australia, 1988.

For teenagers
Fenwick, Elizabeth and Walker, Richard. *How Sex Works*, RD Press, 1994.

For parents

Gelin, Dr Martha. *Sex in Simple Words — explaining the tough sexual facts to your children*, Crawford House Press, 1993.

McKay, Pinky. *How do we tell the kids?*, Prentice Hall, 1995.

For young adults

Locker, Sari. *Mindblowing Sex in the Real World*, HarperCollins, 1995.

For adults

Gray, John. *Mars and Venus in the Bedroom*, Hodder and Stoughton, 1995.

Litvinoff, Sarah. *The Relate Guide to Sex in Loving Relationships*, Vermillion, 1992.

Llewellyn-Jones, Derek. *Everyman*, Oxford University Press, 1982.

Llewellyn-Jones, Derek. *Everywoman*, Faber, 1971.

Montgomery, Dr Bob and Morris, Dr Laurel. *Successful Sex*, Penguin, 1992.

Sexual resources for women

The Pleasure Spot — vibrators, books and videos. Ring and ask for a catalogue. Phone (02) 9361 0433.

Video Ray — specialising in erotic videos for couples, as well as sex toys and lingerie for larger sizes. Phone for a catalogue (02) 9908 4422.

Relationship counselling

Relationships Australia — for the contact number in your state, look under the entry for Relationships Australia in the White Pages of the telephone book.

Improving your communication

Gray, John. *Men are from Mars, Women are from Venus*, Thorsons, 1993.

Hendrix, Harville. *Getting the Love You Want — A guide for couples*, Schwartz & Wilkinson Publishers, 1988.

Montgomery, Dr Bob and Evans, Lynette. *Living and Loving Together — A practical step by step manual to help you make and keep better relationships,* Nelson, 1987.

Tannen, Deborah. *You Just Don't Understand — Women and men in conversation,* Random House, 1991.

Commitment

Abrahams Spring, Janis. *After the Affair — Healing the pain and rebuilding trust when your partner has been unfaithful,* Hodder Headline, 1997.

Colliver, Andrew. *Choosing to Love — Creating trust and commitment in your relationship,* Random House, 1992.

Kirshenbaum, Mira. *Too Good to Leave, Too Bad to Stay,* Michael Joseph Ltd, 1996.

Self-esteem

MacKay, Matthew and Fanning, Patrick. *Self Esteem — Improving and maintaining your self esteem,* New Harbinger Publications, 1992.

Your inner child in your relationship

Jansen, David and Newman, Margaret. *Really Relating — How to build an enduring relationship,* Random House, 1989.

Healing after sexual abuse

Davis, Laura and Bass, Ellen. *The Courage to Heal — A guide for women survivors of child sexual abuse,* Reed Consumer Books, 1990.

Graber, Ken. *Ghosts in the Bedroom — A guide for partners of incest survivors,* Health Communications Inc., 1991.

Hunter, Mic. *Abused boys — Healing for the man molested as a child,* Ballantine Books, 1991.

Maltz, Wendy. *The Sexual Healing Journey — A guide for survivors of sexual abuse,* Harper Perennial, 1991.

Toxic disrespect

Evans, Patricia. *The Verbally Abusive Relationship — How to recognise and control it*, Adams Publications, 1996.

Negotiation skills

McKay, Matthew, Fanning, Patrick and Paleg, Kim. *Couple Skills — Making your relationship work*, New Harbinger, 1994. Also available as audio cassettes.

Creating more sensuality

Love, Dr Patricia and Robinson, Jo. *Hot Monogamy*, Piatkus, 1994.

Sexual fantasies

Friday, Nancy. *Forbidden Flowers*, Arrow, 1975.
Friday, Nancy. *My Secret Garden*, Quartet, 1976.
Friday, Nancy. *Men in Love — Their secret fantasies*, Arrow, 1980.
Friday, Nancy. *Women on Top*, Arrow, 1991.

Increasing your sexual repertoire

Comfort, Dr Alex. *The Joy of Sex*, Mitchell Beazley, 1996.
Hayman, Susy. *Good Vibrations — The complete guide to sex aids and sexual pleasure*, Piatkus, 1992.

Male sexuality

Kaplan Singer, Helen. *PE — How to overcome premature ejaculation*, Brunner/Mazel, 1989.
Williams, Dr Warwick. *It's Up to You. Self help for men with erection problems*, Williams and Wilkens, 1985.
Wolfe, Janet. *What To Do When He Has a Headache — How to rekindle your man's desire*, Thorsons, 1992.
Zilbergeld, Bernard. *Men and Sex*, HarperCollins, 1993.

Female sexuality

Dodson, Betty. *Sex for One — The joy of selfloving*, Crown Paperbacks, New York, 1987. Also available as a 60-minute video (R rated).

Garfield, Lonnie. *For Yourself — The fulfillment of female sexuality*, Barbach, Doubleday, 1991.

Goldsmith, Michele. *Painful Sex — A guide to causes, treatments and prevention*, Thorsons, 1995.

Heiman, Lopiccolo and Lopiccolo. *Becoming Orgasmic — A sexual growth program for women*, Prentice Hall, 1984.

Overcoming sexual difficulties — male and female

Pertot, Dr Sandra. *A Commonsense Guide to Sex*, HarperCollins, 1994.

Spiritual sexuality

Anand, Margo. *The Art of Sexual Ecstasy*, Aquarian, 1992.

Lee, Dr Victoria. *Soulful Sex*, Conari Press, 1996.

Coping with stress

Davis, Martha, Robbins Eshelman, Elizabeth and McKay, Matthew. *The Relaxation and Stress Reduction Workbook*, New Harbinger, 1995.

Montgomery, Dr Bob and Evans, Lynette. *You and Stress — Developing new coping skills and a healthier lifestyle*, Nelson Publishers, 1995.

General health

Carruthers, Dr Malcolm. *Male Menopause — Restoring vitality and virility*, HarperCollins, 1996.

Catalona, Ellen. *The Chronic Pain Control Workbook — A step by step guide for coping with and overcoming your pain*, New Harbinger, 1996.

McKenzie, Dr Francis. *The Penguin Guide to Women's Health*, Viking, 1997.

Margot, Jill. *Man Maintenance — How the male body runs and what to do when it breaks down*, Penguin, 1996.

Molloy, Susan. *Handling It — You and your long term disease*, Hill of Content, 1995.

Addictions

Fanning, Patrick and O'Neill, John. *The Addiction Workbook — A step-by- step guide to quitting alcohol and drugs*, New Harbinger, 1996.

Depression

Dalton, Katherine and Holton, Wendy. *Depression after Childbirth. How to recognise, treat and prevent post natal depression*, Oxford, 1996.

Rowe, Dorothy. *Depression — The way out of your prison*, Routledge, 1996.

Tanner, Susan and Ball, Jillian. *Beating the Blues — A self help approach to overcoming depression*, Doubleday, 1989.

Menopause

Cabot, Dr Sandra. *Menopause — You can give it a miss!*, Women's Health Advisory Service, 1991.

Wren, Dr Barry and Allen, Raelene. *Your choice — A guide to menopause and hormone replacement*, Royal Hospital for Women, 1994.

Pelvic floor exercises

Dr Rosie King's Pelvic Floor Work Out Tape. Sixty-minute audio tape with step-by-step instructions on how to keep your pelvic floor trim, taut and terrific.

Bibliography

Booth, Alan and Edwards, John N., 'The Cessation of Marital Intercourse', *American Journal of Psychiatry*, Vol. 133, No. 11, November 1976, pp. 1333–6.

Cabot, Dr Sandra, *Don't Let Your Hormones Rule Your Life*, Women's Health Advisory Service, Sydney, 1991.

Comfort, Dr Alex, *The Joy of Sex*, Rigby Publishers, Melbourne, 1974.

Crenshaw, Theresa L. and Goldberg, James P., *Sexual Pharmacology: Drugs that affect sexual function*, W. W. Norton & Company, New York, 1996.

Farrell, Dr Elizabeth and Westmore, Ann., *The HRT Handbook*, Anne O'Donovan Pty Ltd, Australia, 1993.

Frank, Ellen, Anderson, Carol and Rubenstein, Debra, 'Frequency of Sexual Dysfunction in "Normal" Couples', *New England Journal of Medicine*, Vol. 299, No. 3, pp. 111–15.

Fromm, Erich, *The Art of Loving*, Allen & Unwin, London, 1957.

Kahn, Ada P. and Hughey Holt, Linda, *The A to Z of Women's Sexuality — A concise encyclopedia*, Hunter House, USA, 1992.

Kaplan Singer, Helen, *Comprehensive Evaluation of Disorders of Sexual Desire*, American Psychiatric Press Inc., USA, 1985.

Kaplan Singer, Helen, *The Sexual Desire Disorders —
   Dysfunctional regulation of sexual motivation*, Brunner/Mazel,
   New York, 1995.

Leiblum, Sandra R. and Rosen, Raymond C., *Sexual Desire
   Disorders*, Guilford Press, New York, 1988.

McKay, Matthew, Fanning, Patrick and Paleg, Kim, *Couple Skills
   — Making your relationship work*, New Harbinger, USA,
   1994.

Maltz, Wendy, *The Sexual Healing Journey — A guide for
   survivors of sexual abuse*, Harper Perennial, USA, 1992.

Pertot, Dr Sandra, *A Commonsense Guide to Sex*, HarperCollins,
   Sydney, 1994, p. 62.

Potter, Hugh, *Pornography — Group Pressures and Individual
   Rights*, The Federation Press, Sydney, 1996.

Rabin, Claire, *Equal Partners, Good Friends — Empowering
   couples through therapy*, Routledge, London, 1996.

Reisner, Paul, *Couplehood*, Bantam, USA, 1994.

Rogerson, Gillian and Wilson, Elizabeth, *Pornography and
   Feminism*, Lawrence & Wishart, London, 1991.

Williams, Warwick, *Man, Woman and Sexual Desire*, Williams
   and Wilkens, Australia, 1986.

Wolfe, Janet, *What To Do When He Has a Headache*, Thorsons,
   USA, 1992.

Index

acetylcholine 106
active listening 163
active sexual behaviour centre 24
addictions 159, 364
adrenal glands 30, 344
adrenaline 30, 212
affairs, extramarital 60, 107, 108,
    159, 172–3
affection 41, 73, 208, 221, 229,
    289, 338, 342
    avoidance of 214
    lack of 72
    during limerence 109–10
    sexual desire and 83, 101,
    213–14, 215–16, 303
ageing:
    erection and 325
    intimacy and 354
    masturbation and 354
    orgasm and 352–3
    relationships and 349, 355
    sexual behaviour and 240,
    349–55, 356
alcohol 321
    excessive consumption of 25,
    59, 63, 65, 71,159, 183
    sexual response and 32,
    313–14, 315, 325
Alcoholics Anonymous 59, 65
amphetamines 316
amputation 314
androgens 26
Angel Dust 316
anger 16, 63, 112, 120, 183, 197,
    318, 325
angina 312, 313
anxiety 35, 70, 318, 325, 326,
    346
aphrodisiacs 73–4, 315
arousal, sexual 24–5, 30, 47-50,
    52, 93, 148, 197, 234, 263,
    271, 286–7, 305–6, 308, 324,
    childbirth and 345–6
    inadequate 328–9

low 241, 313, 327
lubrication during 24, 241, 352
menopause and 349
pornography and 128, 131
pregnancy and 339–40
reduced 148
slow 304, 328, 352, 353, 355
in women 91, 111
The Art of Loving 160
arthritis 312
attraction 41, 71, 73, 185–6, 190, 212
aversion, sexual 62–3, 359

back pain 312
Baker, Dr Martyn 351
behaviour, changes to 215
behaviour exchange 202
benzodiazepines 317
beta blockers 317
betrayal 172–4
birth control 96, 330, 333, 346
blame 14, 55, 65, 120, 147, 149, 159, 160, 184, 226–8, 232
body image 70, 71, 73, 124, 130, 314, 323, 344
body odour 27, 62
bondage 266
brain 20, 21, 23–5, 33
Braxton-Hicks contractions 340
breast cancer 314
breast feeding 29–30, 71, 336–7, 342, 344
breasts 339, 344, 353
bromide 26

cancer 312, 314
celibacy 44, 62
chemotherapy 314
childbirth 28–9, 69

sex after 341–8
childhood 100, 168–9, 213
chronic illness 71, 314–15
CISS continuum 228–9, 237, 283, 287, 295
clitoris 29, 346, 353
stimulation of 236, 286, 328
cocaine 316
codeine 315
Comfort, Dr Alex 352
A Commonsense Guide to Sex 64, 329
commitment 41, 73, 103, 177–81, 190, 310, 361
communication 101, 104, 214, 220, 262–3, 283, 290
active listening in 163
difficulties with 16, 161–4, 328
'I' messages 162–3
improving 162–4, 360
nonverbal 16, 161, 168, 243, 295
in relationships 41, 71, 73, 98, 156, 228–9
verbal 168, 295
companionship 41, 73
comparisons 120–1
compromise 16, 55, 76, 80, 194, 203, 204, 348
condoms 249
conflict 101, 105, 108, 156, 167, 191, 195, 204, 220
avoiders of 192–3
confronters of 194–5
resolution of 41, 73, 191, 192, 194, 195–7
therapy for 197–8
contraception 96, 330, 333, 346
see also specific methods
cot death 59, 340

counselling 58, 158, 159, 167, 238, 268, 319, 325, 328, 360
Couple Skills 199, 203
Couplehood 206
courtship 92, 95, 104, 109, 114, 160, 185, 206, 207–8, 216
cramps 340
cunnilingus 239

dehydroepiandosterone 30–1, 344
dehydroepiandosterone sulphate 30–1, 344
depression 59, 60, 319, 354, 364
desire behaviour zones 46–50, 52, 54, 150, 272
   therapy for 51
desire discrepancy (DD) 7, 19, 55
   emergence of 109, 356
   and premature ejaculation 326
   and pursuer/distancer cycle 149, 226, 234, 346
   symptoms of 124, 269, 280
   and touching 215
   treatment of 17, 234, 239, 244, 248, 250, 253, 258, 270–1
desire enhancers 70, 72–3, 81, 114, 244, 335
   for men 90, 102, 115, 122, 133–8
   in relationships 74–80
   societies attitudes to 113, 116, 132, 136
   therapy for 70, 78, 97, 113, 116, 137
   for women 101–4, 110–14
desire inhibitors 70–2, 81, 90, 95, 335
   for men 96–7, 332
   physical 310–18
   in relationships 74–80, 156

situational 72, 329–30
   therapy for 70, 72, 78, 97
desire, sexual 82–4, 141, 243, 271
   affection and 213
   biological basis of 24–5
   in children 93–4
   conflict and 191
   emotions and 35–6, 84
   frequency of 88, 92, 354
   inhibited 56, 58–61, 65, 95
   levels of 46, 47, 48–50, 113, 227
   during limerence 109–10
   media portrayal of 82
   pregnancy, effect of 339–40
   problems with 192, 221, 234
   in relationships 40–2, 191
   therapy for 12, 61, 99
   trust and 175, 176, 247
   women's 86–9, 100
   desire threshold 88
   in men 89–91
   in women 91–3
DHEA *see* dehydroepiandosterone
DHEAS *see* dehydroepiandosterone sulphate
diabetes 325
diet 32, 313–14, 320, 323
distancers 16, 17, 140, 146–8, 169, 228, 305–7
see also pursuer/distancer cycle; pursuer
divorce 1, 179, 352
dopamine 29, 106
domestic disputes 196–7
Dr Rosie King's pelvic floor work out audio tape 341, 364
drugs 32, 63, 65, 71, 159, 315–17, 321
dyspareunia 313, 328

ecstasy 316
education, sex 12, 63, 71, 72, 128, 237, 322, 325, 328, 347, 359
ejaculation 90, 236, 316, 325, 352
  delayed 327
  premature 326, 341
emotional arousal 212
emotional attachments 103–4, 185, 229
emotional wellbeing 318
emotions 20, 21, 36–8, 42, 112
  in relationships 103–4, 136, 169, 181, 185, 229–30
  sexual desire and 34–6, 71, 72, 318–20
  therapy for 38
  see also specific feelings
endorphins 108
episiotomy 346
equality 156, 188–90
erection 24, 234, 236, 241, 314, 315
  problems with 325, 327, 341, 352, 354
erogenous zones 286
erotica 87, 102, 115–17, 126–32, 135, 270, 304, 305, 347, 353
Evans, Patricia 185
exercise 30–1, 32, 313–14, 320, 323, 355

family 178, 187, 331, 348
Fanning, Patrick 181, 199
fantasies, sexual 60, 70, 71, 73, 125, 129, 323–4, 247, 362
fatigue 70, 71, 310–12, 339, 342
fear 63
feedback, affirming 215
fellatio 239, 266–7

female subordination 127
fertility 113, 117, 138, 316, 338, 340
foreplay 111, 235, 239, 258, 284
Forum magazine 53
Friday, Nancy 324
friendships 166, 178, 354
Fromm, Eric 160
frottage 240, 272, 277

gay couples 3, 257
gender roles, changes in 83
genetic factors in sexual behaviour 83
genital herpes 240
genital stimulation 352
genitals 27, 29, 62, 131–2, 213, 246, 286–7
ginseng root 74
guilt 10, 78, 143, 147, 323, 325, 338

hallucinogenics 316
hardening of the arteries 325
heart attack 313
heroin 315–16
Hite, Shere 328
homosexuality 132
hormone replacement therapy 28, 33, 349, 353, 354, 356
hormones 20, 21, 25, 33, 72, 221
  changes in levels of 71
  disorders of 325, 349
  in pregnancy 340
  in women 26–8
  see also specific hormones
Hot monogamy 220
hygiene 186, 323, 330
hypothalamus 23–24
hysterectomy 351
impotence 314, 316, 325
infatuation 106

infidelity 129, 183, 313
  see also affairs, extramarital
intimacy 41, 101, 104, 176, 208,
  228–9, 244, 247, 290
  emotional 168, 176, 228, 230,
    283
  false sense of 316
  fear of 96, 333
  lack of 71, 156, 189
  during limerence 109
  physical 168, 176, 228, 237
  recreating 167–8, 220
  recreational 167, 205–6, 209,
    221, 298, 302, 348
  selective 166–7
  therapy for 207–8, 209,
    210–12

jealousy 71, 156, 159, 181–3, 190
  therapy for 183
The Joy of Sex 352

kidney disease 314
kissing 213, 265, 300, 305, 342

lesbian couples 3, 253
limbic system 23, 30
limerence 104–10, 114, 124, 185,
  191–2, 195, 208, 337
  therapy for 109
lingerie 102, 115, 117, 124, 134,
  360
lithium 317
lochia 342
love 41, 164, 179, 217, 243, 289
  conflict resolution and 192, 195
  as desire enhancer 160
  distancers and 228
  limerence vs 106–8, 192
  recreating 167
  sex vs 143, 304

Love, Dr Patricia 220
LSD 316

McKay, Matthew 181, 199, 321
Madonna/Whore conflict 341
Maltz, Wendy 297, 300, 323
mandrake root 74
manual stimulation 239
marijuana 316
masculine characteristics 25–6,
  29, 346
Masters & Johnson 329
masturbation 60, 250, 290, 307
  by children 93–4, 246
  display 247
  frequency of 44, 327
  low sexual interest and 58,
    294–5, 307
  noncoital sex and 240
  objections to 245, 249
  puberty and 90
  in relationships 274–80
  religion and 245, 246
  sex addicts and 63–4
  taboos and 247
  therapy for 249–50
media 87, 117, 323, 350
medication 32, 317, 319,
meditation 30–1, 321
men:
  attitude to women 117–21, 127
  cultural conditioning of 48,
    83, 97, 117
  sexuality and 363
Men and Sex 325, 326
menopause 28, 31, 33, 71, 238,
  313, 348–9, 356, 364
menstrual cycle 27, 316
menstruation 240
mercy sex 147
miscarriages 336, 340

morphine 315–16
Multiple Sclerosis 325

Narcotics Anonymous 65
negotiation 16, 76, 362
   conflict resolution and
     198–204
   of sexual participation 150,
     244, 262, 271–8, 280, 348
   therapy for 199–200
nervous system 33, 319
nonverbal communication 161,
    168, 243, 295
noradrenaline 106
nudity 102, 115, 116, 123–5, 132
nurturing 86, 213, 244, 290, 294

oestrogen 24, 25, 27, 91, 317, 349
   ageing and 348
opiates 315–16
oral contraceptives 27–8
oral sex 236, 239, 266–7, 277
orchidectomy 26
orgasm 82, 236, 241–2, 277
   ageing and 49, 325, 352–3
   alcohol, effect on 315
   childrens' 93, 246
   discomfort during 353
   drugs and 316
   erectile difficulties and 325
   expectations about 234
   fantasies and 324
   inhibition of 316
   masturbation and 246–7
   during pregnancy 340, 342
   premature ejaculation and 326
   problems achieving 327–8
   serotonin, effect of 29
   by women 92
ovaries 26, 31
ovulation 27

oxytocin 29–30, 213

Paleg, Kim 199
parenthood 337–8, 348, 360
passion 243, 289, 354
pelvic floor 340–1, 364
penis 62–3, 325, 327
Pertot, Sandra 64, 329
phenylethylamine 106
pheromones 27
phobias 62–3, 65, 178
physical wellbeing 20, 21, 28, 31,
    33, 72, 312, 339, 353, 363
pill, birth control 27–8, 317
pornography 70, 87, 102, 115,
    117, 126–32, 135, 139
Post Natal Depression (PND) 345
pregnancy 30, 69, 240, 316, 330,
    336–8, 356
   sex during 339
premature ejaculation 326
prescription drugs 317, 319, 325
privacy 39, 72, 73, 329
procreation 244, 290
progesterone 25, 26–8, 33, 91,
    317, 349
prolactin 30, 317, 339
promiscuity 44, 83
prostaglandin 325
prostate cancer 26, 28
prostheses 314
psychotherapy 319, 345
puberty 90, 94, 169
punishment 78, 94
pursuer/distancer cycle 16, 140,
    151, 169–70, 214, 226, 231,
    346
reactive distance 142–3
   reversing 231–4, 250, 331
   sexual desire and 143–4
   therapy for 141, 144–5, 148–9

see also pursuers, distancers
pursuers 16, 17, 141, 169, 302–5
  see also pursuer/distancer
  cycle; distancers

radiotherapy 314
rape 327
receptive sexual behaviour centre
  24
recreation 39, 159, 311–12
Reisner, Paul 206
relationships 20, 21, 27, 40–1,
  244
  acceptance in 96, 227, 331
  appreciation in 264, 334
  commitment in 41, 73, 103,
    177–81, 190, 310, 361
  conflicts in 96, 108, 158–9,
    334
  control in 41, 73, 78, 159,
    188, 190
  corporate 189
  de facto 179
  defining 178
  empathy in 226, 230
  equality in 71, 188
  expectations in 318
  improving 159, 299–302, 360
  intrusions in 186–7, 188, 190
  masturbation in 248, 274–80
  needs within 112, 139, 262,
    294, 295
  effect of parenthood on 337–8,
    348
  power in 71, 73, 188–9, 190
  satisfaction in 128–9
  security in 180–1
  sex in 22, 228, 236–7, 256–60,
    262–5, 280
  therapy for 157–8, 179–80,
    186, 189

  trust in 171–5, 176, 262–3
Relationships Australia 159, 360
relaxation 39, 311–12, 321
respect 41, 71, 156, 184–5, 231,
  250, 190
rhinoceros horn 74
romance 208, 216–17
  lack of 185, 206
  limerence and 109
  in relationships 219–20
  sexual desire and 41, 73, 101,
    104, 110

safe sex 96, 330, 333
scarring 314
security 71, 114, 129, 156, 180–1,
  183, 190, 244, 290
self esteem 71, 72, 121, 147, 181,
  182, 183, 321, 339, 361
Self esteem 181, 321
self respect 184–5
sensuality 228, 243, 283, 290
serotonin 29, 106
Sex and Love Addicts Anonymous
  (SLAA) 65
sex offenders 26
sex role stereotypes 87, 188
sex, sexuality:
  addiction to 63–5
  attitudes to 15, 71, 83, 128,
    225, 234
  avoidance of 126, 146 297–9,
    308
  biological sources 21, 33,
    83–5, 103, 117
  boredom with 96, 209, 259,
    331, 349
  coercion 94, 304–5
  comfort level in 71, 312–13,
    332, 353
  compatibility 61, 80, 225, 231

decreasing interest in 31, 140, 54

definition of 43

dependency on 63–5, 359

entitlement to 14–16

environmental factors 39–40, 42, 72, 73, 329–30

expectations of 13, 14–16, 61, 235–7, 245, 284–5, 295–7

experimentation with 266–8

frequency of 44, 53, 269, 326, 338

initiation of 24, 46, 86, 88, 140, 281–4, 287–8, 295–6, 304, 308

interest in 13, 17, 24, 27, 47, 54, 90, 95, 100, 141, 148, 238

knowledge of 12–13, 80

level of 44–5, 46, 56, 86, 244

low interest in 56–8, 65, 95–7, 100, 239, 316

motivation for 43, 91, 243–5, 250, 281, 289, 291, 293, 304, 305, 347

needs 76–7, 127, 134, 147, 281, 289–90

effect of parenthood on 337–8

participation levels in 271–8, 295–6

prescription drugs and 31, 71, 317

primitive man and 84–5, 103, 117

psychological sources 21, 33, 245, 265–6

satisfaction with 96–7, 125–6, 239, 247–8, 291, 305, 325

saying no to 242, 292–4, 305, 308, 333, 347

societal expectations of 48, 58

therapy for 32, 45, 56, 218, 220, 231, 233, 234, 259, 260–1, 285, 290, 291, 299, 334, 363

variety in 102, 114, 115, 122–3, 251–6, 260, 270–1, 273–7, 280, 304, 306, 362

in Victorian era 15

sexual abuse 63, 159, 214, 268, 323, 327, 361

Sexual Corpse Syndrome 331

The Sexual Healing Journey 297, 323

sexual hierarchy 271–7, 292, 295–7, 302, 306, 341

therapy on 280

sexual intercourse 82, 228, 234, 235

anal 267–8

noncoital 235, 237–41, 250, 271–7, 326, 328, 339, 346–7, 355

during pregnancy 339

'quickies' 270

sexual rejection 96–7, 142–3

sexual self esteem 71, 72, 96, 322, 331

sexually transmitted diseases 320, 330

shame 35, 325

smell, sense of 27

smoking 25, 32, 313–14, 321

Spanish Fly 74

sperm 316

spontaneity 96, 102, 115, 122–3, 208, 270, 331, 348

stomas 314

stress 35, 37, 160, 187, 319–20, 363

management of 320–1

in men 193

sexual desire and 22, 32, 39, 69, 75

therapy for 320
stretch marks 339, 344 208–9
survival 85, 103, 117, 319

taboos 267, 324
teenagers 91, 240–1, 359–60
Tenov, Dorothy 104
testes 25, 74, 315
testosterone 21, 24, 33
   in men 83, 84, 283
   in puberty 90
   reduced levels of 30, 71,
     315–17, 354
   sexual desire and 25–6, 28–9,
     48
   in women 31, 86, 91, 346–7,
     349
thoughts 36–8
touching 29–30, 168–9, 213–14,
   300–2, 342
toxic disrespect 184–5, 362
trust 41, 73, 156, 167, 170–5,
   196, 301
   loss of 71, 137
   sex and 175, 247
   therapy for 175
urethra 74
uterus 340

vagina 352, 353
   dryness of 314, 345–6, 349
vaginismus 238
*The Verbally Abusive
   Relationship* 185
vibrators 236, 277, 328, 338,
   353, 355, 360
violence 128
visual stimulation 116–17, 124,
   134, 138

weight 314, 323
women:
   attitudes to 128
   portrayal in movies of 87
   sexual resources for 360
   sexuality of 363
women's magazines 87, 113

Zilbergeld, Bernard 325